FOOD PRODUCTION
IN WAR

BY

THOMAS HUDSON MIDDLETON, K.B.E., C.B., LL.D.

DEPUTY DIRECTOR-GENERAL, FOOD PRODUCTION DEPARTMENT

OXFORD: AT THE CLARENDON PRESS

London, Edinburgh, New York, Toronto, Melbourne and Bombay

HUMPHREY MILFORD

1923

PRINTED IN ENGLAND
AT THE OXFORD UNIVERSITY PRESS

Publications of the
Carnegie Endowment for International Peace
Division of Economics and History
John Bates Clark, Director

ECONOMIC AND SOCIAL HISTORY
OF THE WORLD WAR

British Series

JAMES T. SHOTWELL, Ph.D., LL.D.
GENERAL EDITOR

With the Collaboration of the

BRITISH EDITORIAL BOARD

---

*For List of other Editors and the plan of the Series see end
of this volume*

EDITOR'S PREFACE

In the autumn of 1914, when the scientific study of the effects of war upon modern life passed suddenly from theory to history, the Division of Economics and History of the Carnegie Endowment for International Peace proposed to adjust the programme of its researches to the new and altered problems which the war presented. The existing programme, which had been prepared as the result of a conference of economists held at Berne in 1911, and which dealt with the facts then at hand, had just begun to show the quality of its contributions ; but for many reasons it could no longer be followed out. A plan was therefore drawn up at the request of the Director of the Division, in which it was proposed, by means of an historical survey, to attempt to measure the economic cost of the war and the displacement which it was causing in the processes of civilization. Such an ' Economic and Social History of the World War ', it was felt, if undertaken by men of judicial temper and adequate training, might ultimately, by reason of its scientific obligations to truth, furnish data for the forming of sound public opinion, and thus contribute fundamentally toward the aims of an institution dedicated to the cause of international peace.

The need for such an analysis, conceived and executed in the spirit of historical research, was increasingly obvious as the war developed, releasing complex forces of national life not only for the vast process of destruction but also for the stimulation of new capacities for production. This new economic activity, which under normal conditions of peace might have been a gain to society, and the surprising capacity exhibited by the belligerent nations for enduring long and increasing loss—often while presenting the outward semblance of new prosperity—made necessary a reconsideration of the whole field of war economics. A double obligation was therefore placed upon the Division of Economics and History. It was obliged to concentrate its work upon the

problem thus presented, and to study it as a whole ; in other
words, to apply to it the tests and disciplines of history. Just
as the war itself was a single event, though penetrating by seem-
ingly unconnected ways to the remotest parts of the world, so
the analysis of it must be developed according to a plan at once
all embracing and yet adjustable to the practical limits of the
available data.

During the actual progress of the war, however, the execution
of this plan for a scientific and objective study of war economics
proved impossible in any large and authoritative way. Incidental
studies and surveys of portions of the field could be made and were
made under the direction of the Division, but it was impossible to
undertake a general history for obvious reasons. In the first place,
an authoritative statement of the resources of belligerents bore
directly on the conduct of armies in the field. The result was to
remove as far as possible from scrutiny those data of the economic
life of the countries at war which would ordinarily, in time of
peace, be readily available for investigation. In addition to this
difficulty of consulting documents, collaborators competent to
deal with them were for the most part called into national service
in the belligerent countries and so were unavailable for research.
The plan for a war history was therefore postponed until conditions should arise which would make possible not only access to
essential documents but also the co-operation of economists,
historians, and men of affairs in the nations chiefly concerned,
whose joint work would not be misunderstood either in purpose
or in content.

Upon the termination of the war the Endowment once
more took up the original plan, and it was found with but
slight modification to be applicable to the situation. Work was
begun in the summer and autumn of 1919. In the first place
a final conference of the Advisory Board of Economists of the
Division of Economics and History was held in Paris, which
limited itself to planning a series of short preliminary surveys of
special fields. Since, however, the purely preliminary character
of such studies was further emphasized by the fact that they were

directed more especially towards those problems which were then fronting Europe as questions of urgency, it was considered best not to treat them as part of the general survey but rather as of contemporary value in the period of war settlement. It was clear that not only could no general programme be laid down *a priori* by this conference as a whole, but that a new and more highly specialized research organization than that already existing would be needed to undertake the Economic and Social History of the War, one based more upon national grounds in the first instance and less upon purely international co-operation. Until the facts of national history could be ascertained, it would be impossible to proceed with comparative analysis ; and the different national histories were themselves of almost baffling intricacy and variety. Consequently the former European Committee of Research was dissolved, and in its place it was decided to erect an Editorial Board in each of the larger countries and to nominate special editors in the smaller ones, who should concentrate, for the present at least, upon their own economic and social war history.

The nomination of these boards by the General Editor was the first step taken in every country where the work has begun. And if any justification was needed for the plan of the Endowment, it at once may be found in the lists of those, distinguished in scholarship or in public affairs, who have accepted the responsibility of editorship. This responsibility is by no means light, involving, as it does, the adaptation of the general editorial plan to the varying demands of national circumstances or methods of work ; and the measure of success attained is due to the generous and earnest co-operation of those in charge in each country.

Once the editorial organization was established there could be little doubt as to the first step which should be taken in each instance toward the actual preparation of the history. Without documents there can be no history. The essential records of the war, local as well as central, have therefore to be preserved and to be made available for research in so far as is compatible with public interest. But this archival task is a very great one, belonging of right to the governments and other owners of historical sources and not to the historian or economist who proposes to use them. It is an obligation of ownership ; for all such documents are public trust. The collaborators on this section of the war history, therefore, working within their own field as researchers, could only survey the situation as they found it and report their findings in the form of guides or manuals ; and perhaps, by stimulating a comparison of methods, help to further the adoption of those found to be most practical. In every country, therefore, this was the point of departure for actual work ; although special monographs have not been written in every instance.

The first stage of the work upon the war history, dealing with little more than the externals of archives, seemed for a while to exhaust the possibilities of research. And had the plan of the history been limited to research based upon official documents, little more could have been done, for once documents have been labelled ' secret ' few government officials can be found with sufficient courage or initiative to break open the seal. Thus vast masses of source material essential for the historian were effectively placed beyond his reach, although much of it was quite harmless from any point of view. While war conditions thus continued to hamper research, and were likely to do so for many years to come, some alternative had to be found.

Fortunately such an alternative was at hand in the narrative, amply supported by documentary evidence, of those who had played some part in the conduct of affairs during the war, or who, as close observers in privileged positions, were able to record from first or at least second-hand knowledge the economic history of different phases of the great war, and of its effect upon society. Thus a series of monographs was planned consisting for the most part of unofficial yet authoritative statements, descriptive or historical, which may best be described as about half-way between memoirs and blue-books. These monographs make up the main body of the work assigned so far. They are not limited to contemporary, war-time studies ; for the economic history of the war must deal with a longer period than that of the actual fighting. It must cover the years of ' deflation ' as well, at least sufficiently to secure some fairer measure of the economic displacement than is possible in purely contemporary judgments.

With this phase of the work, the editorial problems assumed a new aspect. The series of monographs had to be planned primarily with regard to the availability of contributors, rather than of source material as in the case of most histories; for the contributors themselves controlled the sources. This in turn involved a new attitude towards those two ideals which historians have sought to emphasize, consistency and objectivity. In order to bring out the chief contribution of each writer it was impossible to keep within narrowly logical outlines; facts would have to be repeated in different settings and seen from different angles, and sections included which do not lie within the strict limits of history; and absolute objectivity could not be obtained in every part. Under the stress of controversy or apology, partial views would here and there find their expression. But these views are in some instances an intrinsic part of the history itself, contemporary measurements of facts as significant as the facts with which they deal. Moreover, the work as a whole is planned to furnish its own corrective; and where it does not, others will.

In addition to this monographic treatment of source material, a number of studies by specialists is already in preparation, dealing with technical or limited subjects, historical or statistical. These monographs also partake to some extent of the nature of first-hand material, registering as they do the data of history close enough to the source to permit verification in ways impossible later. But they also belong to that constructive process by which history passes from analysis to synthesis. The process is a long and difficult one, however, and work upon it has only just begun. To quote an apt characterization, in the first stages of a history like this one is only 'picking cotton'. The tangled threads of events have still to be woven into the pattern of history; and for this creative and constructive work different plans and organizations may be needed.

In a work which is the product of so complex and varied co-operation as this, it is impossible to indicate in any but a most general way the apportionment of responsibility of editors and authors for the contents of the different monographs. For the plan of the History as a whole and its effective execution the General Editor is responsible; but the arrangement of the detailed programmes of study has been largely the work of the different Editorial Boards and divisional Editors, who have also read the manuscripts prepared under their direction. The acceptance of a monograph in this series, however, does not commit the editors to the opinions or conclusions of the authors. Like other editors, they are asked to vouch for the scientific merit, the appropriateness and usefulness of the volumes admitted to the series; but the authors are naturally free to make their individual contributions in their own way. In like manner the publication of the monographs does not commit the Endowment to agreement with any specific conclusions which may be expressed therein. The responsibility of the Endowment is to History itself—an obligation not to avoid but to secure and preserve variant narratives and points of view, in so far as they are essential for the understanding of the war as a whole.

J. T. S.

PREFACE

THE purpose of this book is to preserve, for use in time of peace, facts and considerations respecting the output of food by the soils of the United Kingdom, which were forced on our attention in time of war.

In the compilation of the volume two classes of reader have been kept in view : those who have no knowledge of the technical processes of agriculture, but are interested in the sources of the nation's food supply, and in the capacity of the United Kingdom for supporting its people ; and those agriculturists who may desire to study their subject from a new angle, or at least from an angle new to the farmers of this generation.

With certain qualifications, which will be referred to in Chapter III, it may be stated that in time of scarcity, whether from war or other cause, the soil's output of utilizable energy measures its value to the community depending upon it for food. In contrast to the ordinary business of the farmer and gardener—the winning of a livelihood from land—Food Production, in the sense in which it is used in this volume, may be defined as the art of raising from soil the greatest possible quantity of energy in the form of wholesome foodstuffs.

In time of peace it may be possible for rich nations, as it is possible for rich individuals, to disregard the actual sources from which their food supply is derived, and the conditions under which that food is produced. There is always enough food for those who have money to buy ; the poor, on the other hand, must watch the sources of their food with anxious care. In a heavily indebted nation the difference between poverty and comfort may be determined by the extent to which food can be produced from the home land, just as for a poor man the difference between sufficiency and hunger may depend upon the produce of his garden or allotment.

It is because war has left the nation poor that it has greatly increased the importance to the country of the utilization of its soils. But little increase can be expected if, pursuing our pre-war policy, the non-agricultural classes of the community regard home food production as a subject that does not affect their interests. Concerted measures are necessary in peace, as they were in war, if the output of the land is to be increased.

It is evident that in a country such as ours the framing of any practical measures for stimulating food production must give rise to very complex questions ; but perhaps the greatest of the difficulties with which those who aim at an increase are faced, is the lack of interest which, except under the menace of war, the public take in this subject. Many times, in looking back over the difficulties of the war years, and in comparing the then attitude of the country to its land with that adopted before the war and since the peace, have the words quoted upon page xx of this book come back to the writer : ' The sustenance of nature hidden lies ' is a statement no less true of the great mass of the people to-day, than it was 3,000 years ago when the first writer on food production composed *Works and Days.*

. The plan of the volume may be briefly indicated. Chapter I sketches the situation created by war following on a long term of peace—the ' Waygoing ' after the lease ; and Chapters II to V deal with the stock-taking which the ending of a lease calls for. In Chapter II the resources at the disposal of the farmer, in Chapters III and IV his output of food, and in Chapter V the total amount of the nation's home-grown food supply are discussed. The following five chapters relate the story of the war harvests, Chapter XI briefly refers to the cost of the Food Production Campaign, and Chapter XII summarizes the results of war farming and alludes to some questions which face the farmer under the very uncertain ' tenure ' on which he now holds his land.

Relatively little has been said about live-stock farming in the war years. While broadly it was the case that in any particular year the supplies of meat and dairy produce were determined by the available fodders and feeding stuffs, the seasonal fluctuations in both supplies and prices were governed by other considerations affecting the general policy of the Food Controller. As illustrations the effect on the beef supply of 1918 of the slaughter of cattle in the late autumn of 1917 and the effect on the mutton supply of the prices fixed for mutton and lamb may be cited. The policy adopted with regard to pigs, again, while in the main depending on the supplies of pig-feeding material available, was influenced by other circumstances. Before America joined the Allies, for example, financial difficulties demanded the reduction to the lowest possible amount of the imports of American bacon ; when these difficulties disappeared a powerful incentive for maintaining a high level of pig production in the United Kingdom was removed.

Throughout the war the Agricultural Departments were constantly engaged in efforts to safeguard the milk supply, and to enable farmers to maintain their herds and flocks. They were equally careful to call attention to new or little-known feeding stuffs, such as palm-kernel cake, or to alterations in the demand for produce brought about by the war. When the transference of the Hamburg trade in palm kernels to this country, by increasing our supplies of margarine, reduced our need for butter, the importance of cheese was emphasized, and later a very successful scheme for encouraging cheese-making in place of butter-making was introduced.

But all these activities derive their interest from their effects on food in the later years of the war. Until the end of 1916 there was little change in the production of meat and milk, and thereafter the changes that occurred were so dependent upon the measures which the Ministry of Food took to protect and economize supplies, that no discussion of the subject would be of value in a book dealing with Food Production but not with Food Control.

The figures in the tables relating to the yield of the war harvests and to live stock include the produce of Scotland and Ireland ; but the references to the work of food production in

Ireland are brief, and of the task of Scottish agriculturists very little has been said, as it will be dealt with in a separate volume of this Series.

Personal references, except to Ministers responsible to Parliament for the administration of agricultural questions, have been almost altogether omitted. The names of those charged with the supervision of the work of the Food Production Department in 1918 are given in the Appendix.

T. H. MIDDLETON.

March 1922.

CONTENTS

CONTENTS

LIST OF TABLES IN TEXT

DIAGRAMS

The sustenance of Nature hidden lies ;
The gods have cover'd it from human eyes :
Else had one day bestow'd sufficient cheer,
And, though inactive, fed thee through the year.
Then might thy hand have laid the rudder by,
In blackening smoke for ever hung on high.
Then had the labouring ox foregone the soil,
And patient mules had found reprieve from toil.
But Jove our food conceal'd.

HESIOD, *Works and Days.*
(Elton's Translation.)

CHAPTER I

THE 'WAYGOING'

The End of the Lease of Peace. Early War Measures. Fortunate Harvests. Allotments. Conflicting Views. A changed Situation. Hints from Germany. The Plough Policy. An old Controversy. The Submarine decides. A Subject for further Study.

FROM 1815 until 1914 the farmers of the United Kingdom enjoyed a ninety-nine years' lease of peace. Although there were wars in the interval they touched neither the farmer nor his men. Thus it was assumed—so little did farmers regard war as having any hurtful influence on their peaceful business—that after centuries of disturbance from invasion and civil and foreign wars, British agriculture had in 1815 acquired the possession of peace in fee simple.

When on the 4th of August 1914 this long lease of peace terminated abruptly, the ' waygoing ' found the farmer quite unprepared. The conceptions of his calling, so familiar to his forefathers, were wholly novel to him. The conditions tacitly read into all the farming covenants of 1815 had been forgotten. The rules of good husbandry took no account of the one canon supreme a century before ; in 1914 the farmer was no longer the warden of the nation's food, and agriculture, far from occupying the ' lordly ' position among our industries accorded to the ' loaf-provider ' when the nineteenth century opened, had become a minor contributor to the food supply, and to the country's wealth.

Thus it was that when the nation took stock of its home-grown food supply, it was discovered that, at the ordinary rate of consumption of the years before the war, the produce of our soils would have supplied our needs for one hundred and twenty-five days out of the three hundred and sixty-five ; spread evenly over the fifty-two weeks it would have sufficed to feed the population of the country from Friday night until

Monday morning. We were, as our enemy would have said, ' self-suppliers ' for the week-end, and they knew well that for the remainder of the week we must depend upon our ships. Germany, on the other hand, supplied herself from her own soil for six days out of the seven. She had been careful to ' keep under the protection of her guns the ground upon which her corn grows and her cattle graze '. This was the result of a considered policy to which her military and economic advisers had long given anxious thought.

Early War Measures.

The last days of peace were spent in making plans, and in the first days of war active measures were taken to safeguard the food position in both countries ; measures, however, that were by no means the same.

In this country, dependent as we were on overseas sources, immediate attention was given to the stocks existing on farms, in warehouses, and on passage, or to the supplies which were in sight in those countries from which we could import. In Germany, eyewitnesses tell us that the most obvious signs of preparation for the future could be detected on the land itself. On the central plains all grain was swiftly harvested and secured, and before 31st August old men and women and boys were everywhere strenuously tilling the soil and preparing for the harvest of 1915.

There was no corresponding action ' according to plan ' on the fields of the United Kingdom. Harvest with us is later than in Germany, and at the end of the first month of war we were actively engaged, as at this season we always are, in reaping and carting the crops. A percentage of our younger men had already gone, and in certain districts many of our horses had been requisitioned ; but otherwise a casual visitor to our harvest fields would have detected nothing very different from usual. There was little sign of the intense activity in the preparation of extra land for the following year's crops that was so marked a feature of the German country-side.

It must not be supposed, however, that because no programme for the cultivation of our land in case of war had been prepared before August 1914, we then remained idle.   Our people seldom go out to meet trouble half way, and when trouble comes along our typical statesman has one never-failing resource—he can ask for advice with the certainty that it will be given freely. Thus we had not been a week at war before a Consultative Committee of experienced agriculturists was appointed ; and it can at least be claimed that the difficulties of doing anything to add to our tillage area were very fully explored by all of us who were then responsible for action.

Nor must it be supposed that those responsible for the defence of the country had not given anxious consideration to questions of food supply in time of war.   There had been much discussion of the subject.   Granaries for storing grain had been advocated many times, and measures for ekeing out our home supplies, as for example the offer of inducements to farmers to keep their grain in stack, had frequently been suggested.

It was not a food supply programme, but a food production policy that was lacking in 1914.   The possibility of largely increasing the output of our own land had not been examined by any body of experts capable of framing a trustworthy plan. It was, indeed, the general opinion that in the course of a great war no considerable increase of food could be expected from the activities of our own agriculturists ; hence, for the safe-guarding of the nation's food supply, reliance was placed upon the Navy—and our experiences in the four years' struggle proved how strong were the grounds for confidence in our ships. What the result would have been if war had been delayed until the submarine strength of Germany had been further developed we may ask, but shall not attempt to answer.   Readers, who in the course of the war had not the means of following closely the effects of the submarine campaign, have since had many opportunities of studying the question for themselves.

The Navy and the Mercantile Marine did for our food supply as much as even the most sanguine in 1914 could have dared to hope.   But in the course of the four years' war our ships were set an impossible task ; before food can be transported from

other lands, there must be food to transport ; and long before
November 1918 special measures became necessary to avert
starvation.

These special measures are discussed in the different volumes
of this Economic History. In this volume we are concerned
only with the measures which, in the course of the war, were
necessary and were adopted for the purpose of increasing the
output of food from our own soils.

In the earlier years of the war the activities of the Agricultural Departments in this direction were mainly educational
and administrative in type. So long as food in abundance could
be purchased abroad, so long as we had money to buy without
difficulty, and ships to carry what was needed, it was held to be
unnecessary to interfere with the freedom of farmers in managing
their land as seemed best to them. They were *advised* to grow
special crops, but they were not *required* to do so. No pecuniary
inducements to modify their existing practices were offered
them. The farmer's wants were carefully studied by special
officers of the Departments of Agriculture in each of the three
countries ; difficulties arising because of a shortage of manures,
or feeding stuffs, or other requisites for successful cultivation
were tackled, and the co-operation of traders was enlisted.
Much was done in this way to facilitate cultivation. Close
attention to the labour supply was given from the first weeks
of war, and in this way, too, the farmer's difficulties were
lessened ; but until towards the end of 1916 the Food Production Campaign, to be described in later chapters of this
volume, was not decided upon.

Fortunate Harvests.

Whether it would have been prudent to have intervened at
an earlier stage we need not now discuss, but we should note
in this connexion the extraordinary good fortune of the Allied
Nations in the matter of food supply in the earlier years of war.
In this country especially, dependent for our bread supply on
other countries—and shut off as we were from Russia, a principal
source of wheat—our difficulties might well have been intense

long before the autumn of 1916. We were saved from disaster
by the energy of trans-Atlantic cultivators, and by very
favourable weather conditions in both North and South
America. This combination of hard work and good weather
resulted in gigantic harvests, and a great abundance of grain
for export from the West in the cereal year 1915–16.

Thus it was that after a few weeks of anxiety about food
at the outbreak of war, our people settled down to feeding as
usual, during the first two years of war ; indeed, it might be
said of the great mass of the population to feeding better
than usual, for war energies led them to require more food, and
war earnings enabled them to buy more than before.

Allotments.

Only in one very limited direction was there any parallel
on the land of this country to the intense activity so marked
in the corn and potato fields of Germany.

At the outbreak of war many industrial workers were
temporarily thrown out of employment, and their attention
was then directed to allotment cultivation. The allotment
movement spread continuously and, as we shall see later,
reached large dimensions even before the end of 1916. Except
for the increased interest in allotments, the majority of our
people, with many urgent questions to occupy their attention,
gave little more thought to the sources of their food supply
in the period August 1914 to October 1916 than they did before
the war.

Conflicting Views.

A minority, it is true, from the first insisted that special
action should be taken to modify the systems of farming in
common use in 1914, with the object of largely increasing the
nation's output of food ; and now and again articles in the
daily papers and in scientific and technical journals referred
to the subject ; but the mass of the people were content to
leave these questions to experts, and the experts were not
agreed.

The evidence of the ' Annual Statement of Trade ' was

unmistakable. Four loaves out of five consumed by our people in 1914 were baked from the produce of overseas wheat, and similar figures could be produced for many of our other staples. The exact production of our own land had not been ascertained ; clearly, however, it was relatively unimportant, and in the course of a great war no substantial result could be expected from extending corn growing, while there were obvious risks attending any considerable modifications of the farming system which experience had taught our agriculturists to adopt. These were the arguments on one side. On the other it was contended that a generation before the outbreak of war the country was providing a much greater supply of food than in 1914 ; and that the expansion of food production in the first half of the nineteenth century showed how great were the possibilities of increase, if efforts were concentrated on the cultivation of our soils.

But it is an easier matter, in the pressure of war, to draw deductions from the tabulated figures of a blue-book than to disentangle the results achieved by agriculturists throughout a period so disturbed by political and industrial change as that of the years 1795 to 1840. The circumstances, too, had been wholly altered by time. The experiences of farmers a century before were held to give little guidance in the problems of 1914–16. Thus when, at length, the country adopted the food production policy, it was the recent experience of Germany, not the former experience of the United Kingdom, that weighed most with the general public.

That agriculturists, for the most part, should have been unwilling to adopt any drastic changes in their systems of farming during the first two years of war, while the food position was still satisfactory, need occasion no surprise. The changes which had been adopted during the preceding forty years—the conversion of inferior corn-growing land into grass—had been forced upon them by the fall in corn prices. The wisdom of this change had been proved by the fact that the bankrupt industry of the ' nineties ' had been restored to solvency ; the dangers of an extension of tillage were only too obvious to every thoughtful and experienced farmer. The notable feature indeed is not that agriculturists should have been unwilling to change, but that they should have so willingly backed up the efforts of the Food Production Department in 1917 and 1918, for it must be recalled that not only did this action involve them in risks of personal loss, but that the final results on the food supply of changes in method were at least open to argument. Many agriculturists believed, and still believe, that while the conversion of grass land to corn growing led to an increase in grain, there was a corresponding loss of food in the form of meat and milk. The grounds of this belief we shall subsequently examine in detail. Meanwhile in justification of the attitude adopted by most agriculturists in 1914–16, and by many of them throughout the whole period of war, we may quote the views of so well known an authority as Sir Henry Rew, in the early part of the war, as an Assistant Secretary of the Board of Agriculture and Fisheries, largely responsible for the measures taken to safeguard food supplies, subsequently First Secretary to the Ministry of Food, and in 1921 simultaneously President of the Royal Statistical Society and Chairman of the Farmers' Club. In his presidential address to the former body on the 15th November 1921, in which he reviewed *The Progress of British Agriculture*, Sir Henry said : ' I claim that an examination of the statistics, so far as they are available, points to the conclusion that a larger quantity of food was being produced at the outbreak of war than at any previous period. The food was not the same in kind as it was forty or fifty years ago, but it was greater in quantity.

' There was no doubt a set-back to food-production during the war. By a special effort the amount of cereal food was increased, but there was a marked reduction of other kinds of food, meat and milk particularly.' [1]

While in our own country there was thus a sharp difference of opinion as to whether British agriculture was more, or less, productive in 1914 than it had been forty years before, foreign students of our agricultural changes were in no doubt. These

[1] *Journal Royal Stat. Society*, Part I, 1922.

changes had entered into the pre-war estimates of our military position which were framed by our principal enemy.   An illuminating paragraph occurs in Prince Bernhard von Bülow's *Imperial Germany*, of which the English translation appeared in 1914.   In discussing German fiscal policy in connexion with agriculture in time of war he dismisses free trade as being wholly unsuited to German conditions : ' Agricultural work would grow more and more unprofitable, and would have to be given up to a greater extent ', he writes, and he adds the significant words, ' We should go the way England has gone.'

A changed Situation.

For two years such rival views as those above indicated were discussed at conferences and committees by experts and non-experts ; but in the autumn of 1916 the partial failure of our potato crop, and the information that the American harvests had fallen far short of those of the preceding year, convinced the country that, whatever the merits of its pre-war farming, there must be a change.   And the effects of the unlimited submarine campaign of the spring months of 1917, though only partially known to the public, were sufficiently obvious to prove to them that if changes were not made quickly they would soon be partners in the starvation diet of the German people.   Henceforward the general interest in food questions was as keen as in the progress of recruiting, or in the supply of munitions ; the efforts being made to increase food production commanded widespread attention, the sources of supply were eagerly canvassed in every household, and there is no more need to recall the country's attitude to the progress of the ploughman and the reaper than there is to recall its experiences of queues, or sugar cards, or meat tickets.

Although the words were written some seventy years before, and referred particularly to the two lean years which ushered in the ' hungry forties ', it might truly have been said as the crops of 1917 ripened, ' It is not now the farmer or the corn-dealer only, who watches with painful anxiety the state of the weather.'   Since Tooke wrote these words, there had never been a year in which the townsman felt so anxious about his daily bread as he did in these summer months of 1917, when he was being adjured to eat less of it ; and, it may be added, there had been no intervening year in which the quality of the bread itself made this injunction more easily obeyed !

Hints from Germany.

It was not only the American harvests of 1915 that ameliorated the nation's food position in the later years of war. Our serious food difficulties did not arise until long after the pressure of diminishing supplies was felt in Germany ; thus German methods and German experience furnished this country with valuable hints. Early in the war a voluntary committee of German scientific men [1] undertook a very complete survey of that country's food resources. Their conclusions were of a kind which aroused both interest and discussion. As a result partly of this discussion and partly of independent inquiries in progress in this country, the Royal Society's Food (War) Committee undertook a similar inquiry in 1916. The facts elicited by this inquiry were subsequently of much value in determining the precise line of action to be taken in the production, importation, and distribution of food ; while the authoritative statements which, from time to time, were made by the committee respecting the nature and uses of food carried great weight with the public.

It was possible, again, to show that the systems of agriculture common in Germany resulted in a much larger production of food per hundred acres of cultivated land than the systems common in the United Kingdom.

It was further possible, especially during 1918, to point to the mistakes that had been made by the German food authorities in their attempts to deal with live stock. Needless to say, the methods which the food situation called for in rationing live stock aroused the keenest controversy in both countries.

---

[1] The Eltzbacher Committee. An English translation of its Report by Sir S. Russell Wells was published in 1915 under the title *Germany's Food. Can it last ?*

The Plough Policy.

As in the second stage of the war there was no lack of public interest in food questions, so there was no lack of public discussion. The doings of the Food Production Department were keenly canvassed in both Houses of Parliament, in every farmer's assembly, and at many meetings of representatives of consumers' interests in different parts of the country.

In view of the differences in expert opinion on the policy itself, it is scarcely necessary to state that the carrying out of the policy in detail invited, and received, much criticism. This criticism mainly centred round the ploughing up of grass land ; other sections of the work met with general approval. In a country so well adapted for grazing as is the United Kingdom, and with so vivid a recollection of ' bad times ' present in the minds of agriculturists, it was inevitable that the ploughing of grass land should often have been characterized as ' food destruction ' and that those responsible for the policy should have been condemned. They were indeed regarded by some agriculturists as ' plough-maniacs ' and they were so termed. As acre after acre was furrowed by the plough, and as unavoidably a certain number of failures occurred, and crops had to be resown, or the land left fallow, strong representations were made to Members of Parliament, and criticisms of the plough policy were both severe and persistent. So insistent, indeed, were these critics in proclaiming the high food value of the indifferent pastures then being broken up for corn-growing, that it would almost seem as if they and their constituents hoped to defeat the objects of the submarine campaign by following the example of Nebuchadnezzar !

An old Controversy.

The controversy was chiefly in England. Relatively little of it was heard in the other countries. And it was as typically English as were the pastures round which discussion centred. It was a controversy last heard of, perhaps, during the ' hot-bed ' cultivation of wheat in the early years of the nineteenth century ; but long before the Napoleonic wars it filled the minds of the

English people. From 1488 when the laying to pasture of ' what customably have been used as tillage ; whereby idleness which is ground and beginning of all mischiefs, daily doth increase ', until 1597, when it was enacted that ' arable land made pasture since the 1st Elizabeth (1558) shall be again converted to tillage, and what is arable shall not be converted to pasture ', measures for promoting tillage farming had frequently occupied the attention of the legislature.

It is interesting to note that the enactment of the thirty-ninth year of Elizabeth's reign was literally applicable to the problem which in the seventh year of His Majesty George V's reign the Food Production Department set out to solve. The grass land which the Department sought to bring into cultivation was that which had been ' made pasture ' in the preceding forty years ; and it was as a result of their regulations that the English farmer of the twentieth century, like his predecessor in the sixteenth, was faced with the Order : ' what is arable shall not be converted to pasture.'

The methods of the Food Production Department may have surprised the ' oldest inhabitant ', the follies of the pasture ploughers may still furnish an occasional theme for discussion in the daily papers, or provide gossip for old women in post-war novels, but among the many questions raised by the Great War, this particular question of the ploughing of pastures was not new. Around the relative advantages of grass and tillage farming to the community, discussion has centred for long ages ; for it was not in 1917 that ' plough maniacs ' first appeared in the neighbourhood of Whitehall. The controversy between advocates of the plough and supporters of pasture was certainly not new when the ' laying to pasture of what customably have been used as tillage ' led to the enactment of 1488. Nor can it have been new at the time, three generations before, when William Greville, ' flower of the wool merchants of all England ', grown great through the extension of grazing, was laid to rest in the village church of Campden. There in the very heart of England, where flock masters from the sheep walks of the Cotswolds met wheat growers from the clays of the plains, the rival claims of live stock and of grain were argued 500 years ago as keenly as they were when, in the same district, the Agricultural Executive Committees of Gloucestershire and Worcestershire and Oxfordshire were issuing their ' Cultivation Orders ' in 1917. And around our coasts, centuries before the wool merchants of Campden flourished, did not Mr. Kipling's ' Hobden ' defend the precious old turf of his ' little River-piece ' from Roman and Danish and Norman invaders and innovators with just such arguments as were repeated over and over again during 1917 and 1918 in Sussex and every other English county ? Nor, in spite of what was alleged against the emissaries of the Food Production Department, were Hobden's forceful pleadings ignored. Many a ' little River-piece ', unfitted for the plough, was ' dreened ' with the aid of German prisoners of war in a workmanlike style that would have won the approval of both Hobden and his alien masters.

The Submarine Decides.

But if the controversy between plough and pasture was as old as English farming, never before in the country's history were the issues depending on it so fateful as they were in that period in the spring of 1917, when, driven by the submarine's activity, the ploughmen of the United Kingdom set out on the formidable task of converting once more into corn fields three million acres ' made pasture ' in the preceding generation. The population of fifteen millions which the ' hot-bed ' cultivation of 1800–13 had with difficulty maintained, had now trebled ; there was, therefore, no possibility of providing all that they required ; but every week's supply of bread that could be grown at home lessened the danger of starvation, and the risk that all the sacrifices of the preceding years of war would be in vain. Argument might (and did) continue ; but the time for listening to argument had passed ; action and strenuous action was now imperatively demanded, and it was taken. The measure of success which was achieved we shall subsequently learn.

A Subject for Study.

Meantime, do not let us suppose that England's ancient problem has been settled. Again, and in the not far distant future, this question of the relative value of grass and tillage farming to the nation will be raised, and the answer must be given by the nation, and not only by that small section of the community which is now directly engaged in the growing of crops and the raising of live stock.

Partly because the question is still unsettled, but chiefly because of its direct bearing on the different agricultural policies followed in the early and later stages of the war, we shall have much to say in subsequent chapters about the relative values of grass and tillage farming from the point of view of food supply.

In order that non-agricultural readers may understand the reasons for the conflicting opinions which have been expressed on food production, and may appreciate the reasons which dictated the policy adopted in 1917 and 1918, it will be necessary to refer both to the position of agriculture at the outbreak of war, and to the methods by which the soil's output of food may be determined.

Before dealing with the story of the war harvests we shall, therefore, examine the resources at the disposal of the food producers of the United Kingdom in 1914 ; we shall then attempt to estimate the amount of food which land, growing different crops, may be expected to produce. Special attention must be given to the case of pastures, partly because the grass crop occupies nearly three-fourths of our cultivated area and partly because the yield is difficult to ascertain, so that its actual amount has been very differently estimated by agriculturists. As a check on our estimates, and as an indication of the possibilities of food production in the United Kingdom, we shall then inquire into the actual contribution made by our soils to the total food supply of the country in the years 1909–13, and compare the production of these years with that of an earlier period, when tillage farming was more extensively practised and the area under grass was between four and five million acres less than it was at the outbreak of war.

CHAPTER II

THE RESOURCES OF THE FARMER IN 1914

Area available for Food Production in the United Kingdom. Size and Number of Agricultural Holdings. Number of Persons engaged in Agriculture. Distribution of Principal Crops. Rotations of Crops practised in different Countries. The Distribution of Farm Live stock. Importance of Live-stock Industry. Horses. Cattle. Sheep. Pigs. Poultry. Fertilizers and Feeding Stuffs.

Area available for Food Production.

In 1914 the total area under cultivation in the United Kingdom amounted to 19,414,000 acres of arable land and to 27,350,000 acres of permanent pastures and meadows. Thus farmers had nearly forty-seven million acres of cultivated land at their disposal; and, in addition, they had some fifteen million acres of rough grazings on mountains, moorlands, and heaths.

The following figures show, in thousands of acres, how this land was subdivided between the different parts of the kingdom.

	Total Area.	Available for Food Production.	
		Cultivated Land.	Rough Grazings.
	Acres.	Acres.	Acres.
	000	000	000
England	32,389	24,368	2,448
Wales	4,750	2,746	1,333
Scotland	19,070	4,786	9,148
Ireland	20,248	14,743	2,516
Isle of Man } Channel Islands }	184	121	—
United Kingdom	76,643 [1]	46,764	15,445

No attempt was made to collect agricultural returns on a uniform plan until 1866; in the following year, when the returns were fairly complete, the cultivated area of the United Kingdom was found to be 45,491,000 acres; it rose gradually, chiefly because of improved returns, to 47,400,000 acres in 1876, and then fell slowly to the figure given above. The area of cultivated land varies slightly from year to year, chiefly because

[1] In this and similar cases the figure for the total is given to the nearest thousand, and is not necessarily the sum of the figures in the column above.

there is no sharp distinction between the poorer qualities of cultivated grass land and the rough grazings. Reclamation of the latter accounted for some increase until about 1880 ; but since that time little land has been reclaimed. There has been a slow shrinkage in the cultivated area during the past half century, chiefly because of the encroachment of towns and industrial undertakings ; but it will be seen that since returns were first collected, the area of cultivated land had undergone little change before the outbreak of war.

Detailed information about the areas under different crops and the numbers of live stock kept in each country are published annually in the official Agricultural Returns, but owing to the different sizes of the countries and the very different proportions available for cultivation it is not an easy matter to make direct comparisons by using the figures in the form in which they are issued. Scotland, for example, which is nearly two-thirds the size of England, has only one-fifth as much cultivated land, and although nearly as large as Ireland, it has only one-third of the Irish cultivated area.

The most convenient way of studying the methods of farming adopted in the different parts of the United Kingdom will be to concentrate attention on the cultivated land, and to regard each country as being made up of a large number of thousand-acre sections [1] (of these sections there are in all 46,764). We may then take one section from each country, assume it to be an estate typical of the others, ascertain how it is divided up into farms, and how the land of these farms is, in turn, apportioned between the different crops. The rough grazings having relatively little value, we may conveniently regard as extra land attached to each of our typical estates forming 'outruns' for live stock. The area of rough grazing in Scotland is so large that each estate would have about 1,911 acres of 'outrun ' ; while in England the area would be 100 acres only. Rough grazings, as we shall see, have a very important bearing on the live-stock farming of the different countries.

[1] Non-agricultural readers should endeavour to visualize 1,000 acres. Imagine a straight country road, fields 220 yards wide on either side ; when 6¼ miles have been traversed the fields bordering the road will aggregate 1,000 acres.

Size and Number of Agricultural Holdings.

The first important factor bearing on the capacity for food production of each country is the subdivision of the land between farmers. In Britain it is usual to class holdings of less than 50 acres in area (or of less than £50 rental value, if over 50 acres) as 'Small Holdings'. The following figures classify the holdings of a typical 1,000-acre section into different sizes. (Fractions are omitted) :

| | Over 50 Acres. | | 1–50 Acres. | | All Holdings. over 1 Acre. | |
	No.	Av. Size. Acres.	No.	Av. Size. Acres.	No.	Av. Size. Acres.
England . . .	5	158	10	15	15	66
Wales . . .	6	112	16	17	22	45
Scotland . . .	5	161	11	13	16	63
Ireland . . .	6	85	25	16	31	32
United Kingdom .	6	135	15	16	21	48

In Ireland the holdings are about twice as numerous as they are in England and Scotland. In the case of holdings of more than fifty acres the numbers do not differ much, but the average farms of Ireland and Wales are much smaller than those of England and Scotland. Very small holdings of from five to fifteen acres are much more numerous in Ireland than in any other part of the United Kingdom, except in the Western Highlands and Islands of Scotland. As an indication of the ordinary sizes of holdings in Great Britain, it may be stated that a thousand acres typical of the cultivated land of the whole country would consist of four very small holdings of approximately three acres, seven small holdings averaging twenty acres, five farms of about one hundred and twenty-five acres, and half of one large holding of four hundred and sixty acres. Five-sixths of the total area would be found to be occupied by holdings exceeding fifty acres.

Persons engaged in Agriculture.

From information collected in connexion with the Census of Production 1908, and the 1911 population Census, it may be estimated that at the outbreak of war each thousand acres of cultivated land in Great Britain gave employment to forty-six men and boys and to twelve women and girls. In Ireland the corresponding figures were fifty-nine males and seven females. It may be observed that these Census figures appear to understate the amount of women's time occupied by dairy work, and the rearing of calves, pigs, and poultry. In many dairying and stock-raising districts, and especially in Ireland, the women on the smaller holdings are usually as busily occupied as the men.

Distribution of the Principal Crops.

If in 1914 a survey had been made of each of our four typical estates, we should have found the land to be sub-divided between the crops or groups of crops which are indicated in Table I.

TABLE I

CROPS GROWN ON THE AVERAGE THOUSAND ACRES OF CULTIVATED LAND IN THE UNITED KINGDOM AND IN EACH COUNTRY IN 1914

Crop	*England*	*Wales* [1]	*Scotland*	*Ireland* [2]	*U.K.*
	Acres	*Acres*	*Acres*	*Acres*	*Acres*
Permanent grass . . .	577	748 (500)	311	659	585
Rotation grasses and clovers .	94	95 (343)	312	183	144
Grain	223	118	248	85	176
Potatoes	18	9	32	39	26
Turnips, mangolds, cabbages, &c.	63	27	93	27	53
Miscellaneous . . .	11	1	2	7	9
Bare fallow	14	2	2	—	7

The first line in Table I shows that nearly three-fifths of the cultivated area of the United Kingdom is permanently under grass, and the figures for each country indicate that, except in

[1] The figures taken from the Agricultural Returns for 'Permanent' and 'Rotation Grasses' in Wales are not comparable with those for the other countries. The figures in brackets are rough estimates of the comparable figures.

[2] In the case of Ireland the crops on 100,000 holdings of less than one acre have been included and distributed over other holdings. This will slightly increase the figure for potatoes, but in other cases will not affect the comparison with the figures given for the other countries.

C

Scotland, permanent grass occupies far more land than any other farm crop.

Most parts of the United Kingdom grow grass well ; in our climate we seldom have the keen spring frosts, nor the long spells of hot summer weather common in Central Europe, thus grass flourishes. It is a very cheap crop to grow, for it involves a minimum of labour, and manure is not a necessity as it is for most other crops. The risks from bad weather are, moreover, less than in the case of tillage crops.

The figures indicate, that all parts of the country are not equally suited for grass growing. The cold winters and late springs of the north, and the dry summers of the eastern counties of England are alike unfavourable ; hence we find that the importance of grazing increases as we travel southwards and westwards. While in Scotland there is a certain amount of permanent grass to be found on soils well suited for tillage, this state of affairs is relatively rare ; permanent grass for the most part occupies low-lying land too damp for ploughing, or high land too exposed to ripen oats. In the eastern counties of England permanent grass similarly occupies damp low-lying land, and here the poor high-lying grazings of Scotland are represented by inferior pastures on the stiff clay soils that formerly grew corn.

As a broad generalization it may be stated that whereas the farmers of the north and east grow grass where they cannot profitably till, the farmers of other parts of the country till where they cannot grow good grass ; and tillage, when resorted to, is not so much for the purpose of raising saleable crops, as for providing food for live stock and for home consumption.

When we take into account not only the permanent, but the temporary grasses a somewhat different generalization must be made. As between east and west the remarks already made hold good, the apparent exception in the case of Wales will be explained later ; but when the whole grass area, and not merely the area of permanent grass land is considered, it will be seen that between a northern climate as represented by Scotland and a southern as typified by England there is little difference.   An average English estate of a thousand acres would have 671 acres under grass, while an average Scotch estate would have 623.   Although the mixed herbage of the permanent pasture does not flourish in a northern climate, good crops of the vigorous grasses and clovers sown in rotation husbandry can be raised.

The very high proportion of grass in Wales and Ireland should be noted.   Estates typical of the farming of these countries would have five-sixths of their whole area under grass.

The third line of figures in Table I indicates the relative importance of grain crops in the four countries.   The largest proportion of the cultivated area under grain would be found on the Scotch estate, and the smallest on the Irish.   While the Scotch farmer would have one-fourth of his land under corn, the Irishman would have little more than one-twelfth, and the Welshman about an eighth.   Although the average English farm grows rather less corn than the Scotch farm, the eastern counties of England provide a higher proportion of corn than any other part of the country.   Selecting a group of eastern counties it might have been shown that in 1914 they grew about 400 acres of corn per thousand acres of cultivated land, as compared with 160 acres in six typical western counties.[1]

The potato crop, as is generally known, occupies a more important place in Irish agriculture than it does in the other countries ; but the total area grown amounts to 36 acres only on one thousand acres of cultivated land, and Scotland, with 32 acres, is not far behind Ireland.   It is when we compare the areas devoted to corn and to potatoes respectively that a sharp contrast is found between these two countries.   Ireland has nearly half as many acres under potatoes as under grain crops, but in Scotland we should find nearly eight acres in corn for each acre planted with potatoes.

For a country of small farms Wales grows remarkably few

---

[1] *Eastern Counties*, Division I (a) of Agricultural Returns, Bedford, Huntingdon, Cambridge, Suffolk, Essex, Hertford, Middlesex.

Western Counties, Division III (a), Shropshire, Worcester, Gloucester, Wiltshire, Monmouth, Hereford.

potatoes. Sufficient advantage does not appear to have been taken of the mild climate, which makes early potato growing such an important industry in the south-west of Scotland.

Although the potato crop is readily injured by frost, and may degenerate quickly in the warmer districts, within the limits of the British climate it adapts itself more readily to different conditions than any of the crops already mentioned ; thus the two countries, Scotland and Ireland, which offer the greatest contrasts when grass and grain crops are in question, grow similar quantities of potatoes, while Wales and Ireland, which are alike in climate, occupy the extreme positions in potato cultivation. Again, in the case of England, the chief potato-growing areas are in the district near the Wash with an eastern, and in Lancashire with a western climate.

The next group, the root crops—with which are associated small areas of cabbages, kohlrabi, and mustard—form the chief source of green winter food for live stock ; and because of the special cultivation required by them they also allow the farmer to free his land from weeds. As might be expected, roots are most extensively cultivated in Scotland, where the winter is longest, and they are of least importance in the mild climates of Ireland and Wales. For each acre grown on a typical estate in Ireland or Wales, over two acres would be found in England and nearly three and a half acres in Scotland. This distribution of root crops does not show, however, that the climate of the south-west is unsuitable for their cultivation ; the finest crops of turnips and mangolds in the country are often to be found in Devon and Cornwall. Roots are expensive to grow, thus it is necessity rather than choice—the necessity of providing winter food for cattle and sheep—that leads to their extensive cultivation on every tillage farm in Scotland and the north of England.

In Wales and Scotland other crops, included under the heading ' miscellaneous ', occupy a trivial place, but in England hops and a number of market-garden crops occupy a substantial area, and in Ireland flax takes an important place in this group.

The custom of bare-fallowing land in summer, formerly very common, is now almost confined to clay soils in the southern half of England, where it is practised in preparing land for wheat.

Rotations of Crops practised in the different countries.

The tillage crops of a farm are usually cultivated in some regular sequence known as a rotation. The rotations adopted govern the supplies of labour and manure required, and also determine the additions to the corn area which can be made without resorting to the ploughing of permanent pastures. In studying the capacity of a country to increase its food output during war, therefore, the rotations in use are of much practical interest. From figures given in Table I the approximate character of the rotations typical of each country can be ascertained.

Excluding permanent grass, the remaining crops fall into three groups, viz. rotation grasses and clovers, grain crops, and other crops including bare fallow. Certain other crops, e. g. hops and small fruit, do not enter into the ordinary rotation, and should also be excluded ; but as the total amount is not considerable it will simplify our examination of the figures if these special crops are grouped with roots under the general heading ' green crops '.

Deducting permanent grass the English thousand-acre estate contains 423 acres, and it will be seen that while rather more than half grows grain, almost exactly one-fourth of the land is under green crops, and considerably less than one-fourth grows clover and temporary grasses. Included among the grain crops there are some sixteen acres of beans and peas, and as these often occupy the same place in the rotation as clover, the area under rotation grass and clover may be estimated at a hundred acres, and the grain crops correspondingly reduced. The figures in Table I prove, therefore, that the average system of cropping adopted by the English farmer approximates closely to a four-course rotation (green crops—grain—rotation grasses—grain). While this sequence is exceedingly common, it is frequently departed from in both the eastern and western counties ; in the former three-fifths, and in the latter about two-fifths of the whole of the tillage land would usually be set aside for the growing of grain crops. In those English counties which are best adapted for corn growing as much as two-thirds of the whole of the tillage land is frequently under grain.

Turning to Scotland we find that a completely different style of farming is practised. On a typical estate of one thousand acres no fewer than 689 acres would be occupied by tillage crops ; of this area 129 acres would be set aside for potatoes, turnips, and the other purposes to which the Scotch farmer devotes what he terms his ' fallow break ', while almost twice this quantity of land is used for grain growing. If the average rotation were the common Scotch five-course (viz. roots—grain—grass—grass—grain), the area under rotation grass should be the same as that under grain, and should be double the area under fallow crops ; but it will be seen that there are sixty-four more acres under temporary grass than there are in grain ; the excess equals just half the total area under fallow crops. These figures indicate that the Scotch estate might be divided equally into two groups of farms ; in one group the five-course rotation mentioned above would be followed ; in the other case the temporary grass would remain down for three seasons, thus giving a six-course rotation with the following sequence of crops ; roots and potatoes—grain—grass—grass—grass—grain.

The two rotations indicated by the figures in Table I are, in fact, those generally adopted by Scotch farmers. It will be observed that the percentage of the total tillage area of Scotland under grain is notably lower than it is in England ; this difference in the rotations followed in the two countries had an important influence on their respective Food Production Campaigns in 1918.

From the figures in Table I it would appear that a typical Welsh estate of one thousand acres would contain 252 acres of tillage land, and that almost half of this area would be under grain crops, and rather more than one-third under grass.

These figures bear no relation to the system of farming commonly followed in Wales; it is there usual to plough up temporary grass land, grow one or two crops of grain, follow with a green crop and then with another grain crop, in which a mixture of grass and clover seeds is sown; these 'seeds' then form temporary pastures which may remain down for from six to twelve years, after which the grass is again ploughed up and the process repeated. Since no precise definition of 'temporary' and 'permanent' grass has been laid down, much of the grass land in Wales which in reality is temporary and periodically ploughed up for corn growing is classed by farmers as 'permanent' when making their agricultural returns; and the areas described by them as being in 'temporary' grass are those which have been sown down in the preceding year. In Table I figures have been entered in brackets, which indicate the areas which may be estimated as being occupied by permanent and temporary grass respectively in Wales.

Because of the mountainous character of both countries the system of farming adopted in Wales resembles the agriculture of Scotland rather than it does that of England. As in Scotland, temporary pastures are relatively important. In Wales, however, because of the moist mild climate, temporary pastures last longer in good condition than they do in Scotland; thus whereas in the latter country they become poor in the third or fourth year, in the former they may remain fairly productive for a much longer time. When Welsh temporary pastures are ploughed up they are intermediate in type between the temporary and the permanent pastures of the other countries, and the fertility accumulated while in grass enables many Welsh farmers to grow two or even three grain crops in succession before a green crop is taken. Thus, whereas in Scotland the area occupied by grain crops is just double that allocated to roots, on an average Welsh farm the area under grain would be three times as large as that occupied by the green crops.

In Ireland, as in England, the systems adopted by farmers differ widely in different districts. Except for the prominent place taken by flax, the management of the land in certain parts of Ulster resembles the farming of the south of Scotland. In other parts of Ireland where there are rich grazings, the methods followed resemble those of the English Midlands, but over the greater part of the country the rotations adopted differ markedly from those of Britain; and these differences are indicated by the figures in Table I.

The most striking feature of the management of the tillage land of Ireland is the small area set aside for grain crops, and the relatively large area for green crops. Whereas the average farm of the three other countries would be found to have from twice to three times as much land under grain as under green crops, the typical thousand acres of cultivated land in Ireland grows 85 acres of grain only, as compared with 66 acres of green crops. This relationship between the grain and green crops of Ireland is due to the very extensive cultivation of the potato; one-fourth of all the land not under grass would be used for growing potatoes on a typical Irish estate. A second feature of Irish farming is the important place taken by temporary pastures; as in Wales, the climate favours this crop.

Average Yield of the Principal Crops.

Returns of the produce of all the principal crops have been collected in each year since 1884. The British average yield is estimated from reports sent in by skilled agriculturists to the Agricultural Departments. These estimates are very carefully prepared and the reports on which they are based are written by persons who have inspected the growing crops and have had opportunities of consulting farmers in every parish respecting the character of the harvest. As with all estimates of the kind the tendency is to under-rate the yield in very good seasons and to over-rate the yield in poor seasons; but the averages for a long series of years may be accepted as supplying a close indication of the productiveness of the land of the country.

The average yield per acre of the principal crops of each country and of the whole of the United Kingdom in the ten-year period 1904–13 is shown in Table II. The table also shows the total amount of the crop grown in the average year of the decade.

TABLE II

YIELD PER ACRE AND TOTAL AMOUNT OF THE PRINCIPAL CROPS OF THE UNITED KINGDOM ON THE AVERAGE OF THE TEN-YEAR PERIOD 1904-13

Crop	Yield per acre					Total amount of Crop. Figures in Thousands				
	Eng.	Wales	Scot.	Ireland	U.K.	Eng.	Wales	Scot.	Ireland	U.K.
	Bush.	Bush.	Bush.	Bush.	Bush.	Qrs.	Qrs.	Qrs.	Qrs.	Qrs.
Wheat . . .	31·5	27·2	40·2	36·5	31·9	6,518	135	257	184	7,094
Barley . . .	33·1	31·0	35·9	41·8	34·0	5,864	348	895	859	7,965
Oats . . .	40·8	35·1	37·6	49·0	41·9	9,672	901	4,496	6,497	21,564
Beans . . .	29·5	26·8	36·3	42·7	29·8	1,003	4	43	9	1,059
Peas . . .	26·6	22·8	27·7	28·0	26·6	520	2	2	1	525
	Tons	Tons	Tons	Tons	Tons	Tons	Tons	Tons	Tons	Tons
Potatoes . .	6·2	5·3	6·5	5·1	5·6	2,499	144	926	3,023	6,592
Mangolds . .	19·5	18·0	18·4	19·3	19·4	8,266	195	44	1,429	9,934
Turnips and swedes .	13·0	15·3	16·7	17·3	14·7	13,785	897	7,416	4,803	26,900
	cwt.	cwt.	cwt.	cwt.	cwt.					
Rotation hay . .	29·5	25·5	32·2	39·6	32·5	2,283	230	681	1,623	4,818
Meadow hay . .	24·0	20·3	29·6	45·1	28·9	5,082	539	228	3,482	9,330

The units employed are those made use of in the Agricultural Returns for Great Britain, viz. bushels, tons, or cwt. in stating the yield per acre, and quarters or tons in stating the total crop.

In examining the average yield of any crop, for the purpose of ascertaining the success attending its cultivation in different countries, it is always necessary to take into account the total amount of the crop. Reference to Table II provides examples of the need for this precaution. In the case of wheat it will be seen that the Scotch average yield is over forty bushels per acre, or about eight bushels per acre greater than in England. This does not mean that the soils and climate of Scotland are better adapted for wheat growing than those of England; on the contrary, the climate being much less favourable, Scotch farmers select the best soils only for growing wheat; hence the high yield per acre. Again, although the Scottish climate is particularly suited for growing good crops of oats and turnips, reference to the yield per acre in Table II would seem to indicate that Scotch farmers were surpassed by Irish farmers in the production of both crops. This is not the case; the reason for the low average yield of oats and turnips in Scotland is that these extensively cultivated crops are grown, not only on good, but on very poor soils. In Table I it has been shown that on a given area of cultivated land a Scotch farmer grows about three times as many acres of corn and of roots as an Irish farmer does; thus the latter can use land of better average quality and grow larger crops per acre.

Where, as in the case of potatoes in Ireland, a large total crop is grown, it may legitimately be inferred that cultivation in that country is at least as successful as in England, though in England a greater yield per acre has been secured. In the case of mangolds in England, where not only a relatively large area, but a somewhat better yield is recorded than in Scotland and Ireland, the inference is that conditions in England are much more favourable for mangold cultivation than they are in either of the other countries. The combination of large total and high yield in the case of meadow hay in

Ireland shows how very suitable the Irish climate is for the growing of grass.

The distribution of Farm Live Stock.

Figures showing the descriptions and numbers of live stock kept in the United Kingdom per thousand acres of cultivated land will be found in Table III.

TABLE III

AREA UNDER MOUNTAIN AND HEATH USED FOR GRAZING ; AREA OF PERMANENT AND TEMPORARY GRASS AND THE NUMBERS OF THE DIFFERENT KINDS OF LIVE STOCK ON HOLDINGS OVER ONE ACRE IN EACH COUNTRY AND IN THE UNITED KINGDOM IN 1914, PER THOUSAND ACRES OF CULTIVATED LAND.

	England	Wales	Scotland	Ireland[1]	U.K.
	Acres	Acres	Acres	Acres	Acres
Mountain and Heath used for grazing	100	486	1911	171	330
Permanent and Temporary cultivated grass . . .	671	843	623	842	729
	No.	No.	No.	No.	No.
Horses on farms, all ages .	40	49	38	37	40
Cattle ,, ,, .	210	276	254	343	261
Sheep ,, ,, .	560	1314	1468	244	598
Pigs ,, ,, .	93	81	32	89	85

As about three-fourths of the food consumed by live stock comes from land under grass, the table shows the whole area of grass that would be available either upon, or adjoining, a typical estate in each of the four countries. This grass consists of two qualities :—cultivated grass land forming part of each estate, and rough grazings attached to, but not included within, the thousand acre estate.

It may be noted that the figures in the table give the summer numbers and distribution of farm animals. The annual census of live stock is taken in the first week of June. Extensive movements of both cattle and sheep take place in the autumn,

[1] In the case of Ireland the stock on 100,000 holdings of less than one acre have been included and distributed over the other holdings. This will slightly increase the figure for pigs as compared with the three other countries.

and again in the spring ; a census taken at midwinter would therefore disclose a somewhat different distribution. These changes in distribution are however of more importance in studying the live-stock figures for particular counties than they are in the case of the figures for the countries as a whole.

Importance of Live-stock Industry.

In the first place let us examine the returns relating to the farm live stock of the entire United Kingdom. From the farmer's point of view, the rearing of stock is by far the most important branch of the agricultural industry. In the period before the war the value of the live stock marketed annually, after deducting the cost of imported feeding stuffs, amounted to some £125,000,000, while the value of the two chief tillage crops sold—wheat and potatoes—amounted to about £27,000,000 only. The climate of this country is specially suited for the breeding of most kinds of stock, and our farmers have shown themselves to be skilful breeders. Horse breeding has been a favourite pursuit for centuries, and the country has produced not only the most famous of all horses, the Thoroughbred, but two breeds of carthorse, the Shire and Clydesdale, almost as widely known for their uses in the cart and plough, as Thoroughbreds are for their speed and endurance.

The improvement of cattle by selection was begun about the middle of the eighteenth century, and has made great progress in the past hundred years. In 1914 there were about twenty pure breeds of cattle ; each breed possesses qualities which make it suited to some particular district ; while some, like the Shorthorn, have characteristics which make them popular in many countries. Since the eighteenth century too some twenty-five pure breeds of sheep, and eight or ten breeds of pigs have been evolved. These pure-bred animals are registered in studbooks, herdbooks, and flockbooks, and have a special value for use in improving the quality of the ordinary commercial live stock required in tilling the land, or for meat or milk production. By far the greater proportion of the live stock kept by farmers are unregistered animals, and though a considerable number of these animals may belong to definite breeds, they are generally described as cross-breds, or as 'commercial' live stock. Though individually these commercial animals are much less valuable than pure-bred stock, in the aggregate they are of immensely greater value. It is not possible to give separate values for the pedigree and commercial stock of the country, but some indication of their relative national values may be got from the fact that, in the period 1909–13, the average annual value of the cattle and sheep exported (mainly breeding animals) was £255,000, while the value of the beef, mutton, meat offals, hides, wool, and dairy products sold in the same period may be estimated at about £110,000,000. This latter sum includes the value to the nation of the pure-bred stock which were maintained for improving our meat and milk-producing cattle and sheep.

On an estate of one thousand acres typical of the United Kingdom as a whole, it will be seen from Table III that in 1914 forty horses were maintained; roughly two-thirds of them would be employed in agriculture, the balance being young or breeding animals. Pigs were twice as numerous, and cattle from six to seven times more numerous than horses; while sheep, partly bred on the rough grazings attached to the cultivated land, were in 1914 more than twice as numerous as cattle. Since average cattle weigh about ten times as much as average sheep, and require about nine times as much food, it appears that roughly five times as much of our fodder crops are consumed by cattle as are eaten by sheep.[1] Taking the United Kingdom as a whole, therefore, cattle are by far the most important kind of live stock.

Horses.

The numbers of live stock kept on the farms of each country are shown by the figures in Table III. The number of horses kept per thousand acres does not differ much in the different countries, but when the fact is recalled that tillage land occupies so small a proportion of the whole area of Wales and Ireland, it is clear that both these countries must breed many

---

[1] This statement refers to the produce of rough grazings, as well as to that of cultivated land.

more horses than are actually required for working the land. Irish horses and Welsh ponies are, in fact, bred in large numbers for sale, and they form a considerable source of revenue to the farmer.

In each year English farmers occupying one thousand acres of cultivated land will plough about 320, and Scotch farmers about 375 acres, using twenty-six horses in the former and twenty-four in the latter country. Thus twelve acres in England and fifteen in Scotland are, on the average, ploughed and cultivated by each horse. These figures point to a considerable waste of horse labour. The type of farm horse commonly used in England and Scotland should be capable of ploughing and cultivating from sixteen to twenty-five acres per annum according to the class of soil of which the farm consists. The chief reason for the relatively small quantity of land tilled by the average farm horse is that holdings are very often of an uneconomic size. They are too large for two horses, but not large enough for four, or too big for six and not big enough to employ eight. It is obvious that when a greater number of horses are kept than can be fully employed on the land the chances of profitable tillage farming are much reduced ; and it is chiefly because on large holdings the percentage of loss, from teams not fully employed, is much less than on small holdings, that the former usually prove the more successful in corn-growing districts.

Cattle.

As a cattle-rearing country Ireland is easily the most important of the four. In the month of June a typical Irish farm would carry over 50 per cent. more cattle than an English farm of the same size. In Ireland about one-third, and in England two-fifths, of the herd would consist of cows. In England the cows would be used chiefly for milk supply, in Ireland chiefly in producing butter and in rearing calves. In certain parts of England, notably in Cheshire and Somerset, large quantities of summer milk are employed in cheese making.

In Scotland, as in Ireland, about one-third of the whole herd consists of cows. In the south-west the dairy industry is well developed, and milk and cheese are both among the principal farm products. In other parts of Scotland the dairy industry takes a minor place; the rearing and fattening of cattle, or, especially in the north-east, the breeding of pedigree stock, occupies most of the farmer's attention.

Wales, like Ireland, is a cattle-rearing and butter-making country; but, especially in the south, the milk industry is also an important one. As a result of the excellent local market for milk in South Wales the typical Welsh estate is well stocked with cattle. One thousand acres would maintain a herd of 276, and two-fifths of the whole number would consist of cows.

It should be noted that all these live-stock figures refer to the month of June, and that they do not necessarily indicate the relative importance of the cattle industry in the different countries during the winter months. In the autumn large numbers of cattle from the grazing districts of the west, and especially from Ireland, are sent to the corn-growing districts of the east for winter feeding. There they are kept as stores on roots and straw, as in Lincolnshire, or are fattened, as in Easter Ross, the Lothians, and Norfolk. Whereas the midlands and the west are the chief sources of beef cattle from June to December, the eastern half of Britain is the main source of the cattle sold for beef between January and May. In the winter fattening of cattle large quantities of oilcakes and other concentrated feeding stuffs are used, and manure of high quality is produced; while this manure is generally applied to the green crops its effects persist throughout the whole rotation and maintain arable land in a fertile condition. It is well known that the growing of corn is exhausting when live stock are not kept in sufficient numbers. It was largely because of the increase in the numbers of live stock fed during the winter months that the yield of corn per acre was much greater in the nineteenth than in the eighteenth century.

Sheep.

On the lighter corn-growing soils of England sheep are even more important in maintaining fertility than cattle, and it was

for this reason, quite as much as for direct profit, that large
flocks were kept in the eastern and southern counties. With the
fall in corn prices, and the reduction in the area of tillage land
in the end of the last century, there was a considerable fall
in the number of sheep kept in the south. In other parts of the
United Kingdom, sheep, though always very useful on the
lighter tillage soils, are essentially the live stock of mountain
grazings and upland cultivated pastures; and it is in Scotland
and Wales that the greatest numbers are kept. Because of the
large quantity of hill land attached to the average farm it will
be seen that Scotland can maintain 1,468 sheep and Wales
1,314 per thousand acres of cultivated land. Relatively the
rough grazings of Wales maintain a larger sheep stock than
those of Scotland, for much of the mountain pasture of the
Highlands is extremely poor; but, in comparing numbers, it
should be noted that Scotch sheep are larger than Welsh
mountain sheep, and that in both countries the average size
of the sheep kept is much less than in the east and south of
England.

There is a notable difference in the number of sheep kept
in the two countries, Wales and Ireland, which have most grass
and most cattle. In Wales sheep are five times as numerous
as cattle, in Ireland cattle are more numerous than sheep.
Sheep, as compared with cattle, are of very little account in
Irish farming.

Pigs.

In examining the number of pigs in Table III, it must be
borne in mind that in Great Britain the figures relate to holdings
of more than one acre in area, and that in England many pigs
are kept by cottagers. Contrary to the usual impression, the
'national animal of Ireland' was somewhat more numerous
on the English than on the Irish agricultural holding in 1914,
and, while there have been considerable fluctuations, this
appears to have been generally the case during the past half
century.

In spite of the large quantity of potatoes grown in Scotland

and the extensive dairy industry of the south-west, the pig population of the northern country is remarkably small ; little more, indeed, than one-third of the number found on an equal area of cultivated land in England.   While it is the case that the climate of Scotland may be somewhat chilly for the pig, the comparative neglect of the pig in the north must be traced to other causes.   The southern farm labourer has learned to turn to bacon in order to secure his necessary supply of fat, but fat has been provided for the northern labourer in the grain of the country.   With an oatmeal diet there was no pressing need for a supplementary rasher, and without this pressing need, experience, not the conclusions of the physiologist, taught the frugal Scottish peasant that even the efficient pig is an unnecessarily expensive converter of sound grain and potatoes into human food.[1]

Poultry.

To one class of live stock no reference has been made in Table III.   The statistics available in the case of poultry are fragmentary, and not comparable with those issued for the other animals of the farms.

Information on the subject of the poultry industry was collected in connexion with the Census of Production 1908 and figures for the number of birds on holdings of over one acre are given in the *Report on the Agricultural Output of Great Britain*.[2]

Per thousand acres of cultivated land the figures were as follows :

	Fowls	Ducks	Geese	Turkeys
England . . .	1,060	100	20	20
Wales . . .	820	100	70	30
Scotland . . .	840	60	10	10
Great Britain . .	1,000	90	20	20

Since these figures refer to holdings of one acre and over, they do not include the poultry kept by cottagers in such large numbers.   The returns indicated the importance of the poultry

---

[1] Ethnologists, it may be noted, offer a less prosaic explanation !
[2] H.M. Stationery Office, London 1912.

industry on the smaller holdings ; whereas the average for the country is one fowl per acre, holdings of less than five acres returned about ten fowls to the acre.

The value of the eggs and poultry sold off all holdings which exceeded an acre in Great Britain in 1908 was estimated at the round figure of £5,000,000.

In Ireland the different classes of poultry were not separately returned in 1908. The number of all kinds was equal to about 1,620 birds per thousand acres of cultivated land, while the annual value of the sales of eggs and poultry for the whole country was estimated at £5,280,000, of which £3,526,000 represented the value of the exports from the country. Feathers, valued at £34,000, brought the total value of the exports up to £3,560,000.

The great rise in prices during the war made the poultry industry one of immense importance in Ireland. Its place in Irish agriculture may best be indicated by comparing the values of the exports with those of other important farm products exported from Ireland in the years 1908 and 1918.

			1908	1918
			£	£
Eggs, poultry, feathers	.	. .	3,560,000	18,449,000
Cattle and hides	.	. .	11,420,000	23,881,000
Sheep and wool	.	. .	1,723,000	3,379,000
Pigs and pig products	.	. .	5,084,000	6,692,000
Butter	. .	. .	4,026,000	5,437,000
Cheese	. .	. .	9,000	921,000

In the actual quantities of the products exported there were large reductions under pig products and butter, moderate reductions in cattle and sheep, but a substantial increase under poultry—about 27 per cent.—while there was a forty-fold increase in the quantity of cheese. The export of the last-named product again more than doubled in quantity in 1919, when the value was £2,044,000.

In Ireland, as in Great Britain, poultry increase rapidly in density as the size of the holding is diminished. In 1917, when the number per thousand acres had fallen to 1,550, it was found that whereas holdings of from fifty to one hundred acres had about one fowl per acre, holdings of ten to fifteen acres had three, and holdings of one to five acres, six ; while holdings of less than one acre, which were included in the Irish Census, had no fewer than twenty-two. An interesting fact brought out by the Irish Census is that poultry and tillage land are directly associated. As the percentage under tillage increases, the numbers of poultry rise. It would appear that on the smaller Irish holdings a substantial part of the grain grown must be consumed by poultry.

Fertilisers and Feeding Stuffs.

Among the important resources of the farmer in 1914 were the abundant and cheap supplies of artificial fertilisers and concentrated feeding stuffs on the home market. In the preceding forty years these materials had not only increased in number, but had been reduced in price. The same developments of transport and machinery which gave the towns cheap corn, provided cheap manures for the land and cheap feeding stuffs for live stock. The changes in our farming between 1874 and 1914 were not merely due to the fall in corn prices, but to the fall in the cost of feeding stuffs, which altered the balance in the cost of production of corn and milk or meat. Before 1914 our systems of farming had been planned on the assumption that an abundance both of artificial fertilisers and of concentrated feeding stuffs would be available, and at the beginning of the war delays in the arrival of the usual consignments were almost the first indications of the difficult times in front of him which the farmer experienced.

The fertilisers which the farmer purchases consist of various compounds containing one or more of the elements nitrogen, phosphorus, and potassium—familiarly known on the farm as ammonia, phosphates, and potash.

The annual consumption of these manures in the United Kingdom just before the war was at the following rate per acre of cultivated land :

1·75 lb. nitrogen, equal to 8·5 lb. of sulphate of ammonia.
7·65 lb. phosphoric acid (P_2O_5), equal to 56 lb. (30 %) superphosphate of lime.
1·05 lb. potash (K_2O), equal to 8 lb. kainit.

The total quantities of the chief manures used annually in the years 1910–14 were approximately :

Sulphate of ammonia	60,000 tons
Nitrate of soda	100,000 ,,
Superphosphate of lime	700,000 ,,
Basic slag	280,000 ,,
Bones, guano, shoddy, fish, meal, &c. . .	130,000 ,,
Potash manures, in terms of kainit . . .	180,000 ,,

Several of these substances are largely used for other purposes, and the figures for the total quantity employed in agriculture depend on estimates. The materials about which there is most uncertainty are nitrate of soda, where estimates vary from 80,000 to 100,000 tons, and potash salts, where the consumption has been estimated at the equivalent of from 120,000 to 180,000 tons of kainit.

In the miscellaneous class, bone is much the most important source of manure.

As in the case of the manures, the feeding materials purchased by farmers contain three valuable groups of substances, known as proteins (or, on the farm, as albuminoids), fats, and carbohydrates. Some reference will be made to them in Chapter III. They are purchased in many forms ; the by-products of oil mills (oil-cakes), of flour mills (milling offals), of breweries (brewers' grains and malt culms), and in grains of different kinds.

In dealing with the requirements of live stock during the war, it was usually estimated that in the pre-war period they consumed rather more than eleven million tons of concentrated feeding stuffs annually. With the assistance of former colleagues at the Ministry of Agriculture and Fisheries the writer has revised this estimate. The figures adopted by him in the case of the principal feeding materials will be found in Table IV. They have been classified into Home and Foreign produce. Including materials not specified in the table the total average consumption in the five years 1909–13 is unlikely to have exceeded 10,500,000 tons. The amount of home wheat and barley fed to live stock varies considerably, and if grain has been badly harvested, or if prices are exceptionally low, the quantities used in feeding live stock may be largely increased.

The feeding materials mentioned in the table have widely different values, which are not always reflected in their market prices. The figures in the last column of Table IV show the quantity of starch to which the total quantities of each feeding stuff would be equivalent. These figures approximately indicate the values of the several materials for producing animal increase or work ; they may, therefore, be taken as a rough measure of the relative importance of the feeding stuffs which the farmer has at his disposal, although they do not indicate the values for all purposes.

TABLE IV

ESTIMATED CONSUMPTION OF FEEDING STUFFS BY LIVE STOCK IN THE UNITED KINGDOM. AVERAGE OF YEARS 1909–13. FIGURES, THOUSANDS OF TONS

Feeding Stuff	Home Produce	Foreign Produce	Total	Starch Equivalent
Wheat	300	100	400	290
Barley	290	640	930	630
Oats	2,400	900	3,300	1,980
Maize, and maize products . . .	—	1,675	1,675	1,370
Rye, beans, peas, buckwheat . .	265	185	450	300
Linseed-oil cake	—	300	300	220
Decorticated cotton-seed cake . .	—	80	80	60
Undecorticated cotton-seed cake . .	—	645	645	260
Other oil cakes	—	245	245	160
Wheat offals	250	1,195	1,445	870
Rice meal	—	160	160	110
Brewers' and distillers' grains, malt culms	335	135	470	230
Molasses and mollasses' foods . .	—	95	95	45
Total	3,840	6,355	10,195	6,525

Estimated consumption in terms of starch by :

Cattle and sheep	2,700
Horses (farm horses consume about half the total) . . .	2,300
Pigs	1,160
Poultry, game, rabbits	365

Concentrated feeding stuffs not only provide a large proportion of the total quantity of food consumed by live stock and enrich the manure produced, but serve other useful purposes in the economy of the farm. Feeding stuffs are valued by farmers because of the relatively large quantities of protein and oil which many of them contain ; farm fodders are frequently deficient in these substances, and they do not produce their full effects until blended with concentrated foods. Again, purchased feeding stuffs are of great value because they help to tide live stock over periods of scarcity. If grass fails in the heat of summer, or if the root crop is insufficient to maintain live stock until grass is ready for them in spring, oil-cakes and feeding meals often save the situation.

When in the later years of war feeding stuffs were very scarce, it was not so much the loss in the total food supply, as the difficulty created in providing balanced rations, and in carrying stock through such trying periods as the drought of June 1918, that injured meat and milk production. The circumstances that led to the rationing of feeding stuffs upset the economy of the farm much more than the causes that led to the rationing of human foods upset the economy of the household ; for whereas all men were equal in the eyes of the Food Controller, all animals were not ; thus the owners of live stock that could be given no ' priority ' in the distribution of rations were often in great straits.

CHAPTER III

' THE SUSTENANCE OF NATURE '

The ' Hidden ' Sources of our Food. Purposes served by Foodstuffs. Constituents of Foods. Variation in Composition of Foods. Comparative Value of Foodstuffs. Energy as a Basis of Value. Energy provided by the Constituents of Foods. Quantity of Food necessary. Energy Value and Market Value. The Yield of Energy from Land. Yield of Energy by Crops grown in Rotation.

HAVING examined the extent of the farmer's resources in 1914, we must now consider what the results of his work were ; for on the outbreak of war it was the quantity of food being provided by the land, and the possibility of increasing this food supply, that were of special interest to the public.

But upon these two points the public had little information. Although the statistics taken from the Agricultural Returns, which have been referred to so often in Chapter II, are published annually and are noticed in all our newspapers, those of us who live in towns, and know the country only from an occasional tramp along some winding lane or journey round some unfamiliar district in a motor-car, are little given to interpreting such figures. And when we do try to interpret them how apt we are to go astray !

The pedestrian in the lane, as he looks over the hedges at the farmer's crops and cattle, may dream of colonies of small holders, or of ' factory ' farms, and picture the changes which might come over the countryside if only the political party which he approves were in power. He may perhaps be stirred to write a letter to the daily papers describing the great increase in production that would follow the surveillance of the farmer's business by some wise central authority. But as he saunters along at the rate of three miles an hour he forgets the dimensions of his problem. He does not realize that at his rate of progress it would take him about twenty years, moving steadily for eight hours a day and six days a week, to ' inspect ' the land of England from the roadside. He does not know the close attention required by the crops and the cattle ; he does not understand the matters that daily require thinking about on hundreds of thousands of holdings ; and thus he may reach quite wrong conclusions respecting the ultimate effects which State direction would have on the farmer's business.

In the motor-car, again, as the townsman seeks fresh air in a run through rural England, he may recall Census figures showing that agriculture employs only one million men, whilst many millions work in offices and shops and factories ; and as he speeds along the splendid highways—so largely paid for by English land—he is glad to think that our policy aims at the greatest good of the greatest number. But he fails to understand that these Census figures do not reflect the real value of the agricultural industry to the public ; he forgets that nearly all the persons in the villages, and many of those in the substantial market towns through which he passes, are in one way or another dependent for the earning of their livelihood on the semi-deserted fields—that there are, in fact, many more who live *by* the land than there are who live *on* the land.

The Hidden Sources of our Food Supply.

Nor, although the countryman may be scandalized by the shallow urban musings of those who profit by his winding lanes and his costly highways, does he himself make the fullest use of his knowledge of, and command of the land. He could perhaps estimate with accuracy the number of bushels of corn or of tons of hay that a field would be likely to produce ; and he might distinguish without difficulty between the ' consuming value ' of swedes and turnips when taking possession of them for his sheep. But if, before the war, he had been asked to state the ' consuming value ' of an acre of potatoes or an acre of pasture to his customers in the towns, he would have replied that it was no business of his. He was interested in what his customers paid him for potatoes and beef, but the ' consuming value ' was their own affair.

Thus it was that between townsmen who lacked knowledge, and countrymen whose business it was not, we had, in 1914, very imperfect ideas of the quantity of ' food concealed ' in the land of the country.

But during the war, when food became scarce, and it was necessary to confer power upon public authorities to require that full use should be made of the land, physiologists and agriculturists took counsel together, and our hidden resources were, at least partially, disclosed.

In this and the two following chapters we shall examine the land's output of food. But before doing so it will be necessary to say something of foodstuffs and their uses.

References to the methods of valuing farm products for use as human food must necessarily be brief, and the treatment of the subject must be unequal. The chemist and physiologist have shown us how given quantities of produce may be converted into terms of food, and in dealing with this part of the subject a mere outline, descriptive of the terms used and of the methods adopted, will suffice. On the other hand, very little attention has been given to the actual quantity of food recovered from pasture land, and this question must receive fuller consideration.

By way of preface to the remarks which follow, it may be stated that widely different views are current on food questions. The main principles of nutrition are well known to physiologists and agricultural chemists, and both principles and practice are fairly familiar subjects to many of our medical men and stock-feeders ; but one has only to study the daily papers to learn how contradictory are the ' authoritative ' statements contributed to any discussion on human nutrition.

The principles of nutrition have been formulated as a result of experiments on men and other animals and are applicable to men and animals alike, but in the practice of feeding there is a noteworthy difference. Man, although nourished as other animals are, is an opinionative animal ; thus, for example, it happens that while the studies of the past half century have enabled us to devise dietaries for calves which agriculturists would approve, they have done little to evolve dietaries for schoolboys on which parents and house-masters can agree. Lest the reader should suppose that the statements made below apply to fodder rather than to human food, it should be explained that the writer is well aware of the questionings which may be roused by any brief statement on the subject of nutrition ; and, further, that the experiences of individuals may afford reasons, more or less good, for such questions. But the statements are intended to apply not to particular individuals, but to the feeding of a population of forty-seven millions under war conditions, or under any circumstances when food is scarce and dear ; and it must be recognized that under such conditions it is not the likes and dislikes of the individual, but the maintenance of the population in a state of health and efficiency, that constitutes the business of those charged with the supply and distribution of food.

However different the actual dietaries may be, house-masters and parents would at least agree that schoolboys and calves are both of them warm-blooded animals, that they are forming flesh, blood, and bone ; that each day both exert a certain amount of energy, and that the sources of materials and energy alike must be found in the food. We may note then at the outset the two prime functions of food : the supply of the materials of which the body is built up, and the supply of the energy which the body needs.

By far the larger quantity of the food eaten is required for the latter purpose. The energy exerted by the boy is so variable that any single figure might convey a wrong impression of the relative quantities of food expended in energy, and in materials for growth ; but the calf leads a more monotonous life, and the many experiments made on cattle show that in this case, if fed until about two years old, about nine parts of the food consumed by the animal would be used in providing energy and one part in providing the materials of the body.

The energy produced by food is used partly in moving the muscles and partly in effecting chemical changes which proceed as food material is converted into body material. These movements and changes are accompanied by heat which warms the body. The heat thus produced may suffice to maintain the proper temperature ; but if an animal be exposed to cold an additional quantity of food may be required for the express purpose of keeping the body warm. When any animal grows to its full size it is obvious that the need for body-building material is reduced, but it does not cease altogether. Within the living organism waste and repair of the tissues go on continuously, and to effect repairs the food must always provide a certain quantity of the material out of which tissues are formed.

The Constituents of Foods.

During the past half-century the different constituents present in our ordinary foodstuffs have been carefully studied, and many thousands of analyses showing the chemical composition of foods have been published.

The usual composition of some ordinary foods and fodders is given in Table V.

Before commenting on the composition of foods a few notes on the terms which head the columns in Table V are necessary.

Water. Almost all ordinary foods contain water ; the only exception in Table V is sugar. Although water forms the greater part of the animal body, foods are not valued because of the water they supply. The general rule is that the drier the food of any particular kind the better the quality. There are of course exceptions—for example, over-dryness may decrease the palatability of fruit or vegetables.

Ash. When a food is burned the remaining ash contains mineral substances which, as a rule, were necessary to the plant or animal forming the food, and some of these minerals confer a distinct value on the foodstuff. But if we except common salt the other mineral substances required by the body are usually abundantly supplied in food and water. No money value is assigned to mineral substances when foods are valued for purchase. The only ash constituent, other than common salt, which requires mention is lime. A large quantity is necessary in the formation of bone, and in localities where the water is soft and a proper diet is not used the health of the community may be seriously affected.

TABLE V

PERCENTAGE COMPOSITION OF SOME COMMON FOODS AND FODDERS

	Water	Ash	Fat	Soluble Carb.	Fibre	Protein[1]
Plant products :						
Sugar (white granulated) .	—	—	—	100	—	—
Wheat, grain . . .	14	2	2	68	2	12
,, flour . . .	11	0·8	1	77	0·2	10
,, straw . . .	14	5	1·3	40	37	2·1
Oat, grain . . .	14	3	5	58	10	10
,, meal . . .	8	1·7	8·5	68	0·8	13
,, straw . . .	14	5·5	1·9	42	34	2·9
Bean grain . . .	14	3	1·5	48	7	25
Herbage of pasture . .	77	2·5	0·8	10	5	3·5
Meadow hay . . .	15	6	2·5	40	25	10
Potatoes	77	1	0·1	19	1	2
Swede turnips . . .	89	0·8	0·2	8	1	1·3
Linseed oilcake. . .	12	7	9	33	9	30
Animal products :						
Beef with bone, whole carcass	56	1	25	—	—	18
Bacon, side . . .	20	5	65	—	—	8
Milk	87	0·7	4	5	—	3·3
Butter or margarine . .	14	2	83	—	—	1
Cheese, cheddar . .	27	4	37	4	—	28
Codfish (edible part) . .	81	1	0·1	—	—	18
Herring ,, .	67	2	13	—	—	18
Eggs excluding shells .	74	1	10·5	—	—	14·5

Fat or Oil. This familiar substance is one of the three very important constituents of food. With the two others (carbohydrate and protein) it is assigned an appropriate money value when foods are being valued for purchase. In the plant, as oil, and in the animal, as fat, it serves as a store of energy, and when consumed as food it yields up energy to the body. It is because fat is a very concentrated source of energy, supplying more than twice as much as equal weights of either carbohydrate or protein, that a certain quantity of it is found to be essential in a properly balanced ration. Its share in the processes by which tissues are built up, or repaired, is so small, that for this particular purpose no value is attached to the fat present in foodstuffs. When consumed in excess of requirements, as every one knows, fat may accumulate within the tissues.

Carbohydrate. This is the technical name for the large group of

---

[1] The protein figures here used are N. × 6·25.

substances found in plants, of which starch and sugar are familiar examples. In tables of analyses the more important members of the group are distinguished as soluble carbohydrates (or as nitrogen-free extract) for a reason which will be referred to presently. Like fat, the carbohydrates present in food supply energy, and when consumed in excess of requirements they too may be converted into fat. In the animal body itself but a trifling amount of carbohydrate is present. As milk-sugar it is, however, an important constituent of milk. While fats are specially characteristic of animals and of the food products derived from animals, carbohydrates are specially characteristic of plants. Starch forms the chief material of value in both cereals and potatoes, while sugar, although usually extracted only from cane and beet, is present in many plants and gives them value as food. An important point about the carbohydrates is that, since they are abundantly formed by plants, they are the cheapest foodstuffs. They are, however, useful only in supplying energy. The living tissues of the body cannot be manufactured from carbohydrates in the absence of a supply of protein.

Fibre. This is the name given to certain carbohydrates and modified carbohydrates, which in the chemist's sense are ' insoluble ', that is to say are not dissolved by the special solvents which he employs in analysing foodstuffs. The most important member of the group is cellulose, which occurs largely in hay and straw and forms a considerable source of food for horses, cattle, and sheep. The human digestive tract is not adapted to utilize cellulose, hence our ordinary foods must contain very little.

Protein. The proteins are a large and very complex group of substances abundant in both animals and plants. All of them contain nitrogen in addition to the three elements—carbon, hydrogen, and oxygen—present in fats and carbohydrates. Whereas fats and carbohydrates are relatively simple substances and are comparatively uniform in character, proteins are extremely complex—so complex that their nature has not yet been fully unravelled. Within recent years many important points relating to their uses as food have been discovered that were formerly unsuspected. Proteins have a double function in foodstuffs : they serve as a source of energy, as do fats and carbohydrates ; but they also provide the raw materials out of which the tissues of the body are formed. For this second purpose they have very different values ; the protein found in meat, for example, appears to be about twice as useful as that present in wheat. When, because of scarcity or for any other reason, the quantity of protein allowed in a diet must be cut down to a minimum, these differences in the composition and properties of protein become of great importance ; but when, as is usually the case, the mixed diet contains an abundance of protein, the actual nature of the proteins present in foods is of little account in the feeding of healthy adults.

It has been noted above that if an animal is fed upon carbohydrates it can convert these substances into fats, but there is no similar power of building up proteins from either fats or carbohydrates ; it is essential for the formation of the many kinds of proteins found in the animal body, that some kind of protein should be supplied in the food. The carnivorous animal gets its protein from the flesh of some other animal ; but the ultimate source of all protein material is the plant.

Accessory Food Substances. Vitamins. It has recently been shown that in addition to the substances which the chemist has discovered in foodstuffs, there must be certain other substances present. No mention is made of them in Table V, since they have not been isolated and weighed. Their presence and their properties can be inferred only from their effects on the living animal. Great interest has been created by the discovery of these accessory substances, because of the light which they throw on certain diseases, and on exceptional cases which have puzzled students of nutrition. But the discovery has also been hailed by others, unwilling to regulate their own use of food by bringing it into relation to such a very unappetizing property as chemical composition. Vitamins—substances which the body can detect, but which the chemist fails to find—offer opportunities of disputing the statements of physiologists and chemists which are too good to pass by. Thus the relative value of vitamins as constituents of food, in comparison with the proteins, fats, and carbohydrates, has been widely misunderstood. It is of undoubted importance to the consumer that he should secure an adequate supply of vitamins, but they are widespread in nature and are abundantly produced on every farm. In providing foods for young animals the need for vitamins must be kept in mind ; but in raising and selling the ordinary fresh products of the farm, the grower need not fear that he is providing the public with unwholesome or deficient foodstuffs. The three vitamins so far distinguished are all of them sufficiently abundant in the farmer's produce; the danger of deficiency arises, not because of the quality of the products marketed by farmers and gardeners, but because of the subsequent treatment which foodstuffs undergo in preparation for use. When wheat is converted into white flour nearly all the vitamin present in the grain is removed. When foods are sterilized and put up in cans, some or all of the vitamin may be destroyed. Butter supplies fat with vitamin ; the substitute, margarine, supplies the fat, but little or no vitamin. Hence when for wholemeal bread and butter, or oatmeal porridge and milk, the consumer substitutes white bread and margarine, he may be ill-nourished, not because he is being supplied with an insufficient quantity of the principal constituents of food—the proteins, fats, and carbohydrates referred to in Table V—but because he is using a diet part of which has been artificially impoverished in preparation, and part of which is naturally deficient in vitamins. The remedy is to use milk, vegetables, fruit, and other fresh foods.

There was some evidence during the war that the health of the community in certain districts was suffering from a lack of vitamins, and these symptoms would doubtless have been more marked had it not been for the great growth of the allotment movement, and the large quantities of fresh vegetables which industrial workers were thus able to provide for their households.

Although it is a matter of importance to the consumer that his diet should contain an adequate supply of vitamins, it will not be necessary for us to take them into account in estimating the food value of different soil products, any more than it is necessary to take account of the equally important mineral substances which foodstuffs must supply.[1]

From the point of view of the producer of food the three groups of substances to which special attention must be given are the proteins, fats, and carbohydrates ; let us therefore turn back to Table V and study the quantities of them which are provided by some typical foods. It will be observed that the quantities present differ very widely, and it is because of these differences that the nourishing value of our foodstuffs is so variable.

Taking first the column headed protein, it will be seen that, among cattle foods, linseed oilcake may contain over twenty times as much protein as swede turnips, and in the case of the human foods, that wheat flour may contain five times as much protein as potatoes. The figures in the lower part of the table show that cheese, beef, and eggs are rich in protein.

The percentage of fat in foodstuffs is even more variable than that of protein. The main sources of supply are the animal products : butter, bacon, beef, cheese. Milk, too, is an important source of fat ; the quality of milk is usually assessed by the percentage of fat present. Plant products as a rule supply little fat, the oat being the richest of our home-grown foods in this respect. The fat in margarine is usually of vegetable

---

[1] For further notes on the properties of foodstuffs readers may consult a pamphlet issued by the Ministry of Health, *Diet in Relation to Normal Nutrition*, by J. M. Hamill, D.Sc., H.M. Stationery Office, London, 1921, price 3*d*.

origin, but in many kinds of margarine the fat is derived largely or wholly from animal sources.

Except in the case of milk-sugar, and of a trifling supply coming from certain other animal products, all the carbohydrates in our foods are obtained from plants. It will be noticed that refined sugar is a pure carbohydrate, and that cereal grains and potatoes are rich in this group of substances.

Before taking leave of Table V we must note that, as an indication of the composition of particular foods, the actual figures there given have an unequal value. Seeds and mature plant products vary little in composition; on the other hand, unripe products, such as grass, roots, and potatoes, vary somewhat widely. From the point of view of human nutrition, however, much the most variable products are the different kinds of meat. Meat differs so widely in its character that representative figures are difficult to give, and wide variations from the qualities indicated in Table V must be expected. The figures given show the usual composition of the whole carcasses of well-fed cattle and bacon pigs; but in different individuals very different proportions of lean meat and fat may be found, while every one is familiar with the different quantities of fat and lean present in different butchers' cuts of the same animal.

Thus while it is not difficult to indicate the quantities of protein and fat marketed by farmers in cattle, sheep, and pigs, it is difficult to estimate and to represent by figures the 'average' composition of the meat eaten by consumers. It may, however, be stated that the lean of meat, when freed from all visible fat, contains, as a rule, from 30 to 35 per cent. of protein, the rest being nearly all water; while the fat of meat, from which all visible traces of lean have been removed, will consist of from 80 to 95 per cent. of pure fat, the remainder being water.

A further point to be noted about the figures in Table V is that they represent the composition of food materials as produced on the farm, or as sold in shops; they do not necessarily indicate the composition of the foods actually used by the body, for the foods so used must first of all be digested. The digestibility of fodders is often low, and is so variable that statements of their composition are generally accompanied by figures showing the percentages digested by different farm animals. In the case of ordinary human foods, all of which are relatively digestible by healthy persons, digestion co-efficients are of less importance in estimating values.

A more serious matter in connexion with the utilization of human foods than the losses arising from imperfect digestibility are those losses which occur in preparation and at the table. Careless paring and cooking may result in as much as 25 per cent. of the original value of potatoes being lost; and considerable losses of fat meat—one of the most expensive of all foods to produce—take place in preparation and cooking, and because of the tastes of the individual consumer.

Comparative Value of Foodstuffs.

Having noted the substances of which foods are composed and the percentages of the useful ingredients present in some of the commoner foods, we must next ascertain how the values of different foods may be compared.

Even the brief acquaintance we have made with the subject is sufficient to suggest that a comparison of value is likely to raise awkward questions. The composition of foodstuffs, as we have just seen, varies within wide limits, but this in itself need not give trouble, if a common measure of value could be found. There is, however, the difficulty that most foodstuffs may be used within the body for two quite different purposes, and it is obviously impossible to assess a satisfactory value except with reference to the purpose for which the article is required. A compromise is therefore necessary in comparing the value of foods. One of the two purposes for which food is necessary must be selected, and the value of different materials for that purpose may then be compared.

Each of the three chief constituents of foodstuffs can supply energy, but one only—protein—provides the materials of the body; it is therefore necessary to select energy-value as a basis in comparing different foodstuffs. Energy usually forms an entirely satisfactory basis; by far the larger quantity of the food consumed is needed as a source of energy; and when a nation has at its disposal the ordinary foodstuffs, which experience has taught it to use, in sufficient quantity to provide the necessary energy, there is very little risk that it will suffer from the absence of protein, mineral substances, or vitamins. The supply of an adequate quantity of energy is therefore the object on which those responsible for growing foods for use in times of scarcity must concentrate attention.

While the foregoing statements hold good for the community as a whole, they may not hold good for particular groups within the community. It is always possible that, from poverty or lack of knowledge, the foodstuffs used in certain households may be so badly balanced as to be more deficient in protein or vitamins than in energy. Again, it must be noted that energy-value can only be used as a measure of quantity if the food is appropriate ; the amount of energy which a foodstuff might yield in the body of a healthy man does not necessarily show how much it would supply to an invalid, or to a child. But these reservations bear on the work of the medical man rather than on that of the grower of food. For the guidance of the farmer and gardener we may, with perfect safety, adopt the rule that in time of war, or other cause of scarcity, his business is to produce from the land at his disposal the largest possible quantity of energy. It is by so doing that he will best serve the interests of his fellow countrymen.

The quantity of energy which the different constituents of food can supply to the bodies of healthy persons is not the same. As the results of many tests it has been shown that one pound of either protein or carbohydrate will produce a quantity of energy within the body equal to about 1,860 Calories, while a pound of fat will produce about 4,200. Slightly different quantities may be recovered by the body when the food constituents are derived from different sources, but the foregoing figures are those which are commonly employed in estimating the values of foodstuffs.

Since the public first heard of the Calorie when food became scarce because of war, there is a tendency to class it with the ' meat ticket ' and the ' sugar card ' as a war-time measure of value, wholly inapplicable to peace conditions. It should therefore be noted that the Calorie is the ordinary unit devised for measuring energy in terms of the heat produced.[1] Like the ounce and the inch, and unlike the pound sterling, it is a unit unaffected by war or peace conditions.

Quantity of Food necessary.

The quantity of food required by man varies with size, age, work, and exposure. During the war much attention was given to the subject of the quantities absolutely necessary to maintain health and efficiency under different conditions.[2]

Briefly it may be stated that the body of a man of average size doing moderate work would use energy at the rate of 3,200 Calories per day; with hard work the requirement might rise to 4,500 or 5,000 Calories, and in sedentary occupations and indoor duties it might fall to 2,600 Calories. Averaging the requirements of men of all occupations 3,000 Calories would be required; and, to meet inevitable waste and losses, the supplies on the market must provide 3,300 Calories per man per day. It is estimated that 1,000 persons in the United Kingdom would require as much food as 835 average men. Thus the daily supply per person must provide 2,755 Calories, and for each unit of our population 1,006,000 Calories should be provided annually. In the estimates of the production of food by different farm crops or animals made below, it is assumed that the production of one million Calories is equivalent to the food requirements of one person.

In the practical preparation of suitable dietaries close attention must be given to the size, age, and work of the individual;

[1] A Calorie is the quantity of heat required to raise one litre (0·88 quart) of pure water from 15° to 16° C. When this quantity of heat is referred to, Calorie is spelt with a capital to distinguish it from the small calorie. 1,000 calories = 1 Calorie. A definite conception of the quantity of heat represented by a Calorie may be obtained by filling a quart kettle nine-tenths full of ice-cold water and noting the time it takes to come to the boil over a flame; when it boils 100 Calories have been absorbed and retained by the water: If placed over a very small flame, so that it takes about fifty minutes to boil, the water in the kettle would be gaining heat at about the same rate as the food of an average-sized man should provide him with energy.

[2] See *The Food Requirements of Man*, a Report by the Food (War) Committee of the Royal Society. Harrison & Sons, London, 1918.

for, as has been stated, the energy requirements are very
variable ; but we need not discuss the subject here, since in the
production of food we are concerned only with the average
requirements of the population.   In planning dietaries, too,
careful attention must be given to the sources of the energy
provided.   In the case of an average man supplied with 3,000
Calories, some 400 Calories should be derived from protein
and 800 from fat, leaving 1,800 to come from carbohydrates.
Stated in terms of weight, not less than three ounces each
of protein and fat and about sixteen ounces of carbohydrate
should be provided per day.   Five to six parts by weight
of carbohydrate to one each of protein and fat are usually
allowed in preparing dietaries.   The actual quantity of protein
depends upon its source.   When chiefly derived from vegetable
sources four ounces per day would be desirable in a ration
providing 3,000 Calories.   Much smaller allowances are held
to be sufficient by some authorities ; but experience during the
war indicated that rations providing 3,000 Calories which
supply less than three ounces of protein or two and a half
ounces of fat are not likely to prove satisfactory.

Energy Value and Market Value.

Since the intrinsic value of foodstuffs to a community may
be measured by the energy which they are capable of supplying
to the body, it might be supposed that a close relationship would
exist between the number of Calories which a pound of any
particular food contains and the price at which the food sells.
But that this is very far from being the case is shown by the
figures in Table VI.

The figures in column 3 show the cost of 3,000 Calories in
certain common foods, supplying the number of Calories per
pound shown in column 2, and sold at the prices indicated.
Retail prices vary rapidly, but given any particular price the
cost of 3,000 Calories can easily be ascertained.   In general, it
will be seen that the Calories purchased in plant products are
cheap, while those obtained from animal products are expensive.
The relationship between Calories and price is so slight that

3,000 Calories in oatmeal may be obtained for fourpence, while the same number in veal would cost 10s. 9d.

TABLE VI

COST OF 'ENERGY' IN SOME COMMON FOODS

Food and retail price	No. of Calories per lb. of food as purchased	Cost of 3,000 Calories			
		s.	d.		
Wheaten bread 8d. per 4 lb. loaf	1,000		6		
Oatmeal 2½d. per lb.	1,830		4		
Potatoes 1s. 2d. per 14 lb.	390		8		
Carrots 1s. per 14 lb.	160	1	6		
Beefsteak 2s. per lb.	1,200–1,600	5	0–3	9	
Mutton chop 2s. 6d. per lb.	1,500–1,800	5	0–4	2	
Lamb, leg 2s. 9d. per lb.	1,100	7	6		
Veal cutlet 2s. 6d. per lb.	700	10	9		
Fowl 2s. 6d. per lb.	700	10	9		
Bacon 2s. 6d. per lb.	2,500	3	0		
Milk 6d. per quart	325	1	9		
Cheese 1s. 4d. per lb.	2,000	2	0		
Butter 2s. per lb.	3,600	1	8		
Margarine 8d. per lb.	3,600		7		
Eggs 3s. per dozen (2s. per lb.)	650	9	3		
Cod (edible part) 6d. per lb.	340	4	5		
Herring (edible part) 10d. per lb.	880	2	10		
Sugar, granulated, 5½d. per lb.	1,860		9		

Under ordinary peace conditions the farmer regulates his business without reference to the intrinsic value of the commodities produced; he must have regard to the relative profitableness of the different foodstuffs which his soil and climate enable him to grow. During great wars, however, the circumstances of nations always demand that energy should be produced abundantly and cheaply, and a conflict between the interests of producers and consumers is inevitable. Since this conflict is essentially between the claims to recognition of energy-value and money-value, we must further refer to the reasons for the discrepancies between the results of the two methods of valuation brought out by the figures in Table VI.

In the first place we must recall the fact that energy is derived from three groups of the materials present in foodstuffs, and that while the actual energy recovered from each has exactly the same value to the body, other considerations may give a special value to any one of the three.

Weight for weight, for example, fat provides more than twice as much energy as carbohydrates, and when large quantities of energy are required a concentrated source of supply offers obvious advantages. Even when the total need for energy is small, experience shows that a percentage of the whole should be derived from fats. The effects of fat shortage on the health of the German population during the war were particularly marked.[1]

In the case of protein it is clear that the energy value can only be a measure of its true value if the minimum quantity of protein required for building up or repairing the tissues has already been provided; and in practice conditions justifying a special price may often arise. The farmer is familiar with such conditions, and is accustomed to value protein at about twice the rate of carbohydrate; but it does not follow that experience on the farm justifies a similar value in the case of human foods. Turnips and straw contain very little protein, and it is because oilcakes, which contain a high percentage, enable the farmer to provide a well-balanced ration for cattle and sheep that he finds protein worth paying for. Occasionally conditions in the household may be similar to those on the farm; protein may be specially useful for example when the main food consists of potatoes; and fish, or lean meat, or eggs which supply a high proportion of protein should then be valued for body-building material as well as for energy. But as a rule human dietaries, having cereals as a basis, are well balanced as compared with farm fodders, and when this is the case the true value of the protein would be little, if at all, greater than the value due to the energy it supplies.

In assessing the value of foodstuffs it is not enough, however, to determine the total quantities of protein, fat, and carbohydrates which they contain. Other properties

---

[1] Professor E. H. Starling, C.M.G., F.R.S., on ' The Significance of Fat in Diet ', *British Medical Journal*, 3rd August 1918. See also Professor Starling's *The Feeding of Nations*. Longmans, Green & Co., 1919.

and characteristics may have an important bearing on their usefulness.

Certain foods, for example, may be essential to particular groups of persons, as milk is in feeding young children ; or highly desirable, as meat is for persons requiring an easily digested diet. Again, foodstuffs must be mixed. The degree to which mixture is necessary is not easily determined ; but in all cases some degree of mixture is desirable, apart from the question of composition. The first three foodstuffs mentioned in Table VI, which are the cheapest sources of energy provided by the farmers of the United Kingdom, form the basis of the diet of the poorest classes in the different countries ; but none of them is really well suited to providing more than about two-thirds of the energy required by the body. Oatmeal, because of the considerable percentage of fat which it contains, is the best of the three, and its superiority as a staple food no doubt explains why it is that, in the struggles of the past, the poor Scotchman so often succeeded in developing body and mind, while the resources of the poor of other countries were perforce concentrated on the maintenance of the body alone ; but, until blended with some of the more expensive foods, there are limits even to the merits of oatmeal. Whether, therefore, we appeal to agricultural, or individual, or national experience, we find that there are good reasons why foods should not be valued solely on the basis of the energy they supply ; but none of the reasons so far considered explain why there should be so wide a difference between energy value and market value as is disclosed in Table VI.

The influence of habit on dietary should be noted. The human digestive tract is highly adaptable, and other parts of the world furnish examples of successful dietaries which depart widely from those to which we are accustomed. The hardy Esquimaux derives most of the energy he requires from fat, and the equally hardy Gaucho from lean meat (protein). Even in the case of inhabitants of the same country widely different dietaries may be found in common use among the different classes. The contrast is especially marked in connexion with the use of meat. It would appear that the degree to which meat is necessary is largely a question of habit. There is no doubt that for the ordinary person in this country a certain quantity of meat is desirable—it may indeed be claimed to be essential ; without an adequate supply the health of many members of the community would suffer. But this dependence on meat is to a large extent acquired. Experience proves that, for men living a natural life and securing regular exercise through manual work, a very small meat ration suffices. Among the European dietaries, particulars of which were collected by Atwater,[1] there was one relating to the food of an exceptionally vigorous race of farm workers in the Bavarian highlands. These men were tall, extremely strong and sinewy, well proportioned, and free from superfluous fat. Their diet provided from about 4,500 to 5,000 Calories per day and consisted principally of bread, butter and other fat, cheese, milk, potatoes, and green vegetables ; meat was rarely eaten. In our own country too, it may be observed that the peasantry of the Scottish Highlands, physically perhaps the finest of British races, until recent years consumed very little meat ; their staple foods were oatmeal, milk, and potatoes, with herrings or other fish in coastal parishes. The special value of meat consists in the association of readily digested protein and fat ; thus it forms a useful diet for all engaged in very hard work, and a more or less necessary food for all those whose habits, or working conditions, have brought about a measure of physical degeneration as compared with the hardy and active highlander. It is, however, its palatability which makes it generally sought after by consumers, and palatability is one of the main factors in determining the price of foods.

Another element affecting the cost of food is novelty. This adds considerably to the prices of such commodities as veal, lamb, and new potatoes. Novelty is not without some intrinsic value in the case of those for whom hunger does not provide the necessary ' sauce ' ; but this intrinsic value has but a trifling

---

[1] *Methods and Results of Investigations on the Chemistry and Economy of Food,* W. O. Atwater, Ph.D., Washington Govt. Printing Press, 1895.

relation to the differences in market prices for which novelty is responsible.

When we examine the cost of energy as procurable in different foodstuffs, therefore, we find certain reasons why differences in price should exist which depend on the intrinsic value of the foodstuffs to consumers, and other reasons, more or less good, which induce the purchaser to pay such widely different prices for a daily supply of energy as those indicated in the third column of Table VI.

What fixes the particular price ? Why should 3,000 Calories in oatmeal cost 4d. and in beefsteak 4s. ? In a free market these prices are, of course, regulated by demand and supply. We have discussed at some length the considerations which appeal to the consumer and thus regulate the demand ; but what regulates the supply ?

Harassed by high prices and the difficulty experienced in providing for the household, the consumer has recently attributed the high cost of food to some undefined delinquency on the part of the farmer. But the farmer is neither a philanthropist who sends to market only those commodities in which energy is cheap, nor an autocrat who orders the consumer to expend his money wisely on the articles which provide the best value. The farmer is in no sense a food controller ; his business is to provide what consumers demand ; he estimates the demand by the price offered, and he naturally offers for sale those commodities which pay him best. If he did not do so, some more efficient farmer would oust him from business. Hence the price of the energy offered in any commodity is regulated by the cost of production of the last bushel or gallon or ton for which an effective demand exists. If therefore the consumer, unwisely perhaps, selects foods which are expensive, those expensive foods will be produced ; if he selects materials which are cheap (cheap that is to say in the sense that the energy costs little) those cheap foods will be grown.

Various elements—wages, manures, feeding stuffs—enter into the cost of production of foods ; but the most important element in regulating the cost of the energy which foods supply is the area of land required in their production. Energy is cheap when land produces energy abundantly, and dear when the area employed in the production of a given quantity of energy is large. This statement will be illustrated later on ; in the meantime it is only necessary to mention one point : at the outbreak of war the demands made by consumers on the farmers of the United Kingdom resulted in a very low output of energy per unit area of land, and therefore the average cost of the energy provided in the produce of this country was very high.

The Yield of Energy from Land.

We have seen that when the composition of any foodstuff is known its yield of energy to the body may be calculated. We may now proceed to consider the quantity of energy, in a form suitable for human food, which an acre of land would provide if used in growing some of the common crops.

Table VII contains the figures we shall require in our discussion of this subject. It is assumed that average quantities of the crops mentioned are grown and that farm produce is converted into foodstuffs by the usual processes. The figures in the last column show the number of Calories per acre which the foods would yield if consumed by normal persons.

The method by which the yield of energy has been estimated may be briefly explained. In the case of wheat, after deducting seed and light grain, the produce of an average acre, milled as it was before the war, would yield 1,200 lb. flour and 450 lb. milling offals. A part of the latter is frequently fed to horses, but we shall assume that the offals and light grain are divided between fattening cattle and pigs, and that the small proportion of the wheat straw and chaff which is usually fed to animals is also given to cattle. If the live stock were of ordinary quality we should get the results set out in Table VII. If the extraction of flour were increased to 85 per cent.—a figure which was sometimes much exceeded in the later stages of the war—the yield of energy from one acre of an average wheat crop would be raised to 2,340,000 Calories.

TABLE VII

FOOD VALUE IN CALORIES PER ACRE OF THE PRINCIPAL FARM CROPS

Crop	Form in which used as food	Calories per acre	
Wheat, milling grain . . .	1,200 lb. flour	1,980,000	
Wheat offals, light grain, straw .	57 lb. beef and pork	102,000	
„ whole crop . . .			2,082,000
Oats, milling grain . . .	900 lb. oatmeal	1,650,000	
„ offals, straw . . .	49 lb. beef and pork	68,000	
„ whole crop			1,718,000
Potatoes	10,500 lb. tubers	4,100,000	
„ small and damaged . .	40 lb. pork	80,000	
„ whole crop . . .			4,180,000
Mangolds	230 lb. beef	276,000	
„	350 gallons milk	1,170,000	
Turnips and swedes . . .	150 lb. meat	195,000	
' Seeds ' hay . . .	100 lb. „	130,000	
Meadow hay . . .	90 lb. „	117,000	
„ „ . . .	135 gallons milk	450,000	

The yield assumed is the average yield in the United Kingdom (see Table II). The quantities required for sowing or planting cereals and potatoes have been deducted. ' Meat ' denotes mixed beef and mutton in the proportions in which they are produced. Calorie values per lb. : flour 1,650, oatmeal 1,830, potatoes 390, pork 2,000, beef 1,200, ' meat ' 1,300, milk 325.

The oat crop has been treated in the same way as wheat, and it will be noticed that it is somewhat less productive ; but as already pointed out this is due to the fact that the average oat crop occupies poorer soil. If grown under equally favourable conditions, oats and wheat might be expected to produce about the same quantity of energy per acre.

There is always some loss in potatoes before the whole crop can be marketed. It is here assumed that 'seed' is reserved, that the tubers sent to market amount to 85 per cent. of the average crop of marketable size which was harvested, and that half the balance has been used in pig feeding ; this estimate supposes careful handling and also a year in which there has been little potato disease ; the losses here assumed are often much exceeded.

With the exception of the very small proportion of the turnip and swede crop used as a vegetable, the remaining crops intended for human food must all be converted into meat or milk. The farm animal requires the greater part of the original supply of energy present in the crop for the use of its own body, hence the percentage recovered in meat and milk is always small.

The efficiency of animals as converters of fodder into food varies widely. It depends on the kind of live stock, the age and quality of the individual animal, and on the skill of the stock feeder. A good cow or a pig may be expected to return as human food from 14 to 16 per cent. of the energy present in fodder ; a full-grown bullock fattened at three years old, 5 to 6 per cent. ; a bullock fattened at two years old, 8 to 9 per cent ; and sheep, fattened as a rule when younger than cattle, from 10 to 12 per cent.

The estimates made in Table VII assume good management, and live stock of average quality.

From figures such as those given in Table VII, the yield of human food from arable land may easily be calculated if the rotation and yield of the crops, the system of keeping live stock, and the number of horses required for tillage are known.

Yield of Energy by Crops grown in Rotation.

As an illustration of the quantity of energy resulting from arable land growing crops on a four-course rotation, we may take the case of one hundred acres situated in the eastern counties, and set out the results likely to be secured. Particulars of the crops grown and the methods of using them are given in the foot-note.[1] It may be observed that as the area actually under crops is assumed to be 100 acres, from six to ten acres must be added to the area of the farm so as to provide for roads, hedges, ditches, buildings, garden, and paddock.

---

[1] The crops assumed are : *Course* 1. (*a*) 10 ac. mangolds, 20 ton crop; (*b*) 10 ac. swedes and turnips, 16 ton crop ; (*c*) 5 ac. potatoes, 7 ton crop. *Course* 2. (*a*) 15 ac. barley, 44 bush. crop ; (*b*) 10 ac. wheat, 36 bush. crop ; *Course* 3. (*a*) 20 ac. clover, twice mown, 45 cwt. crop ; (*b*) 5 ac. grazing for farm horses and cows. *Course* 4. (*a*) 15 ac. wheat, 36 bush. crop ; (*b*) 10 ac. oats, 48 bush. crop.

Four horses are kept for tilling the land, and one or two cows to supply the farm with milk. All other fodders are employed in fattening cattle. Wheat, except seed and light grain, sold for milling. 450 bushels barley sold for brewing, the balance after deducting seed used for feeding. Oats used for farm horses and cows. Mill offals and brewer's grain returned to farm for feeding.

The total quantity of energy yielded by one hundred acres of arable land, cultivated as indicated in the foot-note on the preceding page, would be approximately :

Foodstuff	Quantity lb.	Energy Million Calories
Wheat flour.	31,500	58·59
Barley for brewing	25,000	10·00
Potatoes	56,000	21·75
Beef	7,680	17·66
Total production from one hundred acres.		108·00

The methods of estimating the energy value of flour and potatoes have already been indicated. It is here assumed that beer retains one-fourth of the original energy value of barley. Some authorities, however, put the food value of beer at less than, and others at twice this figure. In the case of beef it should be noted that the amount stated consists of the fattening increase of cattle which are nearly full grown, and that the energy value per pound is very high. It has been taken at 2,300 Calories, a figure which would only be applicable to prime fat cattle.

The gross area of the farm on which one hundred acres of tillage crops have been grown is assumed to be about one hundred and eight acres. Thus the yield from arable land managed as indicated would be one million Calories per acre. Medium quality tillage land when well farmed should be expected to yield this quantity of energy, but the amount is much in excess of the average yield of the tillage land of the country.

If we were to examine in more detail the purposes to which the land of this farm has been put, it would be found that twenty-two acres have been used to provide fodder and litter for farm horses and for the milch cows required by the farmer and his labourers, while the remaining seventy-eight acres would have produced the following quantities of energy :

Produce	Area	Million Calories	Calories per acre
Wheat flour	18 acres	58·59	3,225,000
Potatoes	5 ,,	21·84	4,370,000
Beer	8 ,,	10·00	1,250,000
Meat	47 ,,	17·66	375,000

In arriving at the areas contributing to each product, meat has been debited with a proportion of the wheat and barley areas, because of the offals and brewer's grains supplied to cattle. If the energy yield per acre in this case be compared with the figures in Table VII, it will be seen that no crop there mentioned gave so high a yield when converted into meat. It should be noted that the yield of the fodder crops in this example is above the average; and also that the meat figures in Table VII were based on the average production of meat throughout the life of the animal; whereas the above figures refer to the manufacture of prime beef from full-grown store cattle, which it is assumed have been skilfully purchased and fattened. If cattle were reared and fattened on this farm, it is unlikely that the average yield of meat would be found to provide more than 200,000 Calories per acre.

CHAPTER IV

PRODUCTION OF MEAT AND MILK ON GRASS LAND

Large Reduction of Grass Land during War. Importance of Pastures. Production of Meadows and Pastures compared. Methods employed in estimating the Production of Grass Land. Total Production of Beef and Mutton in the United Kingdom. Contribution made by Concentrated Feeding Stuffs to Meat Supply. Meat due to Grass and to Crops other than Grass. Grass available for Meat and for Milk Animals. Production of Milk in United Kingdom. Proportion due to Feeding Stuffs. Conclusions respecting Production on Grass Land. Losses due to Ploughing Grass of average quality. Variations in Productiveness of Grass Land. Production of Meat on Hill Grazings. Food Value of Products of Grass Land.

In the war years more than three million acres of grass land were broken up for growing corn in the United Kingdom. In tracing the history of the war harvests in subsequent chapters we shall examine the methods by which changes in our farming were brought about, and attempt to estimate the additions made to our food supply. But the first stage in corn production was necessarily destruction. Pastures producing milk and meat must be ploughed many months before corn can be harvested. The disappearance of the pastures was the earliest indication the public got of the activities of the Food Production Department, and critics of the plough policy were not slow to call attention to the losses which were being sustained. Assertions were freely made to the effect that those responsible had not counted the cost, and that food destruction, not food production, would result from the Government's misguided efforts.

The production of grain and other tillage crops has been estimated annually since 1884; but no similar estimates of the production of our pastures have been made. Until we know, at least approximately, the contributions which our pastures make to our meat and milk supplies, it is not possible to arrive at any conclusions respecting the real increase in food resulting from the war effort; we shall therefore now examine this subject.

Importance of Grass Land.

We have already seen that of the 47,000,000 acres of cultivated land which the United Kingdom contained at the outbreak of war, no fewer than 34,000,000 acres were in grass. In addition to the cultivated grass land some 15,500,000 acres of mountain and heath land were also available for grazing sheep and cattle.

The areas of cultivated land under pastures and hay in 1914 and 1918 are compared in the following statement :

United Kingdom	1914	1918	Decrease in 1918
	Acres	*Acres*	*Acres*
Permanent grass for hay . . .	6,490,000	5,950,000	540,000
Temporary ,, ,, . . .	2,903,000	2,803,000	100,000
Total grass for hay	9,393,000	8,753,000	640,000
Permanent grazings	20,860,000	19,097,000	1,763,000
Temporary ,, . . .	3,841,000	2,718,000	1,123,000
Total ,, . . .	24,701,000	21,815,000	2,886,000
Permanent hay and grazings . .	27,350,000	25,047,000	2,303,000
Temporary ,, ,, . .	6,744,000	5,521,000	1,223,000
Total grass land	34,094,000	30,568,000	3,526,000

Production of Pastures and Meadows compared.

In Table VII an estimate will be found of the quantity of meat produced by that part of the grass crop which is made into hay. But, in addition to the hay, there is some yield of food from the aftermath of meadows, and from grazing in the early spring ; thus an addition must be made to the figures given in the table. A considerable portion of the temporary grass reserved for hay is mown twice in the season, as is also a small percentage of the permanent meadow land ; and when this practice is followed the grazings will produce little additional food. When the grass is mown once only, the grazing of temporary leys may add from 30 to 50 per cent. to the value of the hay crop, and the grazing of meadow land—mown much later in the year—may add from 10 to 20 per cent. to the value of the hay. Making allowances for the land which has been mown twice, the produce of which has been taken into account in the figures given in Table VII, the total average production (reckoned in terms of meat) of land growing temporary hay should amount to from 120 to 140 lb. per acre, and the total from land growing permanent hay to from 100 to 110 lb. per acre.

The quality of the soil of temporary leys reserved for hay does not differ much from that of the soil of temporary pastures. Where there is a choice the produce of the better land is usually mown. A large part of the temporary grass reserved for pasture is, however, in its second or third season, and it is then of distinctly lower value than in the first season. If the yield of temporary pastures were to be deduced from the yield obtained from the hay crop, the quantity of meat likely to result from the grazing of an average acre might be roughly estimated at 100 to 120 lb.

It is not possible to frame any approximate estimate of the average yield of permanent pastures from a consideration of the production of meadows, for the mixed herbage of permanent grass land varies widely in character. In some cases the crop would yield a greater return if mown than if grazed ; in other cases grazing would give the better return. Nor would the relative production always remain the same ; in some seasons the plants growing on a particular field would yield most if converted into hay, in others if the land were grazed. Moreover, the average quality of the soil of meadows and of pastures differs widely in different districts. In a relatively small proportion of cases, where the grazings are of exceptionally high quality, the best soils are reserved for pastures and inferior grass land is mown ; in other districts permanent pastures and meadows, like temporary pastures and rotation hay, are found upon land which differs little in fertility ; but in by far the greater number of cases the more productive grass land of the farm is reserved for hay. Taking the country as a whole, therefore, the average production of permanent pastures is likely for this reason to be much less than the production of the land mown for hay.

A third difference which prevents any direct estimate of the productiveness of pastures being based upon the output of meadows depends on the utilization. Hay is stored for use, and the surplus of a good year makes up for the deficiencies of a bad ; but pasturage can only be reserved for later use to a very limited extent. In a favourable season there is almost inevitably some waste of grass; for, as it is much more unprofitable to waste flesh than to waste grass, the number of live stock kept is regulated by the production of grass in seasons of average, or under-average, quality. Live stock possess considerable powers of adaptation, so that in a favourable year the yield of meat or milk may be 20 per cent. higher than in a poor season ; but this adaptability is not enough to prevent waste in good grass seasons. The disadvantages of overstocking grass land are so well understood, and the practice is so generally avoided by farmers, that it may be concluded that the production of meat and milk on the pastures of the United Kingdom, even in the best of grazing seasons, is little more than the output of which they are capable in an average grazing year; whereas from meadow land the full advantages of a very good season can be secured.

Methods employed in estimating the Production of Grass Land.

Since the yield of the hay crop does not enable us to estimate the quantity of fodder provided by permanent pastures—much less the quantities of meat and milk provided by grazing animals —other methods must be employed in estimating production.

The total quantities of meat and milk produced, and the total quantities of concentrated feeding stuffs used in the United Kingdom, may be determined with fair accuracy ; thus the net production of meat and milk resulting from all farm crops, other than home-grown grain and its by-products, may be estimated. Further, the numbers of live stock kept in the different agricultural districts are available, and the systems usually followed in feeding them are known. It is possible, therefore, to apportion the production of meat and milk between grass and crops other than grass. The exact apportionment is necessarily a matter of opinion, and an attempt to reach precise figures would involve a laborious inquiry. This has not been attempted, and in view of the desirability, for our present purpose, of giving full credit to grass land, the writer has given it the benefit of the doubt in the estimates which follow.

The figures arrived at below are therefore likely to favour grass at the expense of straw, roots, cabbages, rape, and other crops grown on tillage land, and largely used in the fattening stages of meat production in the corn-growing counties of Britain.

Total Production of Beef and Mutton in the United Kingdom.

Using the figures and methods adopted in estimating meat production before the war, it might be shown that the average yield of meat in the five live-stock years [1] 1909–10 to 1913–14 amounted to about 800,000 tons of beef and veal, and to 320,000 tons of mutton and lamb. The investigations made during the war indicated that the number of cattle available for slaughter in the pre-war period had been somewhat over-estimated, and the Inter-Departmental Committee on Meat Supplies in their Report [2] give the average supplies of home-raised meat (in the 1909–10 to 1913–14 period) as 751,000 tons of beef and veal, and 320,000 tons of mutton and lamb. There is reason to believe that this is again an over-estimate. In a paper read before the Royal Statistical Society on *Variation in the numbers of Live stock and in the production of meat during the War* [3] it is shown that in 1918–19 the production of beef and veal was 620,000 tons, and of mutton and lamb 209,000 tons. There had been a decrease in numbers of 67,000 cattle and calves, and of 1,805,000 sheep and lambs, as compared with the five-year pre-war period ; but it is not possible that the great fall in meat production which was shown by the returns collected by the Ministry of Food can be accounted for by the drop in numbers, or by the shortage of feeding stuffs. The pre-war figures assumed an average carcass weight of 672 lb. in the cattle slaughtered, and of 61·2 lb. in the sheep and lambs. During the later war years the weights of the animals killed at certain slaughter-houses were available. In the above-mentioned paper particulars are given for cattle in 1918–19. Taking the

---

[1] The live-stock census is taken on 4th June.
[2] H.M. Stationery Office (Cmd. 456), 1919.
[3] J. B. Guild, M.B.E., M.A., *Journal Royal Stat. Society*, vol. lxxxiii, London, 1920.

weights recorded in 1918–19, and making allowances for the effect of the heavy slaughter in the autumn months of 1917, which decreased the average size of the cattle killed in 1918–19, and also for the reduction which shortage of feeding stuffs produced, the writer is of opinion that house-fed cattle cannot have averaged more than 650 lb., and grass-fed cattle not more than 630 lb. in the pre-war period. Applying these figures to cattle, and assuming that the calves killed in 1909–14 were 50 per cent. heavier than in 1918–19, the pre-war production of beef and veal may be estimated at 710,000 tons.

The slaughter-houses returning weights of mutton and lamb in the later years of the war were not representative, and the figures they supplied understated the weight of British sheep ; but from an examination of the returns in the years 1918–20, the writer's estimate—after making due allowance for war conditions—is that the average carcass weight of sheep and lambs in 1909–10 to 1913–14 cannot have exceeded 56 lb. per head. This weight is equivalent to a production of 284,000 tons of mutton and lamb. In round figures the production of beef and mutton before the war may be estimated at 1,000,000 tons per annum.[1]

Contribution made by Concentrated Feeding Stuffs to Meat Supply.

A part of the million tons of beef and mutton resulted from the use of concentrated feeding stuffs, and we must estimate the amount produced by feeding stuffs before we proceed to discuss the quantity likely to result from the use of grass, hay, roots, straw, and other farm fodders.

The average quantity of feeding stuffs consumed by the live stock of the country in the five years before the war, as has been stated in Chapter II, was approximately 10,500,000 tons.

These feeding stuffs were of variable value, but if converted into terms of starch the total quantity available has been shown to approximate to 6,500,000 tons. After providing for the needs of other classes of live stock it is estimated that about

---

[1] In addition there was a production of about 50,000 tons of meat offals by cattle and sheep, which have not been included in these estimates.

2,700,000 tons of 'starch equivalent' were consumed by cattle and sheep. It may be shown that the requirements of the dairy herd amounted to about 36 per cent. of this quantity; but, inasmuch as the dairy herd produced meat as well as milk, the quantity used in the production of milk may be taken at 900,000 tons, leaving 1,800,000 tons of 'starch equivalent' available for meat production.

A great many experiments in the feeding of live stock have been made in this and other countries, and, given the conditions —the kinds, ages, and treatment of the animals—it would be possible to predict with fair accuracy the average gain in weight to be expected from the use of particular rations. But this knowledge cannot be applied directly to determining the amount of increase likely to result when a given quantity of feeding stuffs is used in conjunction with the unknown amount of grass provided by our pastures; or when roots, hay, and straw are used with feeding stuffs under the very variable circumstances of the ordinary farm. In estimating production, therefore, it will be necessary to balance a number of considerations, and to take other circumstances than the gain made in feeding experiments into account.

If our cattle and sheep were to be totally deprived of concentrated feeding stuffs, the production of meat in this country might fall by one-half, but this loss would partly be due to the fact that farm fodders by themselves constitute badly balanced rations, and partly to the difficulty of carrying stock through seasons of scarcity without the help of feeding stuffs. It would obviously be unfair to farm fodders to estimate their productive capacity on the assumption that they were used in a way in which no experienced farmer would attempt to use them, i. e. in badly balanced rations. Under ordinary peace conditions the farmer's methods of rearing live stock are based on the knowledge that feeding stuffs will be available. Our problem, therefore, is to attribute to concentrated foods the share which they contribute to production in properly mixed rations. Taking into consideration the classes of stock to which they are fed and the uses to which they are put by the ordinary stock-feeder, it would be reasonable to expect that about nine pounds of ' starch equivalent ' in feeding stuffs would produce one pound of meat. Adopting this proportion, 200,000 tons of meat (160,000 tons of beef and 40,000 tons of mutton) may be attributed to such concentrated foods as cereal grains, oil cakes, and milling offals. The production of meat due to grass, hay, roots, straw, and other bulky farm fodders in the pre-war period is thus estimated at 800,000 tons, viz :

Beef and veal . . . 550,000 tons per annum.
Mutton and lamb . . 250,000 ,, ,,

Proportion of Production of Meat due to Grass, and to Crops other than Grass.

In the case of mutton and lamb the data on which an estimate can be based are scanty ; and, because of the great variation in the size of sheep in different districts, the difficulty of apportioning the production of mutton between grass and tillage crops is much greater than in the case of cattle.

Since we are attempting to estimate the production of cultivated grass land only, we must first write off from the total the production of mutton by mountain grazings. The result of the inquiry referred to subsequently (on page 78) points to the conclusion that our mountain grazings provide no more than the equivalent of from 30,000 to 40,000 tons of mutton annually. Deducting 30,000 tons as the equivalent of the produce of sheep reared on hill land, 220,000 tons of mutton and lamb remain as the production of cultivated crops.

In view of the great extent to which sheep are fattened on roots in the eastern counties of both England and Scotland, and of the size and importance of the flocks kept in the south on roots, kale, kohlrabi, vetches, rye, and other products of tillage land, we may attribute the production of 70,000 tons of mutton to these foods, leaving 150,000 tons to rank as the produce of grass and hay. Assuming one-third of the total root-crop to be available for the use of sheep, this estimate would receive confirmation from the quantity of food which tillage land is known to provide. In the counties in which sheep are most extensively fattened, from three-sevenths to half the root-crop is usually reserved for them.

Taking the total production of beef and veal at 550,000 tons, it may be estimated that the production of beef by grass land must lie between 390,000 and 410,000 tons, and the mean figure 400,000 tons will be taken in our further calculations. It is not necessary for our purpose to examine the detailed figures on which this estimate is based, but it may be stated that the following considerations have entered into it : the number of house-fed and grass-fed cattle slaughtered, their average weight, the length of the final fattening period, the rate of growth of store cattle in winter and summer, the period for which cattle are house-fed in different parts of the country, and the fodders available for winter use.

The foregoing estimates lead to the conclusion that the beef, veal, mutton, and lamb produced by the grass and hay grown on cultivated land in the United Kingdom averaged 550,000 tons per annum in the period 1909–10 to 1913–14.

Area of Land under Grass available for Meat and for Milk Production.

The estimated area of grass land available for cattle and sheep in the period just before the war is shown by the following figures :

	Perm. grass. Acres.	Rotation grass. Acres.	Total grass. Acres.
Total area	27,300,000	6,700,000	34,000,000
Deduct for horses, pigs, poultry, &c. .	3,300,000	4,700,000	8,000,000
Available for cattle and sheep .	24,000,000	2,000,000	26,000,000

The total area producing hay was about 9,500,000 acres, of which, after providing for horses, 6,000,000 acres would have been available for cattle and sheep ; thus the pasturage at their disposal, in addition to aftermath, would have been about 20,000,000 acres.

Although, in fact, cattle and sheep consume a considerable quantity of the hay made from rotation grasses, it will simplify this estimate if it be assumed that horses receive all the rotation hay, and that the hay used by other stock comes exclusively from permanent meadows. The grass and hay available for cattle and sheep would then amount to :

> 18,000,000 acres permanent pasture.
> 2,000,000 acres temporary pasture.
> 6,000,000 acres permanent hay.

If this grass and hay were divided up between the dairy herd and other stock in proportion to the kinds and sizes of the animals and the period during which they require to be provided with grass and hay, the area to be assigned to the dairy herd would be 10,000,000 and to the others 16,000,000 acres. But in practice farmers provide more land for cows than they do for other cattle and sheep, for the consequences of an adverse season and a short supply of fodder would be more serious in the case of cows than in the case of ordinary store sheep and cattle. It will be assumed, therefore, that the dairy herd has about 12,000,000 acres of grass land set apart for its use, viz. 8,000,000 acres for grazing and 4,000,000 acres for hay ; the balance, 12,000,000 acres of pasture and 2,000,000 acres of meadow land, would then be available for other cattle and sheep.

As the dairy herd uses up about one-fourth of its food in meat production, the net area utilized for milk production would be 6,000,000 acres of pasture and 3,000,000 acres of hay ; and the total area employed in meat production would be 14,000,000 acres of pasture and 3,000,000 acres of hay.

We have already (Table VII) estimated the amount of meat produced by an acre of meadow land at 90 lb., or, with the grazing of the aftermath, at 105 lb. If the meat attributable to 3,000,000 acres of hay be deducted from the total quantity of 550,000 tons, the yield of meat from the 14,000,000 acres which we have estimated to be used in the production of beef and mutton in the United Kingdom will be found to amount to 65 lb. per acre. Taking meadows and pastures together the average yield of meat becomes 72 lb. per acre. In view of the excellence of our live stock and the suitability of the British climate for grass growing, the production of 65 lb. of meat per acre from our pastures, and of 72 lb. from pastures and meadows, cannot be regarded as a satisfactory result.

If instead of the writer's estimate of 1,000,000 tons of meat the official estimate of 1,071,000 tons were accepted, it would improve the output but little. The amount of meat due to the use of feeding stuffs, too, is not likely to be substantially, if at all, less than 200,000 tons ; nor is it probable that roots, straw, and the other products of tillage land contribute less than between eleven and twelve weeks' supplies of coarse fodders to our beef animals during the year. The only direction, therefore, in which we can look for some error in the foregoing estimates, responsible for an under-estimate of the production of meat by grass, is in connexion with the apportionment of the grass land between the different classes of live stock.

In view of the total number of farm horses (about 1,800,000), the very considerable number, especially in Wales, raised on mountain grazings, and the requirement of hay for horses kept for industrial and other non-agricultural purposes which was revealed during the war, the allowance of 8,000,000 acres of cultivated grass land for the use of horses would appear to be more than enough for their needs, and for the requirements of pigs and small live stock. In considering the area deducted for horses, &c., it must be remembered that a large percentage of it consists of temporary grass on corn-growing farms, far above the average quality of the grass land of the country. If, there-fore, we have over-estimated the area of grass land used in raising beef and mutton, the error must be sought in the land set aside for milk production. To this subject we shall now refer.

Milk Production of the United Kingdom.

Although, as the result of many experiments, we know the quantity of milk which a given ration ought to produce, this knowledge cannot be applied directly to ascertaining the production of milk by pastures. One figure, however, may be taken from the results got in experimental feeding ; we may assume, as has been done in Table VII, that the rations which ordinarily yield one pound of meat will produce about one and a half gallons of milk. This convenient relationship is suffi-ciently accurate to justify its use in the estimates which follow.

An estimate of the quantity of milk consumed as human

food, and of the quantities made into butter and cheese in the period 1909–13 was made by the Food (War) Committee of the Royal Society in 1916, and was published in their report, *The Food Supply of the United Kingdom*.[1] In the following year the estimate was revised. The figures of the revised estimate are :

					Gallons
Milk consumed as such	.	.	.	965,454,000
,, ,, ,, butter	.	.	.	763,334,000
,, ,, ,, cheese	.	.	.	66,150,000
					1,794,938,000

The writer estimates that the milk used in calf rearing and the proportion of the cows' food converted into meat are together equivalent to a further 600,000,000 gallons of milk. But with this fraction of the production of the dairy herd we need not concern ourselves ; attention will be confined to the 1,800,000,000 gallons used as milk, or manufactured into butter and cheese.

Proportion of Milk due to Feeding Stuffs.

It has been estimated above that feeding stuffs supplying about 900,000 tons of ' starch equivalent ' are used in milk production. Feeding stuffs are even more important to the dairy farmer than to the stock feeder, and were they to be entirely cut off the production of winter milk would fall to a very low level.[2] But in estimating the production of milk attributable to feeding stuffs, we shall follow the principles already applied to meat production and neglect the practical value which concentrated feeding stuffs have in balancing farm rations.

From the cow population of the different agricultural districts of the United Kingdom, and the systems of dairy farming followed, it may be shown that on the average the dairy herd depends upon grass and hay for about forty-four weeks in the year, and on roots, straw, cabbages, and minor feeding crops for the remaining eight weeks. Throughout the whole year, but especially in the winter months, concentrated feeding stuffs are used. The total quantity, as we have already

---

[1] [Cd. 8421], H.M. Stationery Office, London, 1917.

[2] Cf. p. 244 for views of Lord Astor's Committee on the influence of short supplies of feeding stuffs on milk production in 1918.

seen, is equivalent in value to 900,000 tons of starch, and from each ton of ' starch equivalent ' about 380 gallons of milk would result.

The total milk yield may therefore be apportioned between the various sources of food as follows :

		Million gallons
Produced by concentrated feeding stuffs	.	340
,, grass and hay	. . . .	1,200
,, roots, straw, &c.	. . .	260
		1,800

It has already been estimated (Table VII) that one acre of meadow land will produce 135 gallons of milk ; adding one-sixth for the yield from the aftermath there is a total yield of 158 gallons per acre from meadow land.   At this rate the meadow land which is assumed to be at the disposal of the dairy herd would be responsible for the production of 470 million gallons of milk, leaving a balance of 730 millions as the yield from 6,000,000 acres of pasture, or about 122 gallons per acre.[1]

Conclusions respecting Production on Grass Land.

Our inquiry into the quantity of food obtained from those pastures and meadows in the United Kingdom used in grazing, or growing hay for, cattle and sheep leads to the conclusion that at the outbreak of war the approximate yield per acre of meat, or of milk, was as follows :

Pastures	. . . .	65 lb. meat or	122 gallons milk
Meadows	. . . .	105 ,,	158 ,,
Pastures and meadows	. . . . .	72 ,,	133 ,,

With reference to these figures it will be observed that although it has been assumed above that the food required to produce a pound of meat will yield one and a half gallons of milk, pastures are credited with a production of 65 pounds of meat, and of 122 gallons of milk.   If the average quality of all the grass land used for cattle and sheep were the same, these figures could not be correct.   But the average quality is not identical. With the exception of the limited area of rich pasture used in the

---

[1] This apportionment takes account of the quantity of food required by the cow throughout the year.   The actual quantity of milk produced while cows are on grass would be greater, and the amount while on hay less, than here stated.

final stages of the fattening process, cow pastures are on the whole much better than those employed in producing meat. Our figures suggest that the average cow pasture is from 20 to 25 per cent. better than the average of the grass available for meat production. At first sight this difference may appear to be too great, for the pastures usually reserved for cows are classed by agriculturists as second rate. But they are second rate only in comparison with fattening pastures; and if the immense areas of very poor land used for store cattle and sheep are taken into account, there is no reason to question the relative values of milk-producing pastures and meat-producing pastures which are indicated by the above figures.

A second point that calls for comment is the relative production of meat on pastures and on meadows. In spite of the very high quality of some of our fattening pastures, the extent of poor grass land is so great that on the average about 40 per cent. more meat may be expected from meadows than from grazings.

Questions respecting the relative value of different types of pastures, or of pastures and meadows, are of special interest to agriculturists; the main question for the consumer, however, is the total amount of food produced by grass land; and, since the estimated yield of meat and milk in this case does not involve any discrimination between the produce of meadows and pastures, it is more reliable than the other estimates. Although, as has been stated above, these figures can only be regarded as approximate, it may nevertheless be stated with a considerable degree of confidence that the return which the nation gets from its grass land cannot be much more than 72 lb. of meat, or 133 gallons of milk per acre per annum; and—although the benefit of the doubt has throughout these estimates been given to grass land—the return is not likely to be very much less.

Losses due to ploughing Grass of average quality.

From the results of the foregoing discussion it would appear that if no changes had been made by the war in the numbers of our live stock, or in the circumstances affecting their welfare, the reduction in area of pastures and meadows by one million acres of average quality would have reduced the meat supply by 32,000 tons, or the milk supply by 133,000,000 gallons ; and that if the quality of the land ploughed were only equal to that of our average pastures, the loss per million acres would be 29,000 tons of meat, or 122,000,000 gallons of milk.

But in estimating the actual loss in our meat and milk supply because of the ploughing up of grass land, other circumstances have to be taken into account, and it will be convenient to defer further references to this subject until we have studied the changes brought about in the cultivation of tillage land during the war.

Variations in the Productiveness of Grass Land.

One feature of our grass farming must, however, be dealt with at this stage, for it affects not only estimates of production, but the character of the problem which the Agricultural Executive Committees had to attack, viz. the extraordinary variability in the quality of pastures. Whereas wheat crops grown on the best land are seldom three times as great as those grown on the worst, and hay from the best meadows is seldom five times heavier than hay from the worst, the weight of meat produced by our finest pastures may be ten to fifteen times greater than by the worst, and the nourishing value of the meat produced on rich pastures may be forty times greater than that of the lean and watery meat formed on an equal area of semi-derelict grass land.

This wide range in the value of pastures depends upon a combination of qualities which cannot always be easily detected even by the expert, hence the decision as to the land which should, and should not, be ploughed raised difficulties for Executive Committees during the war. The variable quality of pastures further adds to the difficulty of estimating the actual loss in production caused by the ploughing programme.

In illustration of the productiveness of the finest pastures the following particulars may be given :

Without the use of artificial feeding stuffs, and in a season of average quality, the finest pastures in the English Midlands will produce about 120 lb. fat meat per acre in the summer months,

55 lb. moderately fat meat in the early autumn, and 15 lb. of lean meat in the late autumn, winter, and spring, a total of 190 lb. of meat during the year.[1]

Grazing land of such high quality is rare. The proportion of the pastures of the United Kingdom reaching this standard cannot exceed 2 per cent. No land approaching these fattening pastures in productiveness was broken up during the war.

At the other end of the scale are the very poor pastures on which basic slag gives such notable results.[2] These pastures in their unimproved state produce from 30 to 50 lb. of increase per acre in the sheep grazing them, an increase equivalent to from 12 to 20 lb. of very lean meat. The extent of land under these pastures cannot be estimated with any degree of accuracy, but it is probable that the area of grass land producing 16 lb. of meat per acre is at least three times as great as the area producing 190 lb.

Production of Meat on Hill Grazings.

It will also be desirable to refer at this stage to an inquiry made into the production of Hill Grazings in the early summer of 1918. It then appeared to be likely, if the war continued into 1919, that further inroads on lowland grazings might be necessary, and the Food Production Department decided to ascertain what reserves of pasturage, if any, existed in hill districts. At the same time particulars were collected of the output of meat, milk, and other produce on the farms visited.

Thirty-five typical farms in Wales and the western half of England were examined by three experienced investigators, and information was collected from which a close estimate of the actual output could be made. Many of the farms contained considerable areas of cultivated grass, and small areas of tillage land ; and, except in a full report, the products of these different types of land could not be disentangled. In this summary,

---

[1] This estimate was published by the writer in the *Journal of the Board of Agriculture and Fisheries*, September 1915 (vol. xxii). It has since been confirmed by the average of estimates made by four experienced graziers in the district to which it refers ; see *Journal of the Ministry of Agriculture and Fisheries*, July 1922.

[2] See *Manuring of Pastures for Meat and Milk*, by Professor W. Somerville, Sc.D., issued by the Ministry of Agriculture and Fisheries, H.M. Stationery Office, London, 1921.

therefore, reference is made only to those farms on which arable land was either non-existent, or trifling in amount, and on which cultivated grass can have contributed but little to the saleable products.

One of the three investigators [1] who conducted the inquiry in England and Wales subsequently supplied the writer with information of the output on a number of Scotch sheep farms, mostly in the Northern Highlands. These figures were analysed by another of the investigators,[2] and certain of them have been included in Table VIII. The table summarizes the results of the inquiry into production on hill farms in so far as it related to meat. Wool usually amounted to from one-third or one-fourth of the weight of the mutton output, while on many of the hill farms of England and Wales some milk (about equal in weight to the mutton) was produced and sold usually as butter. In the north-west of England the production of milk is much larger than elsewhere, and may amount to three or four times the weight of mutton. Horse-breeding is also engaged in ; on Welsh farms an average thousand acres would rear thirteen ponies. It should be noted that while the columns of the table are headed ' Mutton ' and ' Beef ' very little meat is actually produced. In a few instances sheep are fattened on the hills, but this practice is much less common than formerly. The stock sold consists of wether lambs, draft ewes, and young cattle ; and the meat referred to represents the estimated weight of the carcasses of the animals sold.

The farms in each country have been arranged in order of size. Production usually diminishes as the farms increase in size, the larger holdings being situated in the poorest and most mountainous tracts. Some of the better sheep-farming districts, notably those of the Scotch Borders which are not included in this return, may produce as much as 10 lb. of meat per acre ; but taking the country as a whole it is very unlikely that our hill grazings, apart from the associated cultivated land, produce more than 5 lb. per acre of mutton and beef.

[1] The late Mr. John Robertson, Fodderty, Ross-shire, one of the most skilful and extensive sheep farmers in Scotland. The information sent referred to a number of farms in the occupation of Mr. Robertson himself, and of his friends.

[2] Mr. J. Pryse Howell, now of the Institute for Agricultural Economics, Oxford.

TABLE VIII

Production of Meat on Twenty Hill Farms in Great Britain
Figures lbs. per Acre

Country	Group	Mutton	Beef	Total Meat
England and Wales	I	5·6	1·8	7·4
,, ,,	,,	5·8	0·8	6·6
,, ,,	,,	5·3	0·8	6·1
,, ,,	,,	5·7	1·1	6·8
,, ,,	,,	4·6	0·6	5·2
,, ,,	II	5·1	0·7	5·8
Scotland	I	4·1	—	4·1
,,	,,	9·9	0·1	10·0
,,	,,	6·3	0·3	6·6
,,	,,	2·1	0·3	2·4
,,	,,	3·0	0·3	3·3
,,	,,	3·1	0·1	3·2
,,	,,	2·9	1·0	3·9
,,	II	3·6	0·4	4·0
,,	,,	3·9	0·4	4·3
,,	,,	3·9	0·2	4·1
,,	III	2·4	0·7	3·1
,,	,,	0·9	—	0·9
,,	,,	1·9	0·2	2·1
,,	,,	1·3	—	1·3
Average yield (not weighted) for 20 farms		4·07	0·49	4·56

These farms varied from about 1,500 to over 50,000 acres in area, and are arranged in order of size. Group I contains farms of less than 10,000 acres. Group II, farms between 10,000 and 20,000 acres. Group III, farms of over 20,000 acres.

There is also a small return of venison from mountain land, estimated to amount to 1 lb. per acre of deer forest.[1] The writer has not attempted to check this estimate, but in view of the returns from the larger sheep farms, occupying similar land, it appears to be too high. It is evident, however, that the substitution of sheep for deer would add little to our food supply. From the point of view of food production in a war emergency, there must be many of the 600 English petty sessional divisions [2]

[1] Lord Lovat, *Journal Royal Soc. of Arts*, vol. lxix, p. 103.
[2] The larger divisions usually contain from 50,000 to 100,000 acres. Six exceed 125,000 acres.

in which the opportunities for increase are greater than they are in the whole of the Highlands of Scotland.

Food Value of the Products of Grass Land.

The meat produced by grass land of different types varies widely in composition and food value. Meat resulting from rich pastures consists largely of fat, while that from poor pastures is lean and watery. The quantity of energy which the former is capable of yielding to the body may be well over 2,000 Calories per pound ; the latter may yield no more than 600 Calories. In estimating the total quantity of energy which the meat produced by grass land is likely to provide, 2,000 Calories per pound may be allowed for the richest pastures, 1,300 for the average of all grass land, and 625 for the watery meat produced by the poorest grazings.

While 1,300 Calories per pound represents average meat, it should be noted that a pasture of intermediate quality yielding from 80 to 100 lb. per acre in a season would not, in fact, produce average butcher meat. Such grass land is used in feeding store cattle and sheep, and the energy value of the meat produced would be unlikely to exceed 1,000 Calories per lb.

It should also be noted that although poor pastures and hill grazings have been credited with 16 lb. and 5 lb. of meat per acre respectively, no meat in the ordinary sense is sold off such land. The cattle and sheep fed on these pastures must be fattened elsewhere. Thus when comparing the results got on poor and rich grazings it must be remembered that we are contrasting raw materials and finished products. The use of the Calorie as a unit is not wholly applicable except to foods ready for market. Other properties than the capacity for supplying energy obviously enter into consideration in a comparison of such raw materials and finished products as store stock and meat.

In the case of milk, the figure of 325 Calories per pound used in Table VII may be adopted for the produce of different pastures. Small variations in quality occur, but none comparable to the differences which exist in the case of meat.

CHAPTER V

THE NATION'S HOME-GROWN FOOD SUPPLY

Number of Persons maintained by Produce of One Hundred Acres. The Pre-War Money Value of Home-Grown Food and of Imports. The Food (War) Committee's Estimate of Food Supply in 1909–13. Revised Estimate. The Soil's Contribution to Food Supply in 1909–13. Population fed by the Soils of the United Kingdom in 1831–40. Changes in Agriculture between 1874 and 1914.

BEFORE the war we had very hazy ideas as to the size of the population supported by our agriculture, and it was not until towards the end of 1916 that we were able to state with any degree of accuracy the proportion of our forty-seven million people that was being maintained by our forty-seven million acres.

The lacking information was provided as the result of the work of the Food (War) Committee—a committee of physiologists, chemists, statisticians, and agriculturists set up by the Royal Society in 1916 at the instance of the President of the Board of Trade.[1] Before we refer to the committee's conclusions it will be desirable to summarize the information about the yield of food by land used for different purposes, which has been given in Chapters III and IV.

Number of Persons maintained per hundred acres of land.

The figures in the last two chapters may be summarized most conveniently by indicating the number of average persons who could be maintained (i. e. provided with a sufficient supply of energy) on the products of 100 acres of land.

This information is given in Table IX. It is assumed that each person must be provided with one million Calories per annum, and that the yield of the crop is an average one for the class of land mentioned.

In studying the figures given in Table IX, it must be remembered that, in all cases, the words ' provided the food-

---

[1] This committee took over and extended the work of an earlier body, a sub-committee of the Physiological War Committee, set up by the Royal Society in 1915.

stuffs are suitably mixed' must be read with the statements made; otherwise the figures would lead to quite erroneous conclusions. Thus, for example, it is stated that the meat made from the produce of 100 acres of meadow land would maintain twelve persons. But on the average the inhabitants of the United Kingdom derive from meat one-fifth only of the total energy which they require, and therefore the real meaning of the statement is that the produce of 100 acres of meadow would supply one-fifth of the needs of sixty persons. Again, potatoes provide about one-tenth of the average person's energy, and in this case the meaning of the figure in the table is that 100 acres of potatoes provide about one-tenth of the food of 4,180 persons. In the case of meat it should further be noticed that the same weight does not necessarily supply the same number of persons; for, as pointed out in Chapter IV, meat raised on different qualities of land varies greatly in quality. Where beef and mutton are mentioned it is assumed that they are produced in the proportions 7 : 3 ; that is, in about the proportions in which home beef and mutton were marketed in the period 1909–10 to 1913–14.

TABLE IX

NUMBER OF PERSONS WHO COULD BE MAINTAINED FOR A YEAR ON THE AVERAGE PRODUCE OF 100 ACRES OF LAND GROWING THE PRINCIPAL CROPS OF THE UNITED KINGDOM (COMPARE WITH TABLE VII)

Crop	Edible Products	Persons maintained per 100 acres of land
Wheat	Bread ; beef, pork	208
Oats	Meal ; ,, ,,	172
Potatoes	Vegetable ; pork	418
Mangolds	Beef	28
,,	Milk	117
Swedes and turnips	Beef and mutton	20
' Seeds ' hay	,, ,,	13
Meadow hay	,, ,,	12
Finest pastures	Fat beef and mutton	40
Poorest cultivated pastures	Very lean ,, ,,	1
Average of meat-producing pastures	Beef and mutton	9
,, milk- ,, ,, ,,	Milk	41

The figures in the foregoing table bring out very clearly the great difference in the amount of food produced by different qualities of land, and by the different crops grown in the United Kingdom. Four hundred acres of the poorest grass land would be required to provide as much food (energy) as is produced by a single acre growing an average potato crop, and over two hundred acres to produce as much as an average crop of wheat. At the outbreak of war there were within a hundred miles of London many thousands of acres of these poor pastures, occupying land which half a century before had grown wheat; they had 'tumbled down' to grass because wheat-growing no longer paid.

A second point brought out by the figures in the table is the great variability of food production on grass land. Whereas our poorest wheat soils would on the average provide for 150 persons on 100 acres under grain, and our richest would seldom provide for more than 300, our poorest pastures might provide, in meat, no more than the subsistence needs of a single individual, while our richest pastures might provide for forty.

Again, the table shows how much more economical milk production is than meat production, from the point of view of food supply. The average crop of mangolds grown on 100 acres would, if skilfully used as part of a mixed ration, produce the quantity of meat that would be eaten by 140 people in a year, and since meat forms about one-fifth of our total food this would represent the food supply of 28 persons ; but the same crop of mangolds, converted with equal skill into milk, might provide nourishment equal to the food supply of 117 persons.

The Pre-war Money value of Home-grown Food and of Imports.

In 1908, in connexion with the Census of Production, more complete information about our crops and live stock was collected than is embodied in the annual Agricultural Returns. The results were published in 1912 in two Reports [1] dealing with

---

[1] *The Agricultural Output of Great Britain*, H.M. Stationery Office, London, 1912 (Cd. 6277), 6*d*.

The Agricultural Output of Ireland, H.M. Stationery Office, 1912, 2*d*.

Great Britain and Ireland respectively, and a summary for the whole country appeared in the *Journal of the Royal Statistical Society*.[1]

From this summary it would appear that in the five years' period 1907–11 the United Kingdom produced 19·1 per cent. of its breadstuffs and 55·7 of its meat. The average annual value in millions sterling of the foods produced at home, and also of the imports in this period, were estimated at the following amounts :

| | Values in millions sterling of | | |
	Home Produce	Imports	Total
Grain, flour, meal	10	48	58
Meat	78	51	129
Dairy produce	42	35	77
Poultry, eggs, rabbits, game . . .	15	10	25
Fruit	6	16	22
Vegetables	20	4	24
Sugar	—	26	26
Total soil products	171	190	361
Fish	9	3	12
Total food supply	180	193	373

In addition imported tea, coffee, and cocoa (the last only a food) were valued at £13,000,000.

The Food (War) Committee's Estimate of the Food Supply.

After the outbreak of war, the belligerent nations soon found the necessity of estimating, not merely the weight and money value of the materials available, but the real value of different foodstuffs in supporting life. Close attention was given to the special uses of proteins, fats, and carbohydrates in the body, and to the total quantity of energy which a given weight of each food could supply. Germany, which drew some 10 per cent. only of the total energy required by its people from outside sources, was the first nation to make a careful estimate of its food resources ; for although the total quantity of energy required from abroad was small, it was realized that under war conditions it would be exceedingly difficult to maintain a properly balanced dietary. These difficulties ultimately proved to be

[1] 'The Nation's Food Supply ', R. H. Rew, C.B., *Journal Royal Stat. Soc.*, 1912.

insuperable ; the want of balance in the foods available, and especially the deficiency in fat, undermined the health and powers of resistance of the German people long before the war ended.

In this country relatively little attention was given to the subject of the intrinsic value of our foodstuffs in the first year of the war, as our supplies were ample and no departure from a normal diet was called for. The need for careful study was first prominently brought to notice by the publication of the Report of the Eltzbacher (German) Committee, referred to on p. 9, and by a detailed estimate of British resources which was published by the late Sir Henry Thompson in 1916.[1] It was in the spring of this year that the Royal Society set up the Food (War) Committee to advise on food questions, and the committee decided at its first meeting that, as a basis for its future work, it was necessary to determine the precise character of the food supply available in the years before the war. It therefore proceeded to revise the estimates, made by Sir Henry Thompson (himself a member of the committee) to ascertain the approximate quantities of protein, fat, and carbohydrate present in the foodstuffs consumed in the United Kingdom in the five-year period 1909–13, and to calculate the total quantity of energy with which these constituents of foodstuffs provided the nation. The result of this inquiry was communicated to the Board of Trade in December 1916, and was published in the following year.[2]

A summary of the committee's figures showing in metric tons (2,204·6 lb.) the total weight of the foodstuffs imported, the estimated weight of home-grown produce, and also the energy value, in milliards of Calories, of the foods from both sources, is given in Table X.

Before commenting on these figures certain corrections will be made, which later information and further consideration of the committee's estimates appear to call for.

[1] *The Food Value of Great Britain's Food Supply*, W. H. Thompson, Econ. Proc. Royal Dublin Society, March 1916.

[2] *The Food Supply of the United Kingdom*, H.M. Stationery Office, London (Cd. 8421).

TABLE X

ESTIMATED ANNUAL FOOD SUPPLY OF THE UNITED KINGDOM
AVERAGE OF YEARS 1909–13

Foodstuff	Quantity in thousands of metric tons			Energy value in milliards of Calories		
	Home	Imports	Total	Home	Imports	Total
Wheat flour, shredded wheat, &c. .	840	3,485	4,325	3,051	12,687	15,738
Oatmeal	145	55	200	559	205	764
Other cereal foods	25	315	340	95	1,115	1,210
Beef, veal, unenumerated meats .	820	491	1,311	2,378	1,122	3,500
Mutton, lamb	331	266	597	1,072	706	1,778
Bacon, hams, pork (including home lard)	404	313	717	1,814	1,693	3,507
Meat offals	60	—	60	105	—	105
Milk (including cream) . . .	4,500	—	4,500	3,224	—	3,224
Butter	114	207	321	906	1,645	2,551
Cheese	30	117	147	116	457	573
Condensed milk	—	53	53	—	176	176
Lard (imported)	—	90	90	—	800	800
Margarine	60	58·6	118·6	469	460	929
Potatoes	3,988	262	4,250	3,756	246	4,002
Other vegetables	800	432	1,232	298	512	810
Fruit	341	930	1,271	168	909	1,077
Poultry, eggs, imported rabbits, game	170	161	331	235	226	461
Farm and cottage produce, used at home	—	—	—	2,655	—	2,655
Sugar, molasses, cocoa, &c. . .	—	1,657	1,657	—	6,633	6,633
Fish	715·5	132·9	848·4	392	139	531
Total energy value in milliard Calories				21,293	29,731	51,024

The inquiries made in 1916 were continued in the following year, and it was then ascertained that there had been an underestimate of the production of Irish butter; the later figure required the addition of 12,000 metric tons and of 95 milliard Calories to the butter figure adopted in the original estimate.

It has been pointed out in Chapter IV that estimates of the output of beef and mutton in the United Kingdom made in the early years of the war were too high. The early estimates were those used by the committee. A reduction of 420 milliard Calories should be made to correct for this error.

In the committee's estimates for meat and milk, ' Home Produce ' means the produce of home live stock; but a

considerable part of this meat and milk results from the use of
imported feeding stuffs, and cannot be credited to the soils of the
United Kingdom. In view of the contributions which imported
feeding stuffs make to our home meat and milk supplies,
reductions of 448 milliard Calories for beef and mutton, of
977 milliard Calories for pigmeat, and of 902 milliard Calories
for dairy produce are necessary. Corresponding additions to
the figures for imported produce must be made.

The composition of the potato varies widely with the
variety. When the committee's estimate was made a comprehensive series of analyses of the potatoes in common use in
1909–13 was not available, and analyses made at an earlier
date were used. To supply the lacking information the committee, in conjunction with the Food Production Department,
arranged for the analyses of 681 samples of potatoes taken from
the 1917 and 1918 crops. The value adopted by the committee
for the potato was 427 Calories per lb. The analyses of the crops
of 1917 and 1918 (approximately representing potatoes used in
1909–13), pointed to a gross value of 406 Calories per lb.
Apart from losses in cooking—which, depending on the methods
adopted, may vary from a very small fraction to 20 per cent. of
the original value—there is an inevitable loss of 3 to 4 per
cent. of the substance of the potato in the removal of the
skin. The maximum energy value of the potatoes now in
ordinary use may, therefore, be estimated at 390 Calories per lb.,
and this figure should be substituted for 427 Calories in calcu-
lating the total energy supplied by the crops of 1909–13.

The committee had no reliable figures which would have
enabled them to frame an independent estimate of the value
of the vegetables and fruit retained by market growers for
their own use, nor of the value of the eggs, poultry, and garden
produce marketed or consumed by occupiers of less than
one acre of land ; they therefore accepted the approximate
estimate of the money value of this class of produce used in
Sir Henry Rew's paper in the Royal Statistical Society's *Journal*
quoted above. Converted into energy value the figures adopted
by the committee amounted to 428 milliard Calories for the

fruit and vegetables grown on holdings of more than one acre and retained for home use, and to 2,227 milliard Calories for the produce of gardens, allotments, and small holdings of less than an acre. These figures appear to be much too high. From certain statistics which bear indirectly on the quantity of this type of produce—the number and size of agricultural holdings, the number of allotments and cottage gardens accounted for before the war, and the number of domestic gardeners—it may be estimated that the total energy value of the produce of areas under one acre, together with that of the vegetables and fruit used on farms, is unlikely to exceed 1,600 milliard Calories, or about 9 per cent. of the pre-war produce of the soils of the United Kingdom. In amending the original estimate this figure will be used.

The committee's estimate of the energy derived from fish also requires reconsideration, as the quantity of energy provided by fish affects the estimate of the total production of the soils of the country. The average composition assumed for British herrings was 11 per cent. of protein and 4 per cent. of fat. The percentage of fat in the herring varies very greatly ; in the late summer and autumn 10 to 15 per cent. of fat is frequently present, and in the herring of the Irish Sea much higher percentages have been recorded. The energy value assigned by the committee to the proportion of the total catch of British herrings consumed in the United Kingdom was 82 milliard Calories. It seems probable that a total for herrings of 190 milliard, and of 500 milliard Calories for the entire catch of fish, would more nearly represent the contributions made by the home fisheries to the nation's supply of energy, than the committee's total of 392 milliard Calories.

In connexion with the value of fish as food it may be noted that the abridged figures given in Table X do not fully indicate the importance of the home fisheries. Apart from the herring, which is a considerable source of fat in certain districts, the value of home fish is chiefly due to the readily digested protein which it provides. Although when consumed by itself fish may make but a small contribution to the energy requirements of the body, it is admirably adapted for blending with cereals, potatoes, sugary foods, and other sources of carbohydrates. Further, like the protein of meat, the protein of fish has a high value for tissue-building. It may be noted as an indication of the importance of fish that the home fisheries contribute about three-fourths as much protein to the food supply as is provided by home-fed beef.

Revised Estimate of Food Supply.

We may now summarize the corrections which it is proposed to make in the Food (War) Committee's original estimate.

Corrections in Milliard Calories.			Energy value of U.K. Food Supply 1909–13 in Milliard Calories.	
			Home.	Imported.
Committee's estimate as per Table X . .			21,293	29,731
Add to home produce : butter . .		95		
fish . . .		108	203	
Add to imported produce : feeding stuffs .		2,327		2,327
Committee's estimate with additions . .			21,496	32,058
Deduct from home produce : meat . . .		420		
potatoes . .		322		
cottage produce, &c. . .		1,055		
imported feeding stuffs . .		2,327	4,124	
Revised estimate			17,372	32,058
Total energy available 1909–13 . .			49,430	

The average population of the period 1909–13 may be taken at the 1911 Census figure of 45,274,000 ; it would thus appear that, in this period, the average inhabitant of the country had 1,092,000 Calories per annum at his disposal, or 9 per cent. in excess of the million Calories which we have hitherto taken as being the quantity essential for maintaining the average person in this country. On this supply the nation, as a whole, was living comfortably, and while it cannot be doubted that a very considerable percentage of the people were restricted to the amounts which were absolutely necessary, there must have

been many others who were consuming considerably more than
was required for the maintenance of the body in a state of
physical fitness. Although there was a certain amount of pre-
ventable waste, the above figures suggest, nevertheless, that the
nation must have been reasonably thrifty during this period.

It is interesting to compare the results of the inquiry made
by the Food (War) Committee with similar figures published for
the United States [1] by Dr. Raymond Pearl. According to this
authority, in the seven-year period 1911–12 to 1917–18 the
99,590,000 people of the United States had 129,931,000 million
Calories per annum at their disposal; this is equal to 1,305,000
Calories per head, or nearly 20 per cent. more than in the
United Kingdom. It has been assumed by Dr. Pearl that no
less than 25 per cent. of the total fat and 20 per cent. of the total
carbohydrate in the available foodstuffs were wasted, and that
the foods actually swallowed provided the average person with
1,040,000 Calories per annum. Even the reduced total represents
a generous dietary when compared with 980,000 Calories which
(on the basis of 10 per cent. waste) may be supposed to have
been utilized by our people. The difference may possibly be
accounted for by the larger proportion of self-suppliers in the
United States. In prosperous countries self-suppliers fare much
better as a rule than other members of the community.

The Soil's Contribution to the Food Supply in 1909–13.

The revised figures in the statement above show that
the total contribution made by the United Kingdom to its
own food supply is equal to 17,372,000 million Calories per
annum. Of this number 500,000 million Calories represent the
product of home fisheries, leaving 16,872,000 million Calories as
the estimated product of our soils. If this figure be accepted, it
follows that 34 per cent. only of the food supply of the United
Kingdom is derived from its land; that our home-grown food
would last for about eighteen weeks in the year; that 15,440,000
persons out of a total of 45,274,000 were being provided for, at
the date of the 1911 Census; and that it required three acres of

---

[1] *The Nation's Food*, W. B. Sanders Co., Philadelphia and London.

cultivated land, in addition to the produce derived from mountain grazings, gardens, and allotments, to maintain one inhabitant.

When at the opening of the nineteenth century the long struggle of the Napoleonic wars was beginning, two bad harvests had depleted the stores of the United Kingdom, and strenuous efforts to maintain the food supply were called for. But then the home harvests fed almost the entire population, and the food supply of the country was safe. In 1914 the position was very different ; we had, it is true, some months' supplies stored in the country, but instead of a home food production that could feed our people from Sunday to Saturday throughout the year we had become, as stated in Chapter I, a nation of self-suppliers for the week-end only. Our farmers could have provided us with food from 10.45 p.m. on Friday until 8 a.m. on Monday. If the product of our fisheries were added, a light supper would have been available on Friday night, so that the self-supplying régime might have begun at 9 p.m. on that day.

In addition we had our hares and rabbits, the food value of which the Food (War) Committee did not try to estimate ; nor will the writer make the attempt ; they may be added to the Friday to Monday fare as a contribution to the manufacture of the additional supply of energy which the nation has come to require and to expend during week-ends !

This being the case with the country's home production, it is not altogether a surprising circumstance that, even though ignorant of the actual state of affairs, many British housewives hastened to replenish their store cupboards in August 1914. They showed less courage, perhaps, but they certainly showed more prudence than the authorities who assured them that our food supply was safe ; for no one, at that moment, could have predicted the effect which the submarine would have on our commerce, and from Monday morning until Friday night the nation's food depended upon what its ships brought home.

Population fed by the Soils of the United Kingdom in 1831–40.

It must be admitted that few of those who in August and September 1914 were putting the best possible construction on the country's food position themselves realized the magnitude of the change that had come about in the nation's sources of food supply in the period before the war. It was known, as has already been stated, that there had been a great falling off in the yield of corn; but, on the other hand, it was known that there had been an increase in meat and dairy products, and this increase was widely believed to have compensated largely or wholly in food value, as it did in money value, for the loss in breadstuffs.

It is obvious however, if the statements made in Chapters III and IV respecting the yield of food from land under crops of different kinds are even approximately correct, that the land of the country must have suffered a great loss in productiveness in the past half-century. In East Anglia alone thousands of acres under poor pastures could have been pointed out which, in 1914, were producing one-fiftieth part of the food that they produced fifty years before, and though these derelict pastures are fortunately not typical of British grazings, there must now be many hundreds of thousands of acres under grass which are producing less than one-twentieth part of the quantity of food they formerly provided.

These statements many agriculturists will be prepared to question, for a cursory examination of our agricultural history does not suggest so great a loss in food production. Proofs must therefore be given.

In the first place it should be stated that in the second half of the nineteenth century great improvements took place in the methods and processes of agriculture. That there were advances in this direction cannot be questioned. Land drainage added to the value of much water-logged soil; artificial manures and feeding-stuffs came into common use; farm implements and machines were revolutionized; British breeds of live stock established themselves as first favourites in many lands; our live-stock shows were patronized by the representatives of other countries in search of the best that the breeders' art could produce. At the beginning of the twentieth century again technical education for the agricultural population had been provided in almost every county, and much was heard of the assistance which science gave the farmer. That there had been great progress must be admitted by all who are familiar with farm practice. But with what result? To what extent have our agriculturists succeeded in using the soils of the country for land's primary purpose—the feeding of the people?

We have seen that the number of persons fed in the period 1909–13 was about 15,440,000. Let us compare this figure with the numbers fed in 1831–40. The period 1831–40 is selected for two reasons; in the first place, until about 1840 the country was nearly self-supporting, after that time imports increased rapidly in amount; secondly, the rapid progress in technical processes above referred to had not then begun. From the point of view of 1914 the farming of this period was indifferent; agriculturists had not recovered from the distress which followed the Napoleonic wars.[1]

The population of the United Kingdom in 1831–40 averaged 25,714,000 and the extent to which they were fed on imported foods is shown in Table XI. The figures for average net imports are for the most part taken from Porter's *Tables of Trade*,[2] but for those relating to sugar, maize, and maize meal the writer is indebted to H. M. Commissioners of Customs. To facilitate comparison with the estimates of the Food (War) Committee for the period 1909–13, quantities are shown in metric tons, and the estimated Calorie value of the human food provided by each import is given.

In making these estimates it has been assumed that wheat yielded 70 per cent. flour, and that the offals were used in feeding live stock; that half the imported barley was brewed and half fed to live stock, other than horses; that nine-tenths of the imported oats have been used as horse corn and one-tenth converted into meal; that three-fourths of the peas and beans have

[1] This is the generally accepted view of the state of agriculture in 1831–40. It is a view which, in spite of the references in agricultural writings and histories of the time to agricultural distress, the writer does not altogether accept. Farmers were not prosperous, but farming made great progress in the twenty-five years after Waterloo.

[2] *Tables of Trade of the United Kingdom*, Clowes & Sons, London, 1842. The figures for bacon and hams, pork, salt beef, and eggs have been taken from Appendix IV of Brodrick's *English Land and English Landlords*.

been used as horse corn and the balance fed to other live stock ; that half of the maize and maize meal has been reserved for human food and the balance fed to live stock. The rice imported was at this time partly cleaned and partly in the husk ; the latter has been converted into the equivalent of cleaned rice, and it is assumed that the whole was eaten, although a considerable percentage would, in fact, have been otherwise used. The imports do not distinguish between edible and non-edible olive oil ; it is assumed that half belonged to the latter category, although it is likely that much more than half was used in soap-making, dyeing, lubricating, and for other industrial purposes.

TABLE XI

NET IMPORTS OF FOODSTUFFS INTO THE UNITED KINGDOM, AND THE ESTIMATED QUANTITIES OF ENERGY THEY SUPPLIED TO MAN
AVERAGE OF PERIOD 1831–40

Foodstuff	Metric Tons	Million Calories
Flour from imported wheat and rye, and imported flour .	152,117	553,706
Offals from imported wheat and rye, fed to stock . .	47,500	17,812
Barley, half brewed, half fed to stock	42,872	27,330
Oats, one-tenth assumed to be used for oatmeal . .	33,800	13,600
Maize, half used for human food, half for stock . .	2,168	4,163
Rice, as ' cleaned ' rice	10,066	35,633
Beans and peas, one-fourth fed to stock . . .	30,880	3,088
Sago	· 797	2,869
Raw sugar.	196,909	600,727
Cocoa	590	2,832
Dried fruits, raisins, currants, figs, prunes . . .	17,756	39,211
Olive Oil, half imports assumed to be edible . .	7,500	34,800
Eggs.	4,175	5,845
Butter	9,541	75,851
Cheese	8,729	34,916
Bacon and hams	241	1,203
Pork.	600	2,400
Salt beef	479	1,102
Total million Calories in imports		1,457,088

NOTE. The net imports of wheat grain were 814,900 qrs. and of rye 23,300 qrs. Products ' fed to stock ' are assumed to have been used in meat and milk production. Nine-tenths of the oat crop and three-fourths of the beans and peas have been deducted for horse corn.

The value to be assigned to sugar is doubtful. The quantity imported for home use is that given by H. M. Customs, and is rather more than the weight given by Porter; but the actual quantity which was consumed is of much less moment than the quality. No figures are available from which the average composition of the raw sugar imported between 1831 and 1840 can be estimated. The writer is indebted to Messrs. Henry Tate & Sons for the information that the best sugar of this period came from Barbados. It contained about 92 per cent. crystallizable sugar, and 2 to 3 per cent. non-crystallizable, and produced about 80 per cent. refined sugar, besides edible syrups. Thirty years later, when the average quality would, no doubt, have improved, the imports varied in composition from 67 to 92 per cent. crystallizable sugar. Molasses were used to some extent in stock-feeding, and part of the raw sugar imported may have been used in industries which lessened its food value. On the whole information available it appears to be unlikely that the average food value of imported sugar in 1831–40 could have exceeded 75 per cent. of the food value of refined sugar, and this estimate has been adopted in Table XI.

If the above assumptions (more likely to overstate than to understate the actual values of imports) are made, the average net imports in the period 1831–40 would have provided 1,457,088 million Calories.

During the period 1831–40 there were certain exports of British produce which must be deducted from the net imports of overseas produce; the chief were :

				Metric tons	Energy value million Calories
Salt beef and pork	.	.	.	4,570	14,624
Bacon and hams .	.	.	.	800	4,000
Butter and cheese	.	.	.	3,714	22,248
Beer .	.	.	.	31,140	6,228
Total exports	.	.	.		47,100

In round figures we may therefore place the average net imports of foodstuffs into the United Kingdom in the years 1831–40 at the equivalent of 1,400,000 million Calories.

In 1909–13 the average inhabitant of the United Kingdom had 1,092,000 Calories per annum provided in his food supply, but if we assume that, in 1831–40, the average did not exceed one million, this would mean that, in a total population of 25,714,000, 1,400,000 only were maintained by the produce of other lands. To arrive at the numbers depending on the soils of the United Kingdom we must make a deduction for fish. The quantity of fish caught was undoubtedly much smaller in 1831–40 than in 1909–13, when modern trawlers were at work ; but to avoid any over-estimate of the population depending on soil products we may assume the same contribution by fish to the total food supply in both periods.

We then arrive at the result that eighty years before the outbreak of war, at a time when this country was still suffering from the effects of the Napoleonic campaigns, and when agriculture was a relatively backward art, the soils of the United Kingdom supported no fewer than 23,814,000 people.

There is one exceptional feature of the time, however, to which attention must be directed. The peasants of Ireland, and to a less extent the crofters of the Western Highlands and Islands of Scotland, were then too largely dependent upon the productive, but unreliable, potato. In 1841 the population of Ireland was 8,175,000. As a direct result of the potato famine it had fallen to 6,552,000 in 1851.

The new potato disease, which had been reported in various parts of Europe in the previous ten or fifteen years, suddenly assumed epidemic form in 1845 and 1846 ; thenceforward the potato crop could no longer be relied on ; there was a second bad failure in the period 1860–2, and by 1871 the population of Ireland had fallen to 5,412,000.

There is no question that, under a proper system of husbandry, the soil of Ireland could easily have provided for 8,000,000 people in the period 1831–40 ; but the actual system followed was most dangerous, and it resulted in the population being more than two millions in excess of the numbers who could safely have lived on the products of the soils of the United Kingdom as they were then cultivated. If a correction be made on this account we reach the conclusion that the cultivated land of the United Kingdom supplied the needs of about 21,500,000 inhabitants in 1831–40 as compared with 16,872,000 who could have been fed on the million Calorie standard in 1909–13, and with 15,440,000 who were then actually maintained on the higher standard which the people of the United Kingdom reached before the war.

Taking the figures 21,500,000 and 16,872,000 as affording a suitable basis of comparison, it would thus appear that the soils of the country cultivated as they were in 1831–40 were capable of supporting a population some 27 per cent. greater than they could have fed in 1909–13. In fact—because of the extent to which the Irish depended upon potatoes in the earlier period, and because of the improvement in the standard of living in the later—the population supported by our soils in 1831–40 was about fifty per cent. greater than it was in 1909–13.

If it were indeed the case, as has been claimed, that the output of food by the soils of the United Kingdom was greater in 1914 than it had been in any earlier period, then it would follow that the twenty-three million people who somehow or other contrived to find subsistence from our land in the period 1831–40 had at their disposal a food supply providing rather less than 2,000 Calories per head per day. The times may have been ' hungry ', but it is clearly impossible that the virile people who laid the foundations upon which our Victorian forefathers built up a prosperous Empire could have subsisted on so meagre a diet.

However we may interpret the word ' food ', there can be no question that the land of the United Kingdom was capable of supporting many more people at the beginning, than at the end, of the Victorian period; and the explanation of the change is suggested by the figures in Table IX. The great decrease in the number of persons who could be fed by our soils in the later period was due to the decline of tillage farming. This decline took place in the forty years before the war.

Changes in Agriculture between 1874 and 1914.

As illustrating the character of the changes which took place in the agriculture of the United Kingdom in the forty years before the war, the areas under the principal crops in the years 1874 and 1914 have been set out in Table XII.[1] The numbers of live stock vary considerably from year to year, and the figures for cattle, sheep, and pigs, which are also given in the table, are the averages for the five-year periods 1870–4 and 1910–14.

TABLE XII

CHANGES IN CROPS AND LIVE STOCK OF THE UNITED KINGDOM IN FORTY YEARS

CROPS 1874 AND 1914

LIVE STOCK 1870–4 AND 1910–14

Crops grown on cultivated land	Thousands of acres		Percentage of cultivated land under each crop		Percentage of cultivated land (other than land in grass and clover) under each crop	
	1874	1914	1874	1914	1874	1914
Permanent grass . .	23,680	27,350	50·2	58·5		
Rotation grass, clover, tares	6,285	6,744	13·3	14·4		
Wheat	3,831	1,906	8·1	4·1	22·3	15·1
Barley	2,507	1,873	5·3	4·0	14·6	14·8
Oats	4,089	3,899	8·7	8·3	23·9	30·8
Other grain . . .	938	538	2·0	1·2	5·4	4·2
Turnips, mangolds, cabbages	3,067	2,470	6·5	5·3	17·9	19·6
Potatoes	1,421	1,209	3·0	2·6	8·2	9·6
Other crops . . .	652	426	1·4	0·9	3·8	3·3
Bare fallow . . .	673	349	1·4	0·7	3·9	2·6
Total cultivated area . .	47,143	46,764	99·9	100·0	100·0	100·0
Total cultivated land in grass and clover . .	29,965	34,094	63·5	72·9		
Total cultivated land excluding grass and clover	17,178	12,670	36·5	27·1	100·0	100·0
Total cultivated land in grain crops . .	11,365	8,217	24·1	17·3	66·2	64·9
Live Stock	Thousands	Thousands	Per 100 acres cult. land			
Cattle	9,747	11,934	20·7	25·5		
Sheep	33,052	29,241	70·1	62·5		
Pigs	3,813	3,813	8·1	8·2		

It will be observed that there was little change in the total area of cultivated land, but that the land used for other purposes

[1] Statistics are not available for the period 1831–40. They were not collected until 1866. In the forty years before 1874 changes in the tillage area were relatively small.

H 2

than the growing of permanent, or temporary, grass and clover fell from 17,178,000 acres in 1874 to 12,670,000 acres in 1914, a loss of four and a half million acres; also that, without exception, there was a smaller percentage of cultivated land occupied by the other principal crops in the later than in the earlier period, the heaviest loss being in wheat. The total area under grain fell by 3,148,000 acres.

When, in the last two columns of Table XII, we compare the systems of husbandry followed on the land actually ploughed, we find little change in the proportions used for grain and green crops respectively. In 1874, out of each hundred acres other than grass, sixty-six would have been in grain; in 1914 this area had been reduced by little more than one acre; but the proportions under different grain crops altered greatly, there being seven acres less wheat and seven acres more oats in 1914 than in 1874.

In the case of live stock the changes were less marked. Per thousand acres of cultivated land, cattle increased from 207 to 255, sheep fell from 701 to 625, while the number of pigs was almost the same. The figures taken by themselves suggest a considerable increase in the meat supply; but caution is required in drawing conclusions, as the animals marketed in the earlier period were older and somewhat larger than in the later.

In connexion with the war effort to increase tillage, it is interesting to inquire how these changes in farming during the past forty years affected the different divisions of the United Kingdom. For this purpose it will be desirable to treat the figures as we did in Chapter II, and to compare the changes on typical one-thousand acre estates in each of the four countries between 1874 and 1914. This has been done in Table XIII for the principal groups of crops. The detailed changes in live stock have not been included, the figures for the United Kingdom which were given in Table XII sufficing for our present purpose.

From the figures in Table XIII it is clear that the greatest changes occurred in England. Between 1874 and 1914 each thousand acres of cultivated land on the average lost about 90 acres of grain and also substantial areas of roots and rotation

TABLE XIII

CHANGES IN THE FARMING OF EACH COUNTRY IN THE UNITED KINGDOM IN FORTY YEARS

Crops grown on an average thousand acres of cultivated land in 1874 and 1914. In the figures for ' change' ordinary type shows gain, heavy type shows loss in area in 1914 as compared with 1874.

Crop		England	Wales	Scotland	Ireland	U.K.
Permanent grass	. 1874	435	610	242	665	502
,, ,, ,,	. 1914	577	748	311	659	585
Change		142	138	69	6	83
Rotation grass [1] .	. 1874	125	139	299	123	143
,, ,,	. 1914	94	95	312	183	144
Change		**31**	**44**	13	60	1
Grain . . .	. 1874	313	193	308	121	241
,, . .	. 1914	223	118	248	85	176
Change		**90**	**75**	**60**	**36**	**65**
Potatoes . .	. 1874	13	17	35	57	30
,, .	. 1914	18	9	32	39	26
Change		5	**8**	**3**	**18**	**4**
Turnips, mangolds, &c.	1874	85	29	111	26	65
,, ,, ,,	1914	63	27	93	27	53
Change		**22**	**2**	**18**	1	**12**
Miscellaneous .	. 1874	4	0	0	7	5
,,	. 1914	11	1	2	7	9
Change		7	1	2	0	4
Bare fallow .	. 1874	25	12	5	1	14
,,	. 1914	14	2	2	—	7
Change		**11**	**10**	**3**	**1**	**7**

grass, while it gained about 142 acres of permanent grass. In Wales, while the loss of grain and the gain in grass were less than in England, on the whole the changes were similar.[2] In Scotland, on the other hand, a marked difference is disclosed by the figures, the gain in permanent grass being less than half as much as in England ; and whereas in the southern country there was a great reduction in the area under rotation grass, in

[1] Includes clover, sainfoin, lucerne, and tares or vetches.
[2] The official returns do not, however, disclose the real changes ; cf. p. 23.

the northern rotation grass increased. The loss in the grain area on Scotch farms was about two-thirds of the loss on English land. In Ireland the losses in both grain and potatoes were considerable, these crops having been replaced by temporary grass ; there was no gain in the area returned as being under permanent grass in 1914 ; in this respect Ireland presents a contrast to England.

This then was the position in the United Kingdom in 1914. There had been a large decrease in the production of home-grown food since the middle of the nineteenth century, and a great decline in tillage farming. With the outbreak of war a plough policy became an urgent necessity ; but grass land had so firmly established its position as the basis of economic agriculture in the British Isles that the extension of tillage presented great practical difficulties.

In the chapters which follow we shall trace the development of the plough policy and examine the results which attended its adoption in the later harvests of the war.

CHAPTER VI

THE HARVEST OF 1915

The Autumn of 1914. Consultative Committee on Agriculture. Maintenance of Live Stock. Labour Supply and Weather Conditions. Manure Supply. Harvest Results. Allotment and Garden Cultivation.

THE progress of food production during the war years may be studied most conveniently in relation to the harvests. Though this course may involve some departure from the chronological order of events, it will assist us in following the progress of the food production policy through the war period.

The Autumn of 1914.

At the outbreak of war the British corn harvest of 1914 was just beginning, and the immediate problems facing the Agricultural Departments related rather to the in-gathering of this harvest than to preparations for 1915. Arrangements were made for collecting information respecting the difficulties facing agriculturists in different parts of the country, and for ascertaining the stocks of food, feeding stuffs, and manures available. Duties subsequently performed by the Ministry of Food fell to the Agricultural Departments, and as a consequence members of the staff whose work would, in the ordinary course, have related to food production, were engaged in special inquiries respecting the effects of the war on supplies and labour.

Anxiety on account of the harvest of 1914 was soon relieved. The weather of August and September was fine, and, although there was some scarcity of labour, no real difficulty was experienced in gathering in the corn crops. Later in the year the harvesting of potatoes and root crops in some districts was delayed because of labour shortage; but at the end of the agricultural year 1914, partly because of the fine harvest months, and partly because of the energy which farmers and labourers put into their work, it was found that war had not caused any appreciable losses in the crops of the year.

From an early period in the war, therefore, it was the harvest of 1915, not that of the current year, that gave rise to apprehension on the part of agriculturists. An acute shortage of labour was anticipated almost from the beginning, and doubts began to be expressed as to the possibility of continuing to cultivate as large an area of tillage land in 1915 as had been under the plough before the war.

Consultative Committee on Agriculture.

The President of the Board of Agriculture and Fisheries set up a Consultative Committee of expert agriculturists in the first week of the war, whose members were drawn from all parts of the country and were in touch with local opinion. This committee had access to all the information collected by the officers of the Board, and from time to time, with the object of guiding agricultural action, the Board issued press notices addressed to the farmers of the country in which the opinions and advice of the Consultative Committee were set out. A notice issued on the 18th of August may be quoted *in extenso* as showing the policy favoured at the beginning of the war.

' The following recommendations must in all cases be dependent upon : (1) local conditions, and (2) the circumstances of the individual holding. But, generally, the Agricultural Consultative Committee are of opinion that, in the existing circumstances, agriculturists should do all in their power to secure that the supply of home-produced food-stuffs may be in excess of the normal. In this respect, the requirements of the future with regard both to cropping and to the maintenance of the fullest complement of live stock that holdings can usefully carry, must be carefully borne in mind.

' 1. The acreage under wheat should be largely increased wherever practicable. In this direction it should not be forgotten that on clean land, and by the aid of suitable artificial manure, good crops of wheat can be obtained in successive years. Attention is drawn to section 26 of the Agricultural Holdings Act, 1908, which permits any system of cropping, subject to the holding being protected from deterioration.

' 2. Where wheat cannot be grown, the sowing of winter oats, winter barley, and rye might be substituted. These crops ripen early, and allow the labour on harvest to be evenly distributed.

' 3. The cabbage crop is also one to be considered where land can be spared. It provides a considerable weight of food suitable for either human or animal consumption.

' 4. There is much land of a certain class now under grass which would probably pay for breaking up. If this land is scheduled as arable in the farm agreement, the tenant has the option of ploughing it up. If it is scheduled as grass the Agricultural Consultative Committee suggest co-operation between owner and occupier as to the advisability of breaking up certain fields in view of the national question of increasing home-grown food-stuffs.

' 5. Where a surplus of grass or clover exists, ensilage might be made. Particulars of the best methods can be obtained from the Board of Agriculture Leaflet No. 9.

' 6. The slaughter of immature or breeding stock of every description should be avoided. Where circumstances permit, the total head of live stock should be increased, particularly animals such as pigs, which multiply quickly.

' Ewe lambs might with advantage be put to the ram towards the end of the year.

' 7. While there should be no diminution in the numbers of live stock kept, the strictest economy (subject to proper conditioning) and foresight with regard to feeding is advocated.

' The cheapest efficient forms of food should be used and no waste spaces capable of producing food for animals should be allowed. No recommendation is attempted as to the exact description of the food-stuffs to be grown, as this must depend upon the special circumstances of each case, of which generally the individual farmer will be the best judge; if in doubt, he can obtain advice gratis from the recognized Agricultural College in his ' Province ' or from the County Agricultural Organizer. But the following crops among others are worthy of consideration : trifolium, vetches, rye for spring feeding, and Italian rye grass. By adopting such measures the more valuable foods would, so far as possible, be freed for human consumption.'

A few weeks later, when wheat sowing was about to begin, certain of the foregoing recommendations were again circulated to the press and the following statement upon the breaking up of grass land was made.

' The Committee, of course, do not suggest that good grazing land should be broken up, and they realize that the circumstances of each individual holding must be examined in considering the above recommendations ; but they would point out that should it be found possible to increase the wheat acreage without detriment to the live stock and general organization of the particular holding, there seems every reason to suppose that it might prove to the financial advantage of the grower.'

This guarded utterance is significant. The country was entering on a war which its chief military authorities warned it would be of long duration. Four-fifths of the bread supply was sea-borne. The demands of war had placed an enormous burden on the country's shipping; the submarine was a menace the extent of which the most skilled seamen could not forecast, but many competent authorities attributed a destructive power to the submarine which subsequent events justified. The United Kingdom had thirty-four million acres of land under grass and thirteen million acres only under other crops; per acre of land the latter area was providing at least four times as much food as the former; our chief enemy, with soils no better than our own, was feeding twice as many people per unit of area. All our industrial energies being required for the production of munitions of war, we could no longer afford to pay on advantageous terms for our food by exporting our manufactures.

If, with the position as we now know it, we read again the advice given in August 1914 by a committee representing the best agricultural opinion of the country, we may be able to realize the views on food production widely current in this country in the years before the emergency of 1914. To those of us who, three years later, were struggling to secure every bushel of corn that the land could produce, the committee's advice now reads very much as if one thus addressed a man whose house was on fire : ' There seems every reason to suppose that it might prove to be to your financial advantage to remove your furniture, but we do not, of course, suggest that you should risk injuring the lawn.'

It is due to the Consultative Committee to state that they were, in fact, much more concerned about the future than from their cautious advice the public might have inferred to be the case ; and they pressed upon the Government the desirability of some action that would stimulate wheat production and safeguard supplies. But their public optimism was more acceptable than their private misgivings, and in answer to a question which one of their members addressed to the Prime Minister the following reply was given in the House of Commons on the 9th of September 1914 :

' With regard to next year's cereal crop, the Government have carefully considered all the available information ; it is a highly technical question, and after consulting expert opinion they have arrived at the conclusion that they would not be justified in holding out a financial inducement to farmers to increase their acreage of cereals.'

Presumably the expert opinion followed by the Government was not agricultural, for the policy differed from that recommended by the Agricultural Consultative Committee. The above answer was given by the Parliamentary Representative of the Board, and the final sentence of the reply, which was in the following terms, shows that to a limited extent the advice of the Consultative Committee had been accepted. ' At the same time the Board adhere to the advice which they issued to farmers recently, with the concurrence of the Consultative Committee, that wheat appears likely to be a profitable crop next year.'

While there were not a few who questioned the wisdom of the policy announced by Government, the farmers of the country not unnaturally accepted it. There could, they argued, be no real danger of a shortage of breadstuffs, otherwise Government would have accepted the view of the Consultative Committee that a financial inducement to grow more corn was required. It was only because of the very favourable weather of the autumn months that farmers had been able to carry on the work of their farms satisfactorily ; if the season were adverse the growing and getting of the harvest of 1915 would, they believed, be beyond their powers, and their land would deteriorate. Clearly therefore, farmers reasoned, it would be unwise to add substantially to the area under tillage crops. The farmer's duty, to quote words from a circular issued by a progressive and public-spirited farmers' club for the guidance of its members in the autumn of 1914, was to sow as much wheat as was ' conveniently possible ' ; and fortunately the weather proved so favourable that it was ' conveniently possible ' to sow a great deal more than usual, as we shall see when the results of the harvest of 1915 are examined.

Maintenance of Live Stock.

In the early months of the war, apart from labour questions, the agriculturist's own anxieties related chiefly to his live stock, and from the public point of view there was some reason to share this anxiety; almost the first effect of war conditions was to create difficulties in the milk supply. After mobilization there was a great shortage of milkers in some of the chief milk-producing counties; cases were reported in which dairy herds were reduced, calves were slaughtered in unusual numbers, and a diminution in the herds and flocks on which we depended for more than half our meat supply was anticipated. The census of live stock in 1915 showed that these fears were not realized; but in the autumn of 1914 a Slaughter of Animals Act was deemed necessary, which gave the Departments of Agriculture power to regulate slaughter in the interests of the meat or milk supply.

Much attention was given to securing full rations of the usual imported feeding stuffs, exports of milling offals were stopped for a time, and later regulated by licence; and stock feeders secured a ' windfall ' not fully appreciated until much later in the war, by the transference of the Hamburg palm kernel trade to this country.

At this stage in the war there was in Germany a keen discussion on live-stock policy, since it was recognized that animals, especially the pig, were to some extent competitors with man for foodstuffs; but in Britain no question of competition arose in 1914, except to a very limited extent in the case of calves and the milk supply; and the whole trend of opinion was in favour of maintaining, and, if possible, increasing existing herds and flocks.

Labour Supply and Weather Conditions.

Of all the subjects occupying the attention of the Agricultural Departments in the period of preparation for the 1915 harvest, labour was the most important. As has already been stated, except in the case of milkers, labour shortage was not severely felt during the autumn months because of the fine weather ; and, again because of the weather, which was wet and prevented work on the land in December, January, and February 1915 there was no real scarcity. But as spring advanced, and as farm work fell behind, the keenest apprehensions were expressed by farmers, and efforts were made to increase the labour supply.

A return obtained by the Board of Trade in January 1915 showed that on an average 15·6 per cent. of the farm labourers of England and Wales had then enlisted, or were employed by Government in civilian work. On the other hand, the number of male labourers employed on farms was only 12·4 per cent. less than in January 1914 ; so that, from other sources, farmers had been able to recruit a considerable number of men. The percentage of enlistments varied widely from district to district ; in the south-west it rose to 18 per cent., whereas in some northern districts, where labourers are engaged by the half year or year, it was only half this figure.

During the winter efforts were made by both the Boards of Trade and of Agriculture to get farmers to make use of Labour Exchanges, but with little result. When farmers did apply to the Exchanges it was generally for skilled men, who were non-existent on the registers. Skilled men wanting employment found it immediately in their own districts without recourse to the Exchanges. On the other hand, there were on the books of the Exchanges a considerable number of unskilled workers. By the spring of 1915 about four thousand women had registered ; there were also some men invalided out of the Army, and a number of boys. To facilitate the employment of such persons committees of agriculturists were set up in certain counties. The committees, in co-operation with the Exchanges, were successful in placing many of these workers on the land.

In March the weather improved, the second half of the month was dry in southern districts, and good progress was made on the land. From the point of view of labour, April and May were very favourable, so that by the end of the latter month farm work was in a satisfactory state. But the weather which proved so favourable for tillage was not suitable for the spring corn crops. They had been sown too late because of the wet winter, and both oats and barley suffered from the dry, cold weather of May. By the beginning of June all farm crops required rain, but the weather remained dry until almost the end of the month. The result was a light and easily harvested hay crop. Not until the middle of July, therefore, did the anticipated labour shortage become acute. July was wet, the root crops grew rapidly, but so did the weeds, and farm work fell seriously into arrears. It was then that farmers first benefited by the efforts that had been made to get women to take up agricultural work. In some districts women had already given much help with potato lifting or planting, and in other localities with milking; but until the summer of 1915 there was no widespread demand for their aid. In the difficult conditions of July 1915, however, women workers were everywhere in request. At this time, too, soldiers from the Home Army were granted special furlough for periods of a fortnight to aid with the hay harvest, and their help assisted the farmer to overtake urgent work. The difficult period continued until the middle of August; then, fortunately for the country, the weather became fine and, in spite of the fears generally felt throughout the earlier part of the year, the harvest was gathered in without serious delay, and without loss.

The farmer, reflecting on the course of the agricultural year at Michaelmas 1915, realized that if the weather had not been too kind to his crops, it had at least facilitated his own task. Apprehension, felt in every month for the work of the succeeding period, had only been justified by experience in the weeks between the hay and corn harvest; the casual workers who came to his aid had given him more help than he expected. He had succeeded, but only just succeeded, in growing and saving his crops.

Manure Supply.

There was one other cause for anxiety in the early months of the war, which, like the labour position, created more appre-

hension than experience warranted. This country depended
on Germany for supplies of one of the manures—potash—
which many farmers, especially potato growers, regarded as
essential in the raising of good crops. The stocks of this
manure available when war broke out were inconsiderable.
The Board of Agriculture issued notices in the first weeks of
the war drawing attention to such alternative sources of potash
as wood ashes, seaweed, and properly conserved farmyard
manure, and farmers were advised to use those supplies of the
special potash manures which were available, only on the soils,
and for the crops, for which potash was most necessary. While
the absence of potash must have caused some reduction in the
crops on certain soils, the experience of 1915 and of the subsequent years of war showed that the total effect on our land of
the cessation of German supplies for a period of years was
surprisingly small.

Harvest Results.

From the agricultural policy followed in the first war year,
and from the farmer's early experiences of the effects of war
on his industry, we may now turn to the harvest record of the
crops first grown under war conditions.

As compared with the average of the period 1904–13, the
United Kingdom, in 1915, provided 46,000 fewer acres for the
cultivation of crops other than grass, and there was also a considerable reduction in the grass area. The total area of land
under cultivation had been slowly shrinking for some time, and
in 1915 the rate of decrease was accelerated—partly because of
land taken up for military purposes—so that altogether farmers
had 89,000 fewer acres at their disposal than in the previous
year. When the reduction in the total area available is taken
into account, the actual changes in area in the year 1915 show
that 76,000 acres were ploughed out of grass, chiefly temporary
grass, and added to the corn land. By reducing the sowings
of roots and certain other crops, the total area found for
growing the three principal cereals was increased by 251,000
acres. Towards this total England and Wales contributed

194,000, Scotland 3,000, and Ireland 54,000 acres. In England and Wales there was also the considerable addition of 31,000 acres to the area under potatoes.

With regard to the yield of the principal crops, as compared with the ten years before the war there was an increase of 143,000 tons of corn—about 2·3 per cent.—and of 948,000 tons of potatoes—about 14·4 per cent. The most satisfactory feature of the harvest was the substantial increase in the wheat crop, which amounted to 481,000 tons, or 30·7 per cent. more than the 1904–13 yield. This was chiefly due, as will be seen from the detailed figures given in Table XIV, to the fact that English farmers had adopted the advice given them and had sowed as much wheat as was 'conveniently possible'.

TABLE XIV

HARVEST OF 1915 COMPARED WITH AVERAGE HARVEST OF 1904–13

FIGURES THOUSANDS OF ACRES OR TONS

Country	Crop	Area		Yield		1915 ± 1904–13	
		1915	1904–13	1915	1904–13	Acres	Tons
Eng. and Wales	Wheat	2,170	1,689	1,880	1,468	+ 481	+ 412
Scotland . .	,,	77	51	79	57	+ 26	+ 22
Ireland . .	,,	87	40	86	39	+ 47	+ 47
United Kingdom	,,	2,334	1,780	2,045	1,564	+ 554	+ 481
Eng. and Wales	Barley	1,232	1,510	866	1,192	− 278	− 326
Scotland . .	,,	149	199	112	171	− 50	− 59
Ireland . .	,,	142	164	126	153	− 22	− 27
United Kingdom	,,	1,523	1,873	1,104	1,516	− 350	− 412
Eng. and Wales	Oats	2,088	2,097	1,454	1,484	− 9	− 30
Scotland . .	,,	983	956	680	650	+ 27	+ 30
Ireland . .	,,	1,089	1,060	980	906	+ 29	+ 74
United Kingdom	,,	4,160	4,113	3,114	3,040	+ 47	+ 74
Eng. and Wales	Potatoes	463	432	2,858	2,643	+ 31	+ 215
Scotland . .	,,	144	143	972	926	+ 1	+ 46
Ireland . .	,,	595	597	3,710	3,023	− 2	+ 687
United Kingdom	,,	1,202	1,172	7,540	6,592	+ 30	+ 948

The increased area of wheat was secured chiefly at the expense of the barley crop. Apart altogether from the requirements of the country, the change was a fortunate one for

English farmers, for, whereas the wheat crop of 1915 was above average, the barley crop was a very poor one.

The oat crop in Ireland was rather over average and in the other countries about average, thus the total was satisfactory.

A good crop in Ireland was mainly responsible for a considerable increase in the yield of potatoes.

Apart from the influence of season, the chief change brought out by a study of the detailed figures given in Table XIV was that which was due to the speeding up of autumn wheat sowing by English farmers in 1914. As already stated, the increase in wheat was secured mainly at the expense of barley; but if we compare the crops of 1915 and of the two years immediately preceding it, we find that the root crops also contributed to the result. In the first war year there were about 130,000 fewer acres under swedes, turnips, and mangolds in England and Wales than in the years 1913 and 1914. Fortunately the actual loss of fodder was not great, since the root crops yielded rather more than the average, thus the total supply available for live stock was only 6 per cent. less than in the two previous years; but the restricted area placed under roots in 1915 resulted in a deterioration of the land available for corn in 1916 and contributed to the poor harvest of that year.

The growing of corn after corn is a ruinous practice in most parts of the country, unless skilled management and sufficient labour enable the land to be kept clean. It was, of course, the farmers' line of least resistance, and when urged to grow corn in the autumn of 1914 many of them found the necessary land at the expense of their root crops. For a year or two the practice might be tolerated; but as events proved, with the long war then before the country, no more disastrous policy could have been adopted.

Allotment and Garden Cultivation.

Before we follow the fortunes of the farmer during his second war harvest, we must turn aside to examine the doings of his busy co-workers in the task of food production in the gardens and allotments of the country. We have seen that before the war an appreciable quantity of our home-produced food, possibly as much as 7 per cent. of the whole amount, came from holdings of less than one acre in area.

No satisfactory statistics are available of the land occupied by cottage gardens and industrial allotments ; but from such figures as resulted from inquiries made by the Board of Agriculture and Fisheries in 1895, and inquiries by the Irish Department of Agriculture in 1908, it may be estimated that the area under cottage gardens and allotments of less than one acre, in the period 1909–13, was about 200,000 acres. Adding the vegetable gardens of less than one acre attached to the smaller country houses, farm-houses, and villas, the area under vegetable gardens and allotments might have extended to 500,000 acres. Urban allotments had greatly increased in number since 1900 ; but as the usual size was from one-sixteenth to one-fortieth of an acre, the increase in number did not involve a large area. The total area let for allotment gardening up to 31st December 1913 by local authorities in England and Wales was 31,271 acres only, parish councils being responsible for two-thirds of the whole.

With the outbreak of war there was an immediate extension in the area under allotments, and until the last year of the war the progress made in food production in gardens and allotments was relatively much greater than on farms.

The dislocation of trade and transport which followed the declaration of war not only caused temporary shortages of foodstuffs, which made industrial workers realize for the first time the dangers of entire reliance on food coming from a distance, but it led to the unemployment of many able-bodied men, too old for military service. Sedentary workers, too, in the excitement of the times, felt life in the office and shop to be unbearable, and longed for some form of outdoor activity ; thus in every industrial area there arose a keen demand for allotments. Recognizing the value of the movement, both central and local agencies did much to help it forward.

A few days after the outbreak of war the Board of Agriculture and Fisheries made an appeal to the owners of private gardens to preserve their surplus stocks of vegetable seedlings for distribution to allotment holders ; and the Royal Horticultural Society appointed a committee to assist in the distribution of these surplus plants. Later, leaflets containing detailed instructions for the preparation of land and the planting of crops were issued at regular intervals by the Board.

In the country many local committees got to work, and from amateur and professional gardeners much valuable assistance was secured.

In illustration of the methods by which the very successful allotment movement was developed, three examples from widely separated parts of the country may be referred to.

The first in point of time was the Cumberland and Westmorland ' Home Food Culture ' scheme. These counties had long given much attention to agricultural education, and in the course of the important development of this subject which had taken place just before the war, a capable and energetic horticultural instructor had been appointed. Before joining the Army in the autumn of 1914, this instructor, and others associated with him in educational work, organized a very successful food production scheme. In the first few days of the war a committee representing landowners, manufacturers, and educationists got together, and from an office placed at their disposal by a prominent Carlisle business man they issued a manifesto. This manifesto, dated 20th of August 1914, set out the aims of the committee and the methods they intended to employ. It pointed out that, owing to the dislocation of trade caused by war, local manufacturers were forced to place employees on short time ; that these employees were anxious to augment their earnings by cultivating allotments ; that, already, certain landowners had placed land at the committee's disposal ; that owners of private gardens were contributing seedlings, and that their gardeners were prepared to give instruction to those requiring it. An appeal was made for more land. Parish councils were urged to secure land for themselves, and distress committees were told of the benefits that allotments might confer. A form of agreement for the hiring of land was drawn up, and a leaflet was prepared by the head gardener on a Cumberland estate embodying the results of local experience in the cultivation of vegetables. Large posters were printed indicating the principal features of the scheme and inviting all interested in providing, or obtaining, allotments to apply to the committee.

At the other end of England, the county of Cornwall provided a second illustration of the methods employed in developing food production. As in the Cumberland case, the initiative was taken by persons interested in the work of agricultural education ; but the local conditions being widely different, different methods of securing an increase in the food supply were adopted. In relatively few cases was land required for allotments ; but all over the county small farms and cottage gardens contained land on which production required to be stimulated. The Agricultural Education Committee addressed a circular to each parish council in the county setting out the need for growing more food and suggesting methods that might be adopted for this purpose. As a result meetings were held in sixty-five parishes during September and the first half of October. Many of the meetings were addressed by representatives of the Agricultural Education Committee ; in other cases reports of the proceedings were sent to the committee. As a result of this campaign nearly every parish undertook to grow more potatoes and other vegetables, and a good many farmers promised to increase the area under wheat. About a dozen parishes only reported a demand for more allotments, and from the same number came offers of land at a nominal rent, or rent free.

The third illustration is taken from the London area. In connexion with the pre-war ' Vacant Land Cultivation ' movement, an unsuccessful attempt had been made in 1908 to start a cultivation society at Croydon. On the outbreak of war a local landowner offered a vacant plot for cultivation rent free, and the organizer of the 1908 movement succeeded in forming a society to take up this land. In September 1914 a committee was formed to foster the movement. More land was sought for and secured, rules were drawn up for allotment holders, and guidance in practical gardening was provided. Good progress was made by the cultivators in the winter of 1914–15, and in 1915 very satisfactory crops were raised by many of them. By the end of the year the society held twenty acres of land let to two hundred and sixty cultivators, and there then were one hundred and fifty applicants for land on the society's waiting list. The rents paid by allotment holders were carried to a fund to be used in paying compensation to those whose land might be required for building purposes before the crops were ready for harvesting.

From the outset the Board of Agriculture and Fisheries recognized the value of the allotment movement, not only as a means of adding to the food supply, but because of the recreative value of gardening to many of those engaged in war work, and because of the beneficial results, from a social point of view, which followed the co-operation of all classes in urban or rural areas in such attempts to help the country as were represented by War Food societies, or Home Food Culture committees.

In the Board's *Journal* attention was drawn to such successful attempts to organize allotment cultivation as those made in Carlisle and Croydon ; and from time to time articles were published suggesting the best crops for plots reclaimed from vacant land, and explaining how these crops should be cultivated. These printed hints were of value to persons who already had some knowledge of gardening ; but for beginners practical demonstrations were required, and these could not be organized from a central office. Arrangements for decentralization were therefore made without delay.

In the years immediately preceding the war much attention had been given to the organization of agricultural education, and many counties had committees or instructors who, like those of Cornwall and Cumberland, took immediate action ; in other cases, where a county agricultural staff did not exist, the work was taken up by local agricultural colleges. In 1914 eleven of these colleges, or university agricultural departments, were at work in England and Wales, and with each of them a group of counties was associated. The Board's policy for food production both on agricultural holdings and on allotments was communicated to the heads of these institutions, and at the same time press notices appeared advocating the extension of allotment cultivation ; a circular was issued giving a list of the counties associated with each college, and also the names of the persons to whom residents in a county should apply for assistance and technical advice in connexion with allotment gardening, should there be difficulty in securing aid locally. Thus in such industrial areas as south-west Yorkshire and the Tyne basin the development of allotment gardening centred round the University of Leeds, and Armstrong College, Newcastle; and, as in Cumberland, leaflets explaining how the greatest possible use might be made of small plots of land were prepared by skilled local horticulturists.

It is not necessary to follow the history of the allotment movement during the first two years of the war ; once successfully launched, the progress was remarkable, and the demand for land in the neighbourhood of towns was everywhere greater than the supply. In a subsequent chapter the measures taken to meet this demand will be referred to.

CHAPTER VII

THE HARVEST OF 1916

The Production of Food Committees. Milner Committee's Interim Report. Scotch Committee's Report. Irish Committee's Report. Different Conditions confronting Committees. The Government Decision on Guaranteed Prices. Action taken on Production of Food Committees' Reports. Agricultural Conditions in Season 1915–16. The Supply of Fertilizers. The Acland Committee on Fertilizers. The Harvest Figures.

IMMEDIATELY after the formation of the first Coalition Government in May 1915, the question of the future food supply of the country was carefully reviewed. The Earl of Selborne, the new President of the Board of Agriculture and Fisheries, held views respecting the probable development of submarine warfare which the years 1917 and 1918 proved to be only too well founded ; and, while as fully impressed as were his predecessors with the importance of maintaining the agricultural industry in an efficient and prosperous state, he recognized that the first and paramount duty of the agriculturist was to produce the greatest possible quantity of human food. How much food can be raised from an acre of land ? What are the rations required by groups of persons in various employments ? What average ration would suffice for the nation's needs ? These were the questions which required an answer, and studies were then begun at the Board which had a close bearing on the subsequent food production policy of the country.

The Production of Food Committees of 1915.

Little more could be done for the success of the harvest of 1915, except by assisting farmers to secure labour for summer tillage and for harvesting ; but the harvest of 1916 claimed immediate consideration, and on the 17th June 1915 a committee, with Lord Milner as Chairman, was appointed 'to consider and report what steps should be taken, by legislation or otherwise, for the sole purpose of maintaining and, if possible, increasing the present production of food in England and Wales, on the assumption that the war may be prolonged beyond the harvest of 1916 '. On 23rd June the Secretary for Scotland appointed a committee with the same reference, the word ' Scotland ' being substituted for ' England and Wales ', and on 28th June this reference was given to an Irish committee by the Vice-President of the Department of Agriculture and Technical Instruction. Mr. Eugene Wason, M.P., was Chairman of the Scotch committee, while the Vice-President himself (the late Sir T. W. Russell, M.P.) presided over the Irish committee.

The English committee presented an Interim Report on 17th July, and a Final Report in October. Both the other committees reported in August.

Milner Committee's Interim Report.

Of the four reports, by far the most important in its influence on subsequent events was that submitted by Lord Milner's Committee in July. This report, which was unanimous, stated that the committee had reached the conclusion ' that the only method of effecting a substantial increase in the *gross* production of food in England and Wales for the harvest of 1916 and later consists in restoring to arable cultivation some of the poorer grass land that has been laid down since the 'seventies '. If this were done, wheat could be sown on a much larger proportion of the land already under tillage in the autumn of 1915, and the newly ploughed grass could be sown or planted in spring with crops which wheat had displaced. The committee expressed their belief, and in this they were confirmed by all who gave evidence on the point, that with proper farming wheat and other crops suited for human consumption could be grown on the additional area without diminishing the capacity of the country to ' maintain its existing live stock and its output of meat and milk '.

In order to secure an increased area of wheat which, it was estimated, might be one million acres ' at least ' in 1916, and more in later years, the committee recommended that Government should guarantee farmers a minimum price of 45s. per quarter for a period of four years ; and suggested as conditions, either (*a*) that the farmer should increase the area of his arable land by one-fifth over the area tilled in October 1913, or (*b*) that at least one-fifth of the total area under grass and annual crops occupied by him should be under wheat.

The committee justified their recommendation by pointing out that farmers who increase their tillage area must sacrifice the ' comparative certainty of their present profits ' and take the risks incidental to the farming of arable land with an insufficient supply of labour. While they believed that farmers would continue their 1915 effort to produce wheat if appealed to in the national interests, they were convinced—and in this view they were confirmed by all the witnesses examined—that no substantial increase could be secured in the absence of a guaranteed price.

The method of payment suggested was that the farmer should receive the difference between 45*s*. and the *Gazette* average price of wheat for the year in which the wheat is harvested ; thus the farmer would be left free to get the best price he could for his grain in the market.

The committee recognized that if a minimum price were guaranteed, it would be reasonable in principle to impose a maximum price, and were of opinion that the maximum price, if imposed, should not be less than 55*s*. per quarter. In view, however, of the possible effects of a maximum price on the importation of foreign wheat, the committee did not recommend it.

The committee were unanimously of opinion that if a guaranteed price were offered there should be a rise in wages ; and some of the members advocated the imposition of a ' fair wages ' clause in connexion with the guarantee ; but because of the risk that further conditions might defeat the main object of the scheme, a ' fair wages ' condition was not recommended in their report.

The committee believed that, by itself, the offer of 45*s*. per quarter for wheat would not suffice : they emphasized the necessity for a clear lead being given to the farmer, so that he might know exactly what was required of him ; it was not enough to state that one million acres more wheat were wanted in 1916 ; each district within a county should be informed how much was grown in the 'seventies, what the reduction in tillage since that time had been, and how much was expected next harvest. An organization under the President of the Board of Agriculture and Fisheries was suggested for the purpose of carrying out the programme. This department should be in direct touch with each county council, and these councils, in their turn, should appoint small expert committees for the purposes of the scheme in each rural district. Even in urban districts, if these contained appreciable quantities of agricultural land, committees should be set up. The district committees, it was suggested, should consider the capacity of each farm within its area, fix the increased quantity of tillage necessary, and ascertain the willingness or otherwise of the individual farmer to carry out his share of the task. The district committee should also be responsible for ascertaining what labour and manures were required and they should inform the central department of the needs of each locality.

Lord Milner's Committee did not say what was to be done in cases in which farmers were unwilling to carry out the tasks allotted to them by district committees, and compulsion is not suggested in their report ; but it may be inferred from their proposals that compulsory powers were assumed.

Scotch Committee's Report.

Mr. Eugene Wason's Committee spent a longer time in deliberation than Lord Milner's. They heard evidence from more than twice as many witnesses, and they received one hundred and thirty-five sets of answers to a schedule of questions sent out by them. Their report was of a non-committal character. The caution which characterizes the treatment of the suggestions made in evidence or by letter, may be illustrated by quoting a paragraph dealing with a very contentious topic.

' That the importation of Canadian cattle and Iceland sheep be allowed was advocated by some of the traders and others who gave evidence. The Committee are aware that certain City and Borough Councils have passed resolutions urging the removal of the embargo on the admission of live cattle from Canada, alleging that there are no healthier cattle than those grazed and fed in the Dominion. The Committee are led to think that there is at present in Canada no surplus stock available for export. In these circumstances they make no recommendation. Similarly they have been told that for Iceland sheep, which prior to 1896 were imported in considerable numbers, a new outlet has been found in Norway and Sweden, and in this case also the Committee do not consider it necessary to suggest any steps towards re-opening the question of their admission.'

The Scotch committee were unanimous in rejecting a policy of guaranteed prices for cereals. On this they say :

'The proposal that farmers should be induced to increase their cultivation of cereals by a guaranteed minimum price does not appear to the Committee to be practicable. Witnesses who have advocated this proposal have estimated the minimum price necessary to ensure increased production of wheat very variously—some placing it at 35s. and others at 50s. per quarter. No clear indication has been given as to how a proper discrimination might be exercised between various qualities of grain ; and this aspect of the question, while important in the case of wheat, is even more so in the case of oats which chiefly concerns Scottish growers of cereals, since the differences of value between samples of oats bear a much higher proportion to the average value of the grain. The very considerable increase this year in the acreage under wheat as compared with last year's returns, indicates the inducement to grow it which enhanced prices have created. The Committee cannot ignore the risk that any guarantee of a high price might lead to the cultivation of wheat on land which could make a better contribution to the national needs if it were used in some other way for the production of food, and they direct attention to the fact that the contribution which Scotland can advantageously make to the wheat supply of the country is comparatively slight, and is of much less importance than is the degree in which it can furnish meat and dairy produce. It should further be considered that the fixing of a minimum price for the protection of the producer against loss might entail a maximum price to restrict his profits ; and the disadvantages of this for a country in large measure dependent on world markets need not be emphasized.'

On the subject of compulsory tillage the committee were not in complete agreement and, while the report sets out the case against compulsion in considerable detail, four members appended reservations in which the advantages of compulsion under certain circumstances are argued.

All members of the committee recognized the necessity for providing the farmer with guidance, and with means for bringing his need for labour, &c., before the Government, and they suggested the formation of District Agricultural Committees to include representatives of agricultural societies, the Board of Agriculture, farm workers, the local agricultural college, the committee for secondary education of the county council, and the district committee of the county council.

The committee conclude their report with a series of recommendations, in the main relating to the possibility of securing an increase of production, or the avoidance of waste, by the adoption of methods of proved practical value. Cautious to the last page, their penultimate paragraph explains that while they do not suggest legislation or compulsion of any kind ' they do not disregard the possibility that circumstances might arise in which it would be necessary to recommend Parliament to pass legislation dealing with some of the matters above mentioned '.

Three members of the committee recommended the following measure of compulsion :

' That in the case of all land under rye-grass and other rotation grasses and clover, except such as has been sown with grass and clover in the springs of 1914 or 1915, farmers shall be required to plough up and put under a crop, other than grass or clover, twice as much as they similarly dealt with in 1914–15, provided that such larger area is in existence on their respective holdings.'

Farmers desiring exemption from this obligation were to be given the right of appeal to a local committee acting in conjunction with the Board of Agriculture.

Since grass sown in the spring of 1914 was excluded, these recommendations would not have affected farmers who adopted the ordinary five-course rotation. On the other hand, its general application might have caused some hardship in stock-breeding districts. An alternative plan was therefore put forward by a fourth member of the committee, who in a note of considerable length drew attention to the characteristics of Scotch grass land, and rightly pointed out that much of the permanent pasture of Scotland is unsuitable for tillage ; but that a large part of the temporary pasture could be broken up with advantage to the country and with little difficulty to individual farmers if reasonable discretion were exercised in its selection. He recommended the formation of district committees of four members : the sheriff (or sheriff-substitute) and three farmers. These committees should be empowered to make orders requiring the ploughing out of such grass land as it might appear to them should be tilled. The orders were to be enforced under penalty of a fine. The committees were also to be consulted in the recruiting of farm workers, and in the requisitioning of horses, so that sufficient labour might be available for the additional land to be tilled. In other respects these district committees would take the action for promoting food production suggested in the main report.

Irish Committee's Report.

Sir T. W. Russell's Committee contained more members than the English and Scotch committees combined, it was hence more widely representative ; it included some of the best-known Irish public men and several experienced officials, but its report was disappointing. It may be that efforts to secure unanimity were responsible for the colourless document signed by the majority ; the report gave little indication of the vigour which had characterized recent Irish agricultural movements, both official and voluntary. Unanimity was not secured, and the best result of the committee's work is the reasoned plea for co-operation which forms the Minority Report signed by Sir Horace Plunkett.

The Majority Report sets out the main objectives in increasing the food supply of Ireland in the following order :

(1) A material increase in the area under tillage, not only with a view to producing more human food, but also to the indirect production of the same by increasing the amount of fodder available for cattle.

(2) The maintenance, increase, and improvement of breeding stock of
    all kinds.
(3) The improvement of the farmer's position in regard to the means of
    obtaining the use of machinery and implements.
(4) The conservation of the artificial manure supply of the country.
(5) The maintenance of the Irish fishing industry.

The area under tillage crops in 1914 and 1915 was compared
and the results of the 1915 effort were pronounced to be ' not
unsatisfactory '.   ' But they leave abundant room for improvement, and should our recommendations be carried out there
can be little doubt that this improvement will take place and
that a permanent increase in tillage will be the result.'   This
optimistic statement raises anticipations ; but when the recommendations are examined they do not justify the optimism.
There was to be a guaranteed price of an unspecified amount
for wheat and oats for one year only.   This minimum was to be
an insurance against loss and not a bonus.   Loans were to be
provided to enable small holders to obtain the use of agricultural machinery and implements.   County Committees of
Agriculture were to be charged with the provision of these loans
' without unduly trenching upon any of the special methods of
trading ' ; and the export of artificial manures from the United
Kingdom was to be prohibited.   These were the measures
called for, not merely to increase the second harvest of the war,
but to effect a permanent increase in the tillage land of Ireland,
which for years had been declining in area.

With regard to live stock the census of 1915 had disclosed
a somewhat unsatisfactory position, and the committee recommended that the Maintenance of Live Stock Act, 1915, which
had recently replaced and enlarged the scope of the Slaughter
of Animals Act, 1914, as a temporary measure applicable to
war conditions, should be enacted permanently ; so that the
Department might ' stop alike the slaughter of breeding stock
in Ireland and the movement of animals where slaughter is
prohibited, i. e. the export of such stock to Great Britain, or
even their movement in Ireland '.

With the object of assisting the fishing industry which
provided an important article of food, ' especially among the

poorer people ' of Ireland, loans for the provision of boats and fishing gear were recommended.

The report concluded with an appeal to landholders in which the committee pointed out that there are in Ireland some millions of acres of second- and third-rate grass land which at present produce little, but which if tilled would give good crops. Attention was also drawn to the effects of foreign purchases of food on the balance of trade, and to the serious effects on the ' condition of all classes of the people ' which might follow from a great excess in the value of imports over exports.

Several members of the committee who sign the report submit notes, or reservations. The most important of the reservations relates to the period of the guaranteed minimum price. Six members of the committee were of opinion that it should extend over three years. Three members signing the majority report, including the Chairman's successor as Vice-President of the Department, supported a clause proposed by Sir Horace Plunkett relating to co-operative organization and food production. The rejection of this clause led Sir Horace to prepare a minority report. The minority report refers to the damaging effects on Irish agriculture of official hostility to the co-operative movement. This hostility, Sir Horace stated, was not due to any personal antagonism between the Vice-President of the Department and himself, but was ' simply an inherent conflict between the producers and distributors of food '.

Referring to a brief mention in the majority report of the action taken by some co-operative societies in the west of Ireland to provide implements for small holders, the minority report says : ' In this passage the outside student of Irish agricultural development could find the only indication that the committee considered co-operation to be a factor in the problem it was discussing. If he happened to come from any continental country where Departments of Agriculture recognize that their own utility depends essentially upon the degree in which the farmers with whom, and for whom, they work are co-operatively organized for every branch of their industry, he would go home with the impression that in rural Ireland the Dark Ages had hardly passed.' The report proceeds to show that the ' situation is not quite so bad ', and references are made to the successes of the Irish Agricultural Organization Society in organizing the dairying industry. Similar success might be anticipated if the same methods were adopted in organizing ' better farming '.

Sir Horace pointed out that measures involving compulsion, pecuniary inducement, or persuasion might be adopted with the object of increasing tillage farming. He agreed with the majority of the committee in rejecting compulsion, ' the controlling of agriculture would be a much more formidable task than the controlling of munition factories ' ; he further agreed with the majority in recommending inducements ' in the form of insurance against loss '. He strongly dissented from the attitude adopted by the majority on the subject of persuasion. On this point the majority report had stated that in Ireland ' persuasion on the people in this direction had been exerted to the fullest extent '. Sir Horace examined the statement with the object of showing how far it was from the truth. In subsequent paragraphs the minority report criticized the inadequacy of the proposals made by the majority for securing an increase of tillage, pointed out that, in a business like agriculture, increased production can only be secured if the tillers of the soil are themselves ' persuaded ' of the desirability of a particular line of action, and that alike for the success of the policy, and for the measures required to make a tillage policy practicable, reliance must be placed largely on the co-operative organization of producers. The chief recommendation of the minority report is that a small joint committee should be set up ' consisting of representatives of the Department and of the Irish Agricultural Organization Society, with an impartial chairman, to co-ordinate State assistance with organized voluntary effort in food production, and to move the Government to take certain measures in regard to labour, the supply of agricultural implements and manures, and the provision of funds needed for the combined campaign of better farming and better business '.

Milner Committee's Final Report.

The series of reports issued by the Production of Food Committees of 1915 concluded with the issue in October of that year of a Final Report by Lord Milner's Committee. Members of the committee were divided. The Majority Report, which was drafted after the decision of the Government, not to guarantee the prices of cereals, had been announced, relates to the other measures which might be effective in increasing the supply of food.

A Minority Report was submitted by two members of the committee, the substance of which is contained in the following paragraphs.

' The submarine menace since we made our report is apparently " well in hand " and the Government are not now afraid of a short supply of wheat from abroad. They consider it unnecessary, therefore, to adopt any extraordinary measures to ensure a home-grown supply, even if the war should extend beyond the Autumn of 1916.

' The recommendations now put forward by our colleagues are meant to apply to conditions after the war with which we were not invited to deal.

' We expressly abstain from adhering to the opinion that the nation's purchasing power will hereafter be reduced, or that it is necessary and possible to raise in this country a very large proportion of nearly 300 million pounds worth of food now purchased abroad. We are not prepared to say that, even if possible, there would be an economic gain in doing this.'

The minority apparently held the view that a number of suggestions made by the majority for the improvement of farming methods could not become operative during the period of the war. In this they were mistaken ; subsequent experience showed that recommendations which were made, e. g. with respect to labour-saving machinery and the use of waste land, were in fact of value at a later stage of the war ; but the criticism of the minority was clearly directed not so much against the technical methods suggested by the majority as at the tillage policy which was advocated. The passages dealing with this subject contain much the most important conclusions in the majority report. After expressing agreement with the practical recommendations submitted by the Scotch committee, in so far as they apply to agriculture in England and Wales, and referring to the Government's decision not to guarantee prices, the report proceeds to express the views of the majority on the subject of the increase of tillage farming in the following terms :

' At the same time we wish to place on record our conviction that there is great need to increase the productivity of the soil of our country, which, as we believe, falls far short of what it might be, by stimulating more intensive cultivation and by bringing under the plough a large area of land at present wastefully devoted to inferior pasture.

' Any increased production of food must rest upon a greater output from the soil, and from all the evidence laid before us we concluded that, speaking generally, the land of England is being kept at a comparatively low level of cultivation, and that it might be made to produce a greater amount of food without the withdrawal of labour from more profitable industries.   In particular the conversion of arable land into grass, which has taken place to the extent of nearly four million acres during the last forty years and is still going on, must necessarily be attended by a diminution in the amount of food produced.   We received evidence that a great deal of this land would produce twice as much meat and milk when under the plough as when in permanent grass, and that more, and not less, stock could be maintained on it if it were restored to arable cultivation, while it would also be producing corn for human consumption.

' It does not follow that the larger gross returns from arable, beneficial as they would be to the nation, would always be attended by a corresponding profit to the farmer.   His labour bill would be greatly increased, and account must also be taken of the greater capital required, the increased risk, and the call for more skill and management. . . . We wish to emphasize the point that the conversion of a considerable area of grass land into arable, bringing with it, as we believe it must, a great increase in our food supply, will be in the permanent interest of the nation.   The intensification of our agriculture will be even more necessary after the war than now, for then the nation's indebtedness will have reduced its purchasing power abroad, and the need will be felt for the extra employment of labour that arable land provides.   Moreover at all times a State purchasing the greater part of its food from foreign sources is *ipso facto* more open to attack and in a more unstable economic position when war comes.   We hope, therefore, that the importance of bringing our poorer pastures under arable cultivation will be recognized by the Government and the agricultural community. In our opinion it is only on these lines that a substantial increase in our home production of food can be achieved.'

The report then proceeds to discuss various measures for increasing the productivity of the soil as that of the Scotch committee had done. The measures suggested call for no special notice ; but attention may be directed to a Note appended to the report by the Chairman and five other members which expresses the belief ' that it is necessary and practicable to produce within this country a very large proportion of the foodstuffs and other agricultural products natural to its soil, but now purchased abroad at a cost of nearly three hundred million pounds per annum '.

Different Conditions confronting Committees.

The contradictory views expressed by the three national committees on the subject of guaranteeing prices for wheat and oats might, at first sight, suggest that two of the three committees must have erred in their judgement of the agricultural situation in framing the recommendations which they submitted ; and that it was to this conflict of expert opinion that the Government policy of 1915 was due. If the English committee were right in advising the necessity of a guarantee of prices for four years, then both the Scotch and Irish committees would appear to have been wrong in their estimate of the agricultural problem presented to them ; if the Scotch committee were right in advising against a guarantee, then both the English and Irish committees would seem to have been in the wrong ; and finally, if the majority of the Irish committee were right in believing that a guarantee for the year 1916 only was necessary, then the English committee would appear to have been in error in recommending the State to undertake a guarantee for four years and the Scotch committee were equally .at fault in believing that no guarantee was desirable. But the fact is that these three committees were dealing with systems of farming which were essentially different, and there is no agricultural reason to assume off-hand that any of them misjudged the situation, or the measures necessary for stimulating food production in their respective countries in 1916.

That the problems were quite different may be seen by referring to the figures of Table I on p. 17.

To take first the case of Scotland. In that country there was a very large area (roughly 31 per cent. of the cultivated land) under rotation grass, usually broken up after two or three years. The manual labour required, though reduced by the war, was still to be found on almost every holding, the horses were there, and the necessary implements and buildings ; all that was called for was a speeding-up of the work, the ploughing out of the land after two years grass instead of after three, or after one year in grass instead of after two. Some inconvenience might have been caused to breeders by a reduction in summer grazing, but the hill land of the country offered substantial reserves of summer grass. An increase in the number of working hours would be wanted, especially should the weather prove unfavourable ; but under war conditions it was as reasonable to expect the ploughmen to make an extra effort as the farmers. Some financial risk would be necessary, but on the other hand the Scotch committee— and many of the practical farmers of Scotland—judged the risk to be relatively small. In fact under war conditions, with a prospect of rising prices, the increase of the area under grain and potatoes at the expense of temporary grass was known by a large number of Scotch farmers to be sound business.

In Ireland the position was somewhat different. As in Scotland, there was a large area of temporary pasture, but the intervals at which it was broken up were less regular. An increase in the ploughed area meant more of a change of system and was to a less degree a mere speeding-up of normal methods. Some pecuniary inducement was deemed advisable to overcome agricultural inertia, but no great sum was necessary and the committee judged—and again they may have judged rightly— that a guarantee for a single year would result in a large increase in the area sown with grain.

In England the position was entirely different. Instead of 31 per cent. of the cultivated land being in temporary grass regularly broken up, as in Scotland, temporary leys occupied only some 9 per cent. of the land at the farmers' disposal. Most of this consisted of clover, or clover and rye-grass, sown down for a single year, so that any large increase of grain at the expense of this crop could only be got by omitting it altogether—a very undesirable proceeding. In certain English counties, as in Scotland, temporary grass remained down for two or three years, and in such cases corn-growing could easily be increased, but some of this temporary grass had already been ploughed in 1915, and no great extension of the practice was possible. Grain could also be grown at the expense of roots and fallows, and this method, too, had been followed in 1915 ; but the extension of the system was undesirable, for if extended the land could not be cleaned satisfactorily and would rapidly deteriorate in fertility. Apart, therefore, from make-shift methods of farming, which were good enough for a single year, but highly undesirable should the war be prolonged, the only method of increasing grain open to the English farmer was the ploughing out of permanent grass. Whatever views may be held as to the relative merits of grass and tillage to the farmer himself, the proposal that he should altogether alter the system of farming to which he had been accustomed, of which he had experience, and for which he had sufficient capital, was clearly a very different matter from suggesting that he should speed up his existing methods. The figures in Table I plainly show that an alteration in system is what would have been required of the average English farmer if he were to increase largely the area under grain in the harvest of 1916. Any considerable change in system would have involved, not merely a speeding-up, but the purchase of additional horses in a depleted market, the provision of implements, and the finding of additional men. In view of the conditions in the summer of 1915, it would have been unreasonable to have expected, and impossible to have secured, any substantial increase in the English harvest of 1916, except by the adoption of such methods as those recommended by Lord Milner's Committee.

The Government's Decision on Guaranteed Prices.

The decision of Government on the recommendation that guaranteed prices should be offered for grain was first disclosed on 26th August 1915 at a meeting of agriculturists convened by the President of the Board of Agriculture and Fisheries. Referring to this proposal Lord Selborne said : [1]

' After the report (Interim Report of Lord Milner's Committee) had been received I need not say that the Admiralty were consulted, and that all through the Government have acted in consultation with them, and what is of great importance as bearing on this question was fresh information which reached them after that report had been received and before it had been considered. Shortly after it had been received the Agricultural Returns of 1915 came to hand. . . . In addition to that we had the final reports on the Canadian and Australian harvests . . . as compared with the year 1913 there are at the present moment 500,000 more acres of wheat under cultivation, or an increase of nearly 30 per cent. The increase in cattle is 384,000 and the increase in sheep 450,000. . . . In view of these remarkable figures disclosed by the Agricultural Returns ; in view of the fact that it was borne in upon us as the struggle in the east of Europe developed that the call on men, on agricultural labourers, for the colours would be very heavy in the coming year ; in view of the difficulties with which the farmer would thereby be confronted ; in view of the superabundant harvest in Canada and Australia, and in view of the great financial stringency which will certainly prevail after the war, the Government decided that they would not incur the additional financial liability involved in the guarantee.'

The Government's policy at this time caused surprise to most agriculturists. It was generally understood that in recent months the submarine menace had become serious, and the financial risk called for appeared to be very small in comparison with the object which the guarantee of prices was intended to secure.

We now know that between the second quarter of 1915—the period which the Milner Committee had in view in considering their recommendations—and the end of August, there had been a great improvement in the submarine position from the point of view of the Allies. Commander Groos, the German official historian of the war, in a paper quoted in *The Times* news-

[1] *Journal of Board of Agriculture and Fisheries*, vol. xxii, p. 485.

paper of 12th April 1921, states that the success of their submarine warfare in the spring months of 1915 exceeded German
anticipations, but that the sinking of neutral ships led to such
political difficulties that von Bethmann-Hollweg insisted on
the cessation of attacks upon them. On 9th May the Kaiser
ordered submarine commanders not to attack in doubtful cases.
The effect of this order, according to Commander Groos, was
that whereas in the first half of May, before it was acted upon,
fifty-two ships in addition to sixty-two fishing vessels had been
sunk, in the last week of June seven vessels only were sunk ; in
the meantime, too, twelve U-boats had been destroyed. Thereafter in the autumn of 1915 the submarine war on commerce
became ' a pretence of activity '.

But even greater than the change in the situation between
May and August 1915 which resulted from the decreased losses at
sea, was the change in the outlook for supplies caused by the
' superabundant harvest ' in other countries to which Lord
Selborne drew attention.

Both Canada and the United States had largely increased
the area sown with wheat, and the season had been extraordinarily favourable ; thus in both countries, especially in
Canada, the yield of the wheat crop of 1915 was remarkable,
and it was apparent that, given the means of transport, there
would be no difficulty in meeting the wheat requirements of the
Allies in the cereal year 1915–16. The Argentine crop of 1915–16
also proved to be somewhat above average ; thus the combined
crop of the three countries available for consumption in the
cereal year 1915–16 was no less than seventeen million tons in
excess of the average yield of the years 1901–14. The effect of
this great harvest on the Allies' bread supply will be appreciated
when it is pointed out that the average annual imports of wheat
and flour by the United Kingdom, France, and Italy in the five
years before the war amounted to about eight million tons.

Nor was this all, the additional supply of wheat in the
New World had not been secured at the expense of other cereals.
The average yield of the four cereals—wheat, barley, oats, and
maize—in Canada, the United States, and Argentina had been

125 million tons in the years 1907–14 ; in 1915 the total yield was 160 million tons ; there was therefore available, not only an abundant supply of breadstuffs, but more fodder grain for animals.[1]

The actual figures given above were not forthcoming until the following year ; but it was generally known by September 1915 that the American harvest had been exceptionally good, and the fact that there was no immediate danger of a short supply influenced agriculturists, as it did Government, in making their arrangements for the harvest of 1916.

Action taken on Production of Food Committees' Reports.

Although Government refused to accept the main recommendation made by Lord Milner's Committee, several of the suggestions made by the committee, and by the corresponding committees in Scotland and Ireland, were acted upon.

At the meeting referred to above, Lord Selborne announced the measures he proposed taking in the immediate future. Of these the most important was that which led to the formation of War Agricultural Committees. Referring to the organization which Lord Milner's Committee had suggested for increasing food production, Lord Selborne announced that he proposed

' to adopt a valuable recommendation made in the Interim Report of Lord Milner's Committee, that the County Councils should be asked to act as the link between the Board of Agriculture and the farmer. . . . What I am going to ask them to do is to establish in each county a sub-committee, or one of their committees, if there is such a committee adapted for the purpose, to deal with the whole county and then to appoint, in the smaller areas of the county, committees which will be in continuous correspondence with it.'

A few weeks later the Board of Agriculture and Fisheries published a scheme for the appointment of War Agricultural Committees on the lines indicated by the President. It was explained that these committees, however formed, must represent landowners, farmers, and labourers, and should include others locally interested in food production. Where committees had already been formed to organize farm labour, their work

[1] Further figures on the American crops will be found on p. 160.

was to be co-ordinated with that of the War Agricultural Committees. It was suggested that an existing official of the county council should act as clerk to the committee, and the Board intimated that they would be represented by a commissioner or inspector. District sub-committees were to be constituted in each rural district, and also in each urban district where there was a considerable area of agricultural land.

The main functions of the War Agricultural Committees were:—(1) To organize the supply of agricultural labour; for this purpose they were to be supplied with the information available under the National Registration Act, and with all relevant information which the Board were able to command; special attention was directed to the training of women. (2) To consider how, under the conditions obtaining in the county, food production could be maintained, or increased; figures showing the existing acreage under the principal crops in each petty sessional division of the county in 1915, and in certain other years, were provided by the Board for the guidance of committees. (3) To secure information about the need for fertilizers, feeding stuffs, machinery and implements, and to report deficiencies to the Board with a view to supplies being secured; also to promote co-operation among farmers in the ordering of supplies, and in the using of such machines and implements as there might be difficulty in procuring.

Lord Milner's Committee had emphasized the need for guidance in the selection of crops and the management of stock, and the Board was careful to see that the new War Agricultural Committees, and agriculturists generally, should be thoroughly informed respecting the products which the nation was most likely to want in 1916.

On 28th September 1915 Lord Selborne issued an appeal to farmers and occupiers of land from which the following passage may be quoted:

' As Minister of Agriculture in this present time of war, I desire to appeal to you who live by the land to assist your King and Country by producing as much food as possible in the coming year. It is always a wise precaution for a nation at war to produce as much food as possible within its own borders. You must remember that this war has to be fought with money as well as men, and every additional pound's worth of food which you can grow means a reduction in the quantity to be purchased from abroad, and is therefore a distinct contribution to Victory.'

The appeal then proceeded to outline the commodities which were most required, and to make suggestions for the breaking up of poor grass land, the reduction of bare fallows and other measures likely to increase the quantity of food which the soil was able to provide.

It was hoped and expected that farmers would respond freely to this appeal; but subsequent experience proved these expectations to be ill-founded. An opinion commonly expressed by agriculturists at this time was that there could be no real need, otherwise the advice of Lord Milner's Committee would have been accepted. Thus while almost every farmer looked to his neighbour to make an effort, he found his own particular conditions so difficult that he interpreted the appeal, in his personal case, to mean ' carry on '. Lack of labour and supplies prevented him ' *farming* as usual ', but he would at least attempt ' *cropping* as usual '.

We are anticipating, however; the harvest of 1916 is still twelve months ahead. Let us therefore follow the farmer's fortunes, as he tills and sows and plants throughout the dismal months that were to follow.

Agricultural Conditions in Season 1915–16.

We have seen that, favoured by good weather and assisted by a considerable number of casual workers, the 1915 harvest was saved without loss and, indeed, without any particular difficulty.

The experiences of farmers in July 1915, nevertheless, showed how very serious their difficulties might be in adverse weather, and from the summer of 1915 onwards the efforts of the Departments concerned were closely concentrated on the problems presented by the carrying out of essential farm work. An instruction was issued from the War Office informing recruiting officers that they were not to induce certain skilled farm workers to enlist, unless there were evidence that their places could be filled ; foremen, head carters, shepherds, necessary milkers, blacksmiths, were among those specified.

About the same time postmen were offered special leave for harvest work, and pensions officers were instructed not to question an old age pensioner's right to his weekly payment, in cases where he was temporarily employed in work arising out of the war.

Immediately after harvest, special arrangements were made to supply soldier labour for autumn cultivation. Men were provided, in cases where no local labour existed, at a wage of 4s. per day, or 2s. 6d. if board and lodging were supplied. The only outlay for travelling expenses which the farmer was called upon to bear was conveyance from the nearest railway station. Attempts were made to secure soldiers accustomed to horses, and as a result quite a number of useful men found their way to the land. When, in the autumn of 1915, the Derby Scheme of recruiting was introduced, most of the necessary farm workers were ' starred '. These men could not be enlisted for immediate service ; but, if they wished it, they might join the Army Reserve, and pass into one of the forty-six classes into which the Reserve was divided.

The season for autumn cultivation was on the whole satisfactory until the middle of November, when very cold weather set in and frost endangered mangolds and potatoes in late districts. Sowing was carried on under less favourable conditions than in the previous year, and it became evident as the season advanced that less wheat was being put in. Competition for labour at the November ' hirings ' was keen, and in nearly every district there was a substantial increase in wages.

Thereafter for some months the labour situation was eased by the state of the weather ; for, until the middle of March, conditions were so unfavourable that it was almost impossible to make headway with field work. December was wet and stormy ; January, on the other hand, was mild and open, and some arrears in ploughing stubbles and ley were overtaken in this month ; but a wet spell, which began in February and lasted until the end of March, prevented spring sowing until an unusually late period. The position of the farmers of the country in April 1916 was most trying ; and, to add to the difficulties created by prolonged bad weather and shortage of labour, the Army was calling for more men.

At the beginning of the year the Military Service Act had come into operation, and all agriculturists qualified for service who had not attested under the Derby Scheme were, like the rest of the civil population, automatically enlisted on 2nd March ; but men previously ' starred ' were exempted as being in occupations certified to be of national importance. The ' certified occupations ' were somewhat wider in their scope than the occupations previously ' starred ', and included farmers themselves and a few other groups of agricultural workers. During March, however, the military position necessitated a review of the exemptions at first agreed to, and thereafter no exemptions were granted to unmarried bailiffs under thirty years of age, or to other unmarried skilled farm workers under twenty-five. Further, it was ruled that no exemptions could be granted in respect of men who had not been occupied in the same, or similar, work since before 15th August 1915. These changes caused great uneasiness, and increased the despondency with which farmers contemplated the tasks lying ahead.

As a set-off to the increased recruiting of farm hands the Military Authorities agreed to extend the system of granting furlough to soldiers for agricultural employment. Previously furlough had been granted for harvesting only—it could now be given for other types of farm work. Arrangements were also made which enabled convalescent soldiers to undertake work on the land.

The policy of the Government with respect to Food Production at this stage of the war is indicated by the following quotation : [1]

' *Mr. T. Davies* : I beg to ask the Minister of Munitions whether, in view of the Statement made on behalf of the Government yesterday that still further demands for men must be made upon the agricultural

[1] *Parliamentary Debates, House of Commons,* 22nd March, 1916.

industry, he can make any statement as to the necessity for maintaining agricultural production and retaining on the land a sufficient number of agricultural workers ?

'*Mr. Lloyd George* : It is true, as my hon. Friend says, that it will be necessary in the national interest to review the exemptions granted to certain classes of agricultural workers, but it must not be supposed that in taking this action the Government have failed to realize the importance of maintaining the highest possible output of home-grown food supplies, which remains a national subject of a most essential nature. We should deprecate the removal from work on the land, of labour which is really essential and irreplacable for this purpose.'

This then was the position of farmers at the beginning of April 1916. Government was proclaiming the importance of their work, the Departments of Agriculture were doing what they could to supply casual labour ; but the soil was sodden, the spring crops were unsown, and the recruiting authorities were enlisting their most active men. Fortunately April was a dry month. The first three weeks were cold, and this added to the trials of stock owners, if it did not retard the progress of tillage. Then the weather improved and, until the end of May, favourable conditions continued ; spring corn was sown rapidly on a raw and ill-prepared seed bed, potatoes and mangolds were got in somehow, and thus by the end of May the proportion of the land sown or planted was not much less than usual. June set in cold but dry and the first three weeks of July were also cold ; the hay crop was light, the corn crops and roots were backward, but the chilly weather at least checked the growth of weeds. Turnip hoeing was greatly in arrears, but the effects of neglect were less noticeable at this stage than they would have been in a warm moist season. Towards the end of July the weather turned hot and forcing. Grain crops ripened rapidly and in the south some harvesting was done under favourable conditions. In the second half of August and the first week of September the rain which fell, though it interfered with harvesting, was, on the whole, beneficial ; but the remainder of the month of September was cold, dull, and unfavourable ; the corn harvest made slow progress, potatoes suffered from disease, and mangolds did not ripen well. The corn harvest lasted until late in October, except in the south and east ; but it was secured with little loss except in a few upland districts. It was otherwise with the potato crop : the second half of October and most days in November were wet, and the lifting of the crop was carried on under very unfavourable conditions which resulted in much waste.

Throughout the difficult summer and autumn months great efforts were made by the Departments of Agriculture and the War Agricultural Committees to provide labour.   The sowing of the corn crops had been carried out by the farmer's regular staff ; but casual workers were wanted for potato planting, weeding, and harvesting, and it was in the summer of 1916 that farmers began everywhere to appreciate the value of woman labour.

The efforts made to get employment for women in 1915 had been disappointing. Lord Selborne recognized this, and, in his address, from which we have already quoted, in referring to the great labour difficulties ahead, he drew attention to the unwillingness of farmers to avail themselves of the services of women. As we have seen, when War Agricultural Committees were set up they were asked to give special attention to inducing farmers to accept women's help, and in November 1915 a circular letter was addressed to War Agricultural Committees, and also to Local Education Authorities, asking them to appeal for volunteer workers, to provide training for those who needed it, and to urge farmers to employ women on all work for which they were suited. Attention was drawn to methods of training which had already proved successful, and also to the grants for training which education committees could earn under the regulations of the Board of Agriculture for grants-in-aid of agricultural education.

In February a second circular on the same subject was sent to the committees referring to recent extensions of the activities of the Labour Exchanges. The Board of Trade had appointed organizers of women's work in connexion with the Exchanges for the purpose of establishing women's organizations, and it had been decided to set up Women's Farm Labour Committees

in each county. These women's committees were closely associated with the War Agricultural Committees. Attention was
also directed to the Women's National Land Service Corps—
a central association which had been set up to assist the Women's
Farm Labour Committees established locally.

Frequent articles and notes on women's work on the land
appeared in the Board of Agriculture's *Journal*. Attention
was drawn to successful training schemes, to evidence given
by farmers of the value of women's work in different parts of the
country, and to local measures taken to encourage the employment of women. A great fillip was given to the movement by competitions. The first to attract general attention were held in the
county of Cornwall, a county frequently in the van when any new
movement is afoot. Some cautious (or incautious) member of
the Launceston Board of Guardians stated publicly that women
could not do certain types of farm work. In the local press
women challenged this statement, and a public demonstration
was arranged for 9th March. Eight competitors appeared, and
acquitted themselves so well that a month later a county
demonstration was arranged at Truro. Competitions were
arranged in seven types of farm work, including harnessing and
driving horses in wagons, ploughing, manure spreading, and
potato planting. There were forty-three competitors, they
were given stiff tasks, some that could only be well done by
skilled labourers ; but they won praise from the judges, one of
whom wrote : ' Some of the work was very well done indeed.
The dung-spreading and planting were excellent, and the way
in which several of the competitors handled the horses in the
harrowing and in the wagons was a surprise to many of the
spectators. . . . I should like to see some of the men who have
been cheaply sneering at the ploughing have a try themselves.
. . . However, the heavy work on a farm must be done by men,
but there is a lot of work that women can do very well.'

Before the war was over there were women in this same
south-western division of England who took a farm and worked
it by themselves, presumably to prove that men could ' very
well ' be done without !

It was thus partly the lead given by the Agricultural Departments and the War Agricultural Committees, partly the pressure which the adverse conditions exerted on the farmer, but above all the performance of the women themselves, that led farmers, in those parts of the country where women had not formerly been employed on the land, to welcome them in the summer of 1916.

Soldier ploughmen, who had already become popular, were eagerly sought by many farmers ; and there was also a great extension of the demand for soldiers for general farm work. Between 3rd June and 28th July 1916 applications for over 33,000 soldiers were made to the Labour Exchanges, and about 14,000 men were provided. On the 5th of August the Military Authorities announced the conditions on which soldiers could be released for harvest, and—although few farmers were then in a position to say when men would actually be required for this purpose—by the 9th of the month 3,244 men had been requisitioned to begin work on the 14th.

The labour difficulties of the summer of 1916 were responsible for introducing one other source of assistance. In February the attention of agriculturists had been drawn to the possibility of employing selected civilian prisoners of war, but the suggestion evoked no enthusiasm. During the summer, however, a further circular was issued, advising farmers to utilize these men and explaining the conditions on which they would be released for farm work ; applications were made for their services, and farmers who employed them often spoke well of their work. Thus a beginning was made in the employment of the prisoner labour which, in the later years of the war, proved to be so useful.

The Supply of Fertilizers.

Next to labour questions the subject causing most apprehension in the minds of tillage farmers in the winter of 1915–16 was the future supply of fertilizers. Allusion has already been made to the shortage of potash ; but with this relatively unimportant exception, no trouble had been experienced in procuring the manures required for the 1915 crop. It was obvious, however, in the summer of that year, that, if the war continued, the position in the spring of 1916 would be much more difficult. The manufacture of explosives was making large demands on the stocks of nitrate of soda, and the imports of phosphatic rock for the manufacture of superphosphate had been considerably reduced in the first half of 1915 ; thus two of the farmer's most important manures were threatened, and prices had risen sharply. In the year before the war, nitrogen in nitrate of soda could be purchased at from 14s. to 16s. per unit (22·4 lb.) ; the price in November 1915 ranged from 19s. to 20s. 6d., although in this month the demand for the manure is very small. Similarly, phosphates, which before the war could be purchased in superphosphate of lime of ordinary quality at from 1s. 9d. to 2s. per unit, cost from 2s. 10d. to 3s. 3d. in October 1915. Moreover, to those who were watching the fertilizer position on the farmers' behalf there were elements in the situation which pointed to much reduced supplies and increased prices in the spring months. It was known that arrangements for the manufacture of explosives would then be in force which would call for large quantities of sulphate of ammonia, a manure of which there was a full supply in the autumn of 1915 ; further, a great demand for sulphuric acid had arisen, so that even if rock phosphates could be imported, it might be impossible to convert them into superphosphate.

The Acland Committee on Fertilizers.

In October 1915 Lord Selborne appointed a Departmental Committee to make arrangements for the shipment, sale, and distribution of nitrate of soda, and of any other fertilizers purchased by the Government, and to deal generally with all questions relating to the supply of fertilizers for the use of farmers in the United Kingdom. The committee included representatives of the Board of Agriculture and Fisheries, the Scottish Office, the Irish Department of Agriculture and Technical Instruction, the Board of Trade, the Ministry of Munitions, and the Admiralty. The Rt. Hon.

F. D. Acland, M.P., Parliamentary Secretary of the Board of Agriculture and Fisheries, was Chairman. This committee continued in existence, watching the interests of agriculturists and regulating the trade in fertilizers, until December 1916, when the Board of Agriculture's functions with respect to the supply of fertilizers were transferred to the newly formed Ministry of Food.

The great demand for explosives in the first year of the war had entirely altered the character of the trade in nitrate of soda. After August 1914 shipments consisted chiefly of the refined nitrate used in the manufacture of munitions, and relatively little of the unrefined material employed as manure was imported. As a precautionary measure, in the autumn of 1915 the Government decided to purchase 50,000 tons of nitrate of soda for use as a fertilizer, and the immediate purpose of the Fertilizers Committee was to make arrangements for its importation, sale, and distribution. Unfortunately, at this stage a block occurred in the Panama Canal, and as the duration of the interruption of traffic was uncertain, an endeavour was made to get the manure shipped via Cape Horn. Arrangements for the sale and distribution in this country were completed before the end of the year, but ships for transport could not be found. Finally, as the weeks passed and the Admiralty were unable to provide tonnage, it became apparent that the manure would be too late for the crops of 1916. Part was therefore resold in Chile and part exchanged for refined nitrate for the manufacture of explosives. The committee then concentrated their attention on an alternative nitrogenous manure— sulphate of ammonia. This material, a by-product of gasworks, coke ovens, and shale oil manufacture, is a more concentrated source of nitrogen than nitrate of soda, and its value as manure is well known; but although some 400,000 tons per annum were manufactured in the United Kingdom, the greater part of the home product was exported. Thus in the period before the war it is estimated that not more than fifty to sixty thousand tons per annum were applied to our soils, as against some eighty to one hundred thousand tons of nitrate of soda. Moreover, at

least nine-tenths of the sulphate of ammonia used was sold
to farmers in mixed manures, whereas nitrate of soda was
nearly always supplied as imported ; thus the farmer was much
less familiar with sulphate of ammonia and its uses than he was
with nitrate of soda. It was clearly necessary in the national
interest that the use of this very valuable home supply of
manure should be stimulated, and the policy of the committee
was therefore directed to increasing the demand for sulphate
of ammonia, and to ensuring an abundant supply at reasonable
prices. The success of this policy was not immediately apparent,
as farmers do not readily change their methods ; they were not
satisfied that sulphate of ammonia would prove profitable, since
they were unable to forecast the prices of corn, and if the abundant harvests of 1915 should be followed by similar good crops
in Canada and the other overseas sources of supply, British corn
might, they argued, fetch low prices in the autumn of 1916.
They therefore purchased very cautiously throughout the
entire season.

The first step taken to popularize the use of sulphate of
ammonia was in the autumn of 1915. The ordinary sales of
this manure for application to autumn-sown wheat were very
small ; on the other hand, experience, acquired for the most
part in the period before corn prices fell and forgotten by many
of the present generation of farmers, showed that under suitable
conditions the use of nitrogenous manures in autumn would
considerably increase the yield of wheat. The Board of Agriculture and Fisheries, accordingly, issued a circular pointing out
the value of sulphate of ammonia as an autumn manure, and
they urged farmers to use this means of increasing the production
of food. At the same time arrangements were made by the
committee which ensured that a sufficient supply of sulphate
of ammonia should be placed on sale at very favourable rates.
From the quantity of manure disposed of under this arrangement in November and December 1915, it may be estimated
that about 75,000 acres of wheat were manured. By negotiations with the Sulphate of Ammonia Association, through which
the manure for autumn use had been provided, the committee

next secured an understanding with manufacturers of sulphate of ammonia on the subject of spring prices. No actual price was fixed—at this time the committee had no power to fix prices—but the agreement which was come to ensured that in most parts of the country sulphate of ammonia would be on sale at an advance of about 30 per cent. on pre-war figures. The committee were satisfied that the increase in the cost of production, chiefly due to the sharp advance which had taken place in the price of sulphuric acid, justified this increase in the price of sulphate of ammonia. Relatively to other manures, sulphate of ammonia was indeed one of the cheapest fertilizers available in the spring of 1916.

While Government had at this time not taken powers enabling them to fix the prices of manures, they were able, by controlling exports, to ensure that a sufficient stock of sulphate of ammonia was retained within the country for the needs of agriculture ; and the principal duty of the committee in the winter and spring months was to ascertain the production of sulphate of ammonia, estimate the needs for all purposes, and release for export as much as could be spared. Apart from considerations depending on the position of the industry itself, it was necessary in the national interest that all the material not required at home should be exported ; for not only did this valuable export assist the nation's trade balance, but the manure was largely required for growing sugar in tropical countries, and thus for producing a commodity of which increased supplies were urgently required.

By the beginning of 1916 the difficulty of securing acid, on the one hand, and the prospective demands of munitions, on the other, led the committee to think that the whole of the sulphate of ammonia manufactured during the first six months of the year might be required for home use ; in January, therefore, the issue of licences to export the manure was suspended.

This course of action not only deprived merchants of a profitable trade, but led to much inconvenience in certain factories. The practice of makers being to dispose of sulphate of ammonia as produced, storage accommodation as a rule was very limited, and complaints in great numbers soon reached the committee. Steps were taken to relieve the congestion in a few instances, where the position was specially bad, by granting permits to export to France ; but the restrictions on export were retained until 31st March, by which time it was clear that the quantity of sulphate of ammonia in stock, or in sight, was sufficient to meet all the demands of the crop of 1916.

The Board of Agriculture and Fisheries, at the instance of the committee, did everything possible to stimulate sales and to induce farmers to purchase early in the season. Information was published in leaflet form on the uses of sulphate of ammonia for spring crops and grass land, and attention was drawn to its relatively low price. Circulars on the subject were addressed to War Agricultural Committees, and over 50,000 copies of a ' Notice to Farmers ' drawing their attention to the various uses of sulphate of ammonia were issued. Letters were also addressed to some three hundred agricultural societies ; and the Royal Agricultural Society, the National Farmers Union, and many other associations of farmers assisted the Board in popularising the use of sulphate of ammonia in the spring of 1916. As already indicated, the response was disappointing. In all, about 80,000 tons were sold ; but those who tried sulphate of ammonia in 1916 found that it justified the recommendation given it, and there was a greatly increased demand in the later years of the war.

While the Fertilizers Committee did everything possible to mitigate the inconvenience caused by the accumulation of large stocks of sulphate of ammonia in the hands of manufacturers in the spring of 1916, it must be admitted that the committee's precautions, by preventing export to certain foreign customers until late in the season, caused traders not only inconvenience, but loss ; and it should be recorded that manufacturers, and the Sulphate of Ammonia Association which represented them, acted throughout in a public-spirited manner. They made efforts to carry out the wishes of the committee, and materially assisted with the distribution of the manure to farmers in all parts of the country. This distribution was no easy task, for apart from the difficulties common to the transport of all bulky commodities at the time, in the case of sulphate of ammonia there was the special difficulty that it was largely a product of the industrial north, while it was chiefly required by the farmers of the corn-growing counties in the east and south. It is, moreover, a manure which farmers are very apt to demand at short notice, and in spite of the Board's warnings many delayed its purchase until it was wanted for use ; then, the local supply being exhausted, consignments had to be railed from a distance. In arranging supplies under these circumstances, the committee got much help from the Sulphate of Ammonia Association.

At the beginning of 1916, when it seemed possible that the demands of the Ministry of Munitions might reduce the supplies of sulphate of ammonia available for agriculture below the quantity required, the attention of the committee was directed to the possibility of manufacturing additional supplies by such synthetic processes as had been worked in Norway before the war, or developed in Germany since 1914. They therefore approached the Chemical Society, who readily came to their aid and undertook to provide the information asked for. Later the Society sent to the Board of Agriculture and Fisheries a valuable report prepared by three leading authorities on the subject. This report described the processes which had been worked successfully, and estimated the possibilities of each under the conditions of 1916.

In the interval, while this report was in preparation, material changes in the position had taken place, and the prospective demands for nitrogen compounds for munitions were so great that the Ministry of Munitions had decided to refer the whole subject to a committee of experts, including those who had prepared the above-mentioned report. At the same time the farmers' demands for nitrogenous manures for the season of 1916 had been met. It seemed to the Fertilizers Committee, therefore, that the responsibility for the further development of processes for manufacturing compounds of nitrogen should rest with the new body—the Nitrogen Products Committee—set up by the Ministry of Munitions,[1] and to it the information which they had collected was transferred. One of the members of the Fertilizers Committee joined the Nitrogen Products Committee, so that touch between the two might be maintained.

A second manure which claimed much attention in the winter of 1915–16 was superphosphate of lime. No measures to popularize this material were necessary, for farmers were well aware of its uses ; but as the supplies of sulphuric acid and rock phosphate required for its manufacture were much reduced, and as labour difficulties were severely felt in manure factories, action was necessary to assist manufacturers both with raw materials and with labour. Attention was also given to the measures required for securing the economical distribution of the available supplies of superphosphate.

To replace the acid needed by makers of fertilizers, ' nitre cake ', a by-product accumulating in quantity as a result of the manufacture of explosives, had been used with some success in the making of sulphate of ammonia ; and one or two firms had experimented with it as a substitute, or partial substitute, for acid in dissolving rock phosphate. The committee arranged for an investigation of the subject by an expert. Experiments carried out on the manufacturing scale proved that a superphosphate indistinguishable from the ordinary superphosphate of commerce in its manurial properties (though containing a lower percentage of soluble phosphate) could be made from nitre cake and rock phosphate. These results were brought to the notice of manufacturers ; but very little use was subsequently made of nitre cake as an acid substitute in the manure trade, partly because of technical difficulties which it introduced into the process of manufacture, and partly because the low percentage of ' soluble phosphates ' which could be guaranteed, led makers to fear that the reputation of the superphosphate sold by them would suffer.

[1] A valuable Report (Cmd. 482) was issued by this Committee. H.M. Stationery Office, London, 1920, 4s.

Nitrogenous and phosphatic artificial manures constitute by far the most important classes of fertilizers required in British husbandry. Of the five or six millions sterling paid by farmers for artificial manures in the years before the war, nine-tenths was expended in the purchase of manures belonging to these two classes. The balance was spent on potash manures, and, as has already been stated, the supplies of these were almost cut off by the outbreak of war.

Although the injury caused by the loss of potash was much less than had been feared, its absence was felt by the growers of certain crops in most parts of the country. New, or possible, sources of supply, therefore, frequently engaged the attention of the Fertilizers Committee. Of possible sources, the most promising, at the beginning of 1916, appeared to be felspar. In a process known as ' Rhodin's ', employed in preparing a white cement from felspar, a substantial percentage of potash in a soluble form was produced as a by-product.

Certain felspars, abundant in this country, contain from nine to eleven per cent. of potash ; it is present, however, in a form valueless to plants, and many attempts had been made to devise an economic process for its extraction in a soluble form. Before the war, Rhodin's process, as applied to a very pure Swedish felspar, had been shown to have commercial possibilities. There was a limited demand for white cement in this country, and to the extent to which the cement could be sold at the prices ruling before the war, the potash by-product could be sold for manure at the prices which farmers were then paying for German potash. But the process had not been applied to any British felspar and the quality of the cement that might result was unknown. A sub-committee of the Fertilizers Committee was therefore set up to arrange for practical tests. Through the Geological Survey and by personal inquiries, supplies of the best British felspars were located and samples procured ; these felspars were treated by Mr. Rhodin, the patentee of the process, on premises placed at the disposal of the committee by Messrs. Cubitt & Co., who owned the necessary plant ; and careful tests were made under the supervision of the Government Chemical Laboratory. A short description of these tests has been published.[1]

While Rhodin's process effected all that had been claimed for it, the Fertilizers Committee were unable to recommend the Government to adopt it as a means of providing potash. The potash present in the felspar was extracted in a form suitable for manure ; but the best of the British felspars produced only 8 tons of potash per 100 tons of raw material and per 220 tons of the main product—cement. Thus to have produced about one-fourth of the quantity of potash used by farmers before the war, it would have been necessary to manufacture 136,000 tons of cement. The market for the class of cement produced was limited, and though it was stated by experts that a market for a very large quantity at remunerative prices could be created, it was believed by the committee that other sources of potash, which in the interval had been brought to light, would prove to be more advantageous from the point of view of agriculture.

The work of the Acland Committee of 1915–16 has been referred to in some detail, partly because its operations laid the foundation for the policy followed in connexion with the supply of fertilizers in the later years of the war, and partly because its activities illustrate the possibilities, in the direction of influencing prices and supplies, of a body not armed with the authority entrusted to the ' controllers ' of the subsequent period. In spite of limited powers, and the great difficulties with which they were faced, the main purpose of the committee was accomplished, and, save in the case of potash, farmers were provided, at reasonable prices, with practically all the artificial manures they were prepared to purchase for use on the 1916 crop. If pre-war prices had prevailed farmers would no doubt have been ready to purchase more freely ; but, even if the committee could have fixed prices, any attempt to enforce pre-war prices at this period would inevitably have reduced supplies, and no additional quantity of manure would have reached the soil.

[1] *Journal of the Board of Agric. and Fisheries*, vol. xxiii, p. 1087, London, 1917.

The Harvest Figures.

We have followed the farmer through his troubles from seed time till harvest, and described the methods adopted in stimulating, advising, and assisting him through this difficult year; let us now examine the results of all these efforts to maintain, and if possible to increase, food production in 1916.

The necessary figures will be found in Table XV.

TABLE XV

HARVEST OF 1916 COMPARED WITH AVERAGE HARVEST OF 1904–13

FIGURES THOUSANDS OF ACRES OR TONS

(FOR AREAS AND YIELDS OF 1904–13 SEE PAGE 112)

Country	Crop	1916		1916 + 1904–13	
		Area	Yield	Acres	Tons
England and Wales .	Wheat	1,912	1,498	+ 223	+ 30
Scotland . . .	,,	63	61	+ 12	+ 4
Ireland . . .	,,	77	76	+ 37	+ 37
United Kingdom . .	,,	2,052	1,635	+ 272	+ 71
England and Wales .	Barley	1,332	974	− 178	− 218
Scotland . . .	,,	170	117	− 29	− 54
Ireland . . .	,,	150	140	− 14	− 13
United Kingdom . .	,,	1,652	1,231	− 221	− 285
England and Wales .	Oats	2,085	1,452	− 12	− 32
Scotland . . .	,,	991	650	+ 35	0
Ireland . . .	,,	1,072	891	+ 12	− 15
United Kingdom . .	,,	4,148	2,993	+ 35	− 47
England and Wales .	Potatoes	428	2,504	− 4	− 139
Scotland . . .	,,	130	531	− 13	− 395
Ireland . . .	,,	586	2,433	− 11	− 590
United Kingdom . .	,,	1,144	5,468	− 28	1,124

The total area of land at the farmer's disposal in 1916 was almost the same as in the previous year. The Agricultural Returns showed an increase of 12,000 acres. The gain was 21,000 acres in England and Wales; the other countries showed small reductions. But if the total area remained unaltered, its management underwent a marked change, and the area of cultivated land, other than grass, was less by 148,000 acres than in the previous year. Nor was this all. During the year bare fallows had increased by more than 113,000 acres, so that whereas in 1915 the farmer had cultivated 12,567,000 acres, apart from grass and bare fallow, in 1916 he cultivated 12,306,000 acres only. The sharp increase in the area under bare fallows was partly due to the extra area put under corn in the previous year, and partly to labour difficulties in the late spring and early summer months. The total increase in the area under grass was 160,000 acres, but the Returns indicated that a certain amount of permanent grass had been broken up. This ploughing was, however, more than counter-balanced by a reduction in the ploughing of temporary grass. In the winter of 1914–15 a considerable inroad had been made on temporary grass land, but in the winter of 1915–16 the balance was restored, so that in the summer of 1916 the area of temporary grass in the country was almost the same as before the outbreak of war.

These circumstances resulted in a reduction of the area sown with corn; there was some increase in barley, but the wheat area fell by 281,000 acres, and for the three cereals the reduction was 163,000 acres.

The figures in Table XV compare the areas and yields of 1916 with those of the pre-war period. It will be seen that as compared with the average of 1904–13 the area of wheat in the United Kingdom had risen by 272,000, and of oats by 35,000 acres, while barley had fallen by 221,000. In themselves these figures were not unsatisfactory, for although the effort of 1915 had not been equalled, the normal areas had been more than secured; but unfortunately the yield was very poor. Thus while the total crops of wheat and oats were about the pre-war level, there was a great loss of barley, and for the three cereals the yield was 261,000 tons less than the average pre-war crop.

The area planted with potatoes was nearly normal; but the crop, especially in Scotland, was one of the worst that had been known for years, and the failure led to some of the sorest perplexities of the winter and spring months.

After all the effort that had been expended—the committees, the appeals, the advice, the assistance given by women, by soldier labourers, and, at harvest time, by not a few volunteer workers—the corn and potato crops of 1916 made a melancholy recompense to the food producer. To what was this result due? First, of course, there was the weather; this was mainly responsible for the poverty of the crops of 1916. Want of manure had relatively much less effect. The weather was also to some extent responsible for the low acreage of 1916; with better weather from the middle of October to the end of November more wheat would have been sown; with better weather in December and February more temporary grass would have been ploughed, and so the area under oats would have been greater. But even if the weather had been that of an average year, it is questionable if the total area under crops, other than grass, would have been substantially different in 1916 from the figures recorded in the above table. The farmer had put all his available tillage land under grain in 1915; and, in England at least, there was bound to be a reaction.

Given a definite area of arable land, it is an easy thing to increase the area under grain for a single season, but to maintain this increase is a very difficult matter. With the land distributed as it was between the different farm crops in September 1915, the total area under grain in 1915 could only have been equalled in the following year if a substantial quantity of grass land had been ploughed up between October and March and sown with oats. But this course was not adopted, and though the weather was partly responsible, the main reason was the farmers' uncertainty as to the future. It does not cost much to plough grass land, but it may cost a great deal to maintain it under cultivation after it has been broken up; and in the circumstances in which the farmer was placed in the winter of 1915–16 there were reasons for misgivings as to the future.

The methods adopted for increasing the area under tillage in 1916, the appeals to patriotism, the good advice, the promises of assistance in the future, were bound to fail. The risks were present to the mind of every farmer. 'Government', he argued, 'could not have any real fear of food shortage or they would themselves have accepted some risks and not have left them

all for him to face.'   He waited, therefore, until some other
farmer made a move.   And no move was made.

Proof of the need for a change in policy was the most
obvious contribution which the harvest of 1916 made to the
food problems of the war years.

CHAPTER VIII

THE HARVEST OF 1917

Measures Taken to arouse Public Interest in a Plough Policy. Change in Food Situation. Help for the Allotment Movement. Lord Ernle's Policy. Formation of Food Production Department. Agricultural Executive Committees. Powers conferred on Executives. Survey for 1917 Harvest. Early Organization of Food Production Department. Enlargement of Department's Scope and Powers. Scotch Procedure. Irish Procedure. The Supply of Labour. Manure Supply. Seed Supply. The Weather in Season 1917. Harvest Figures. Allotment Cultivation. 'Seed' Potatoes for the 1917 Allotments. The Improvement of Tillage. Crops on Newly broken Grass. Maximum and Minimum Prices.

THE result of the harvest to which reference has been made in the preceding pages was not known until towards the end of the year. Those who were anxiously watching the effects of the policy adopted for maintaining, or increasing, the crops of 1916 were well aware by the spring of that year, however, that the pre-war standard of production would with difficulty be maintained ; and that, unless new methods for stimulating farming were introduced, no substantial increase in the foodstuffs required by this country would be made by the soils of the United Kingdom. In the autumn of 1915 an effort had been made to attract attention to the very small contributions which are made by grass land to the total food supply of the country, but the public had subjects to think about at that time which were of much more interest to them than were such technical questions. Another method was therefore decided upon. It was known that the soils of Germany were supporting a much greater population than the soils of the United Kingdom ; but most of those who thought about the subject at all were under the impression that the standard of subsistence had been higher in this country than in Germany, and that it was this difference in consumption which enabled German agriculture to support a greater population. In the sense that the cost of the food eaten by the average Englishman was higher, this was true ; but in the sense that Germans had been less well nourished than the inhabitants of this country, it was untrue.

There was further the widespread impression that British agriculture was, without any possibility of question, the best in the world. That it had been the best fifty years before was true ; but that it still was the best was at least debatable. In the sense that this country bred the most valuable live stock, British agriculture was still supreme ; but the value was represented more in the quality than in the quantity of the foods produced, and in the quality to a less extent than is usually supposed. The yield per acre of the principal crops was also higher than in most other countries ; but while other countries had increased the area under tillage and also the yield of the crops, our tillage area had been greatly reduced, and, with few exceptions, the yield of our crops on the better soils now reserved for cultivation had shown no marked increase.

It appeared to be desirable therefore to set before the public some statement indicating the quantity of food that was grown in the United Kingdom in a form that would attract attention. This led to the issue by the Board of Agriculture and Fisheries of a Memorandum,[1] in which the productivity of the soils of this country and of Germany was compared. It was shown that per unit of area German soils supported in comfort many more persons than did the soils of Great Britain, and that this result was possible because of the relatively large proportion of German land which was kept under the plough.

The issue of this pamphlet in the summer of 1916, at a time when food difficulties were becoming more felt by the whole population, secured some attention to the merits of a plough policy ; and the events of the next few months supported the arguments for increasing the area under tillage, with the result that renewed attention was given to the proposals which had been made by Lord Milner's Committee in the preceding year.

[1] *The Recent Development of German Agriculture*, by T. H. Middleton, C.B. (Cd. 8305), H.M. Stationery Office, London 1916.

Change in Food Situation.

By the middle of the autumn of 1916 it was obvious that a complete change had taken place in the food situation. The main factors in the change were the comparative poverty of the American harvest, the failure of the home potato crop, and the decrease in the supplies of sugar.

Both in Canada and in the United States the great cereal harvest of 1915 had been followed in 1916 by comparatively small crops. The extent of the decrease was not known at the time, but the effect on the subsequent food situation produced by the American harvests of 1916 (including the poor Argentine harvest of 1916–17) was so great that it will be of interest to refer at this stage to the grain crops of Canada, the United States, and Argentina. Table XVI shows the total production of wheat, and of barley, oats, and maize, in Canada and the United States for each of the years 1910–16, and also in Argentina for the seasons 1910–11 to 1916–17. The figures, which come from the Statistical Bulletins of the International Agricultural Institute, Rome, are expressed in millions of metric tons.[1]

TABLE XVI

PRODUCTION OF WHEAT, AND OF BARLEY, OATS, AND MAIZE, IN CANADA, THE UNITED STATES, AND ARGENTINA IN MILLIONS OF METRIC TONS

Year	Canada		United States		Argentina		Total		
	Wheat	*Other Cereals*	*Wheat*	*Other Cereals*	*Wheat*	*Other Cereals*	*Wheat*	*Other Cereals*	*Four Cereals*
1910	3·6	4·7	17·3	94·3	4·0	1·4	24·9	100·5	125·4
1911	6·3	7·1	16·9	81·2	4·5	8·6	27·7	96·8	124·5
1912	6·1	7·5	19·9	104·8	5·1	6·2	31·1	118·5	149·6
1913	6·3	7·7	20·8	82·3	3·1	7·6	30·2	97·6	127·8
1914	4·4	6·0	24·2	88·7	4·5	9·1	33·2	103·8	137·0
Av. 1910–14	5·3	6·6	19·8	90·3	4·3	6·6	29·4	103·5	132·9
1915	11·6	9·8	27·9	103·5	4·6	5·3	44·1	118·6	162·7
1916	7·2	7·4	17·3	87·3	1·9	2·0	26·4	96·7	123·1

As was pointed out in Chapter VII, the cereal harvest of 1915 in these three countries greatly exceeded the average.

[1] One metric ton =2204·6 lb., 1,000 metric tons =984·2 British tons.

Comparing it with that of the preceding five years—on the whole a period of satisfactory production—there had been an increase of nearly thirty million tons of cereals. This great crop, partly exported as breadstuffs, and partly in the form of meat, had made the Allies' food situation in the cereal year 1915–16 relatively easy ; but in 1916 there was a sudden change, the wheat crop being less than in any year since 1911, and some three million tons below the average for the five-year period 1910–14. The total grain crop was lower than any since 1909, and it was nearly ten million tons less than the average crop of 1910–14.

These figures, while they explain the change in the autumn of 1916, also bring out very clearly the great good fortune of the Allies in the earlier years of the war. If the American crop of 1915 had been a poor one, or even if the yield had been average, this country would no doubt have experienced in the summer of 1917 food difficulties comparable with those then confronting the German nation.

The British potato crop of 1916 was late in being planted, but during the summer and early autumn months the prospects were fair ; the cold autumn, however, retarded the growth of the maincrop varieties, and wet soils in October intensified the effects of potato disease. A large part of the crop was harvested with difficulty, and by the beginning of November it was clear that the yield would be much below the normal. The figures for the total yield of potatoes, given in Table XV on p. 154, are those which, like other figures appearing in the Agricultural Returns, were based on estimates submitted by the official Crop Reporters, and reasons will subsequently be given for the view that they were over-estimates.

The Food (War) Committee of the Royal Society, to whose Report reference has been made in Chapter V, had recently completed their review of the food supplies of the country for the cereal year 1916 ; and, so far as they had been able to estimate the supplies, the foodstuffs available for the civilian population up to June of that year did not appear to have altered materially from those available in the period 1909–13.

In the pre-war period it had been shown that over and above the minimum requirements the foodstuffs then available had provided a considerable margin of the essential constituents— proteins, fats, and carbohydrates. The excess had been least in the last instance, amounting to some 10 per cent.

The deficient harvests of 1916 altogether modified the hitherto favourable situation ; the supplies of the three principal sources of carbohydrate—cereals, potatoes, and sugar— had all been greatly reduced, and by November 1916 it was obvious that very great difficulties must be faced before the next year's harvest was ready.

The fact that in all three cases the deficiency affected the supplies of carbohydrate had a graver significance than consideration of the reduction in the percentage of the total supplies might suggest, since carbohydrates form by far the cheapest sources of food, and are accordingly consumed in greatest proportion by the poorest classes. In this case, therefore, the reduction in supplies meant that the less the consumer had been able to spend on food in the past, the more would the percentage cost of his dietary be likely to rise. Far more suffering would thus be caused than if the same percentage reduction had taken place in the supplies of meat.

An increase in the production of corn and potatoes, which in the previous year had been advocated as an insurance against the shortage that would arise if the submarine prevented the landing of food in the country, now became a necessity ; since it was by no means clear that, even if the submarine menace continued to be ' well in hand ', there would be a sufficiency of breadstuffs for the Allied Nations.

In a memorandum which he prepared in November 1916 for the President of the Board of Agriculture and Fisheries, the writer emphasized the radical change which had taken place in the food situation, proposed an immediate effort to enlarge the areas under oats and potatoes in 1917—these being the only crops in which it was then possible to effect a substantial increase—and urged that preparation should be made for the harvest of 1918 without further delay. It was pointed out that in the event of a second unfavourable season in 1917, or of interference with shipping, the ploughing of the grass land of the United Kingdom presented the only considerable means of adding to the food supplies of the Allies. A shortage of shipping would diminish the importation of fertilizers even more than the importation of food, and without fertilizers good crops could not be expected from tillage land which had been subjected to the treatment which English tillage land had received since the outbreak of war. In any event, it was argued that an increase in home production would release tonnage for other essential services. This memorandum was brought before the Agricultural Consultative Committee, who expressed themselves as being in general agreement with the proposals made.

A few days later the second Coalition Government was formed by Mr. Lloyd George, and Lord Ernle (then Mr. Prothero) succeeded Lord Crawford as President of the Board of Agriculture and Fisheries. Lord Ernle immediately applied himself to the work of preparation for the 1917 harvest, and a period of great activity set in.

Before describing the action taken by Lord Ernle it will be convenient, however, to refer to the Cultivation of Lands Order of 1916, which was issued just before the change of Government.

Help for the Allotment Movement.

The remarkable growth of the allotment movement in the first year of the war has been described in Chapter VI. During 1916 it made steady progress, and much attention had been given by the Board of Agriculture and Fisheries to the publication of the information of which inexperienced cultivators were in need, and also to overcoming the obstacles with which they were confronted in gaining access to land. The land readily procurable at the beginning of the war was quickly occupied, and in the winter of 1915–16 many would-be cultivators could not obtain allotments. The failure of the potato crop and the high prices current in November 1916 greatly intensified the demand for land. Lord Crawford decided to deal with the situation that had arisen by a Regulation under the Defence of the Realm Acts. Accordingly on 5th December there appeared in the *London Gazette* the first of a series of Regulations which were to exercise a notable effect on food production in the remaining years of the war. This particular Regulation, No. 2 L, in the form in which it existed at the Armistice, is printed in Appendix I. The original did not apply to Ireland nor, for the first few months, did it authorize access to cultivated land, except with the consent of the owner.

Regulation 2 L empowered the central authorities of the three countries to make Orders delegating their powers to local authorities, and on 8th December the Board of Agriculture and Fisheries made the Cultivation of Lands Order 1916, which *inter alia* authorized urban local authorities to take possession of unoccupied land for the purpose of forming allotments without obtaining the consent of the owner; it further authorized them to create allotments on occupied land, provided that the consent of both owner and occupier were obtained, and on common land subject to the consent of the Board.[1]

The tenure conferred by the Order in Council was for the duration of the war; but it was explained that powers would be taken to enable an occupier to harvest the crop growing on the land at the end of the war. Compensation was payable for loss caused by disturbance. At first this compensation was limited to cases of disturbance before the 1st of January 1918, but the period was subsequently extended.

No rent was payable by local authorities for unoccupied or common land; but for occupied land a rent, limited by the Order, might be offered. Cultivators were expected to pay such rents as would recoup the expenses of providing the land. Local authorities were authorized to prepare the land for cultivation and to supply seed, manure, and implements at cost price. They were encouraged to provide expert assistance and to take advantage of an offer made by the Royal Horticultural Society to furnish advice through its members.

The powers conferred by this Order resulted in a great extension of allotments in the following year; and, as will be noted later, one of the most difficult tasks undertaken by the Food Production Department in the first months of its existence was the provision of 'seed' potatoes for eager cultivators.

[1] For this Order in its final form, see p. 362.

Lord Ernle's Policy.

Lord Ernle, who had been a member of Lord Milner's Committee in 1915, decided to adopt the recommendations of that committee, in so far as they were applicable to the conditions of December 1916, and his policy was clearly stated in two memoranda addressed to the War Agricultural Committees on the 28th and 29th of the month.

The first of these memoranda began with the sentences :

' We have two objects before us. One is immediate—the spring sowing in 1917. The other is more remote—the preparation of an arable area for the next cereal year. Farmers want—and the nation expects them—to grow all the essential food they possibly can, both for human consumption and for the maintenance of live stock.'

The memorandum then set out the country's chief food requirements, drew attention to the area cultivated and the crops produced in each county in 1874 and 1894, and, after alluding to the difficulties of the times, concluded ' Do not let us be discouraged by the many circumstances against us. For the nation's sake let us take as our motto for 1917 and 1918 " Back to the 'seventies and better ". We cannot do more. I am sure that farmers will not do less.'

The memorandum of the 28th December dealt with aims, that of the following day with methods. Attention was drawn to four subjects : the organization of War Agricultural Committees ; the survey of badly cultivated land, or of land for any other reason requiring the attention of the committees ; the ploughing of grass land ; and the stimulation of potato-growing and pig-keeping by villagers.

On three of these subjects no difference of opinion arose, but the policy of ploughing more grass land was then warmly debated. Most agriculturists believed that it was more prudent to concentrate all available labour on the existing tillage land than to undertake additional cultivation.

' This is a matter ', Lord Ernle wrote, ' which, I am sure, will receive the careful attention of the Committee. Apart from improvement of existing methods, use of fertilizers and seeds, &c., there can be no increase in gross production without adding to the arable area. The ploughing of temporary grasses for corn only increases the area by substituting one arable crop for another. An actual addition to the land under the plough is, therefore, urgently needed, and the Committees will fail in their duty if they do not satisfy the need. I am sure that landowners, as a body, recognize the paramount claim of the necessities of the nation. In the hands of practical agriculturists, I do not think that compulsory powers for ploughing grass will be abused. Steps are being taken to arm the Board with these powers. But it seems to me necessary that their use should be carefully regulated.'

In a series of public meetings, beginning with one in his own county, Bedford, where because of the character of the soils the difficulties to be surmounted in securing a considerable increase in the tillage area were greater than in many others, Lord Ernle explained the policy set out in his memoranda, and rapidly secured the assent of the majority of agriculturists to his proposals.

The author of *Pioneers and Progress of English Farming* and of *English Farming Past and Present*, who had studied the English farmer in every period of his long history, could appreciate his difficulties and his point of view, and could follow the workings of his mind in an intimate way impossible to other statesmen. Mr. Prothero, as he then was, was held in very high personal esteem by those agriculturists who knew him best; but it was his familiarity with England's story, and his clear perception of the urgent and immediate needs of the country, that enabled him, at this stage, to win for the plough policy the support of many of the most progressive of England's farmers. The mission which began in Bedfordshire was, in the following months, carried to the ends of England, and everywhere farmers were stirred by the watchword ' back to the 'seventies '.

Formation of the Food Production Department.

For the purpose of concentrating attention on questions relating to the increase of the supply of food, Lord Ernle created (on 1st January 1917) a special department of the Board, the Food Production Department, with the writer as Director. The new Department immediately took in hand the organization of the measures required by the Government's tillage policy.

The first need of the new Department was for additional powers ; for, beyond the authority to enter on unoccupied land conferred by Regulation 2 L under the Defence of the Realm Acts, persuasion was its only weapon ; and in such enterprises as were then projected, persuasion, to be an effective weapon, must have its edge tempered by compulsion. On 10th January 1917, therefore, a new Regulation (2 M) was made by Order in Council, which gave the Board of Agriculture and Fisheries and the Board of Agriculture, Scotland, in consultation with the Food Controller, power to make Orders bearing on the better cultivation of agricultural land. A copy of this Regulation in its final form will be found in the Appendix, p. 352.

As authorized by Regulation 2 M the Board of Agriculture and Fisheries on 12th January 1917 made the first of a series of Orders having reference to the cultivation of ordinary agricultural land. Subsequently some minor amendments were found to be necessary ; the Order is reproduced on p. 358 in the form which it took at the date of the Armistice.[1]

The powers conferred on the Boards of Agriculture by Regulation 2 M were of a comprehensive character, and the English Order of 12th January delegated all these powers to local committees.

Agricultural Executive Committees.

The first step taken in England and Wales was to arrange for the selection of members of local committees. The War Agricultural Committees, to whom the powers conferred by Regulation 2 M were nominally delegated, were much too large to undertake executive functions ; they were therefore required to set up Executive Committees consisting of not less than four and not more than seven members nominated by themselves, with such additional members as the Board might nominate ; and these new county committees, known as the Agricultural

[1] Readers interested in the development of legislation, regulations, and orders, as affecting food production, should consult *Food (Supply and Production) Manual of Emergency Legislation*, edited by Alexander Pulling, C.B., H.M. Stationery Office, London, 5s. Monthly editions recording changes were issued until after the Armistice, price 6d.

Executive Committees, were the bodies authorized to exercise, as the Board's representatives, and at the Board's expense, the powers conferred by Regulation 2 M. In the case of the Welsh counties two members were nominated by the Agricultural Council for Wales, a body that had been created in 1912 to advise the Board of Agriculture and Fisheries on agricultural subjects of special importance to the Principality.

The Agricultural Executive Committees appointed their own chairmen, filled up such vacancies as occurred in their body, and, subject to financial regulation, were given a free hand in dealing with local questions. England and Wales were divided at first into seventeen and subsequently into twenty areas, for each of which a local Commissioner was appointed, and he was the Food Production Department's representative on the committee of each county in his area. The Commissioner formed a link between the local Executive and the Department, and an effort was made to reduce written communications on questions of detail to a minimum, with a degree of success which varied considerably in the case of different counties. At frequent intervals letters on questions of general policy were addressed to committees, and in these circulars subjects on which there was a general desire for information were dealt with.

Faced with so many new problems and with differing phases of the same problem in every day of the year, it was inevitable, in spite of the efforts made to curtail it, that there should be much correspondence, and as the work progressed the correspondence became very large in volume ; but the original policy of a free hand for the Agricultural Executive Committees was maintained throughout, the attitude taken by the Department being, ' this is what we want done : you know how it can be done '. To this policy much of the success which was ultimately achieved may be attributed.

Powers Conferred on Executive Committees.

In the first circular letter on the subject of Executive Committees, addressed to the War Agricultural Committees on the 23rd January 1917, the Department's policy was set out at considerable length, and the powers of Agricultural Executive Committees were thus referred to :

' The powers that are placed in the hands of the county Executive Committees are very wide and far reaching, but Mr. Prothero is confident that he can rely on the Committees to exercise them with a single eye to the national interests and with a due regard to the urgent necessity of economy in public expenditure. Mr. Prothero feels that any conditions which would involve constant reference to the Board must be avoided, in order that progress may be made with the least possible delay. It is clearly desirable in carrying out a policy which aims at promoting good farming and stimulating food production that the fullest use should be made of local knowledge and experience. But the Committees will be acting as the agents and at the expense of the Board, and it is necessary that the Board should be fully informed of their proceedings. The Board direct, therefore, that a report should be sent to them at the end of each week by the executive officer of each Executive Committee, which should contain information as to any action taken by the Committee under the powers conferred on them by the Order, and should include a general account of the proceedings of the Committee during the week.'

With respect to the measures which Agricultural Executive Committees were authorized to take, it may be noted that in the original Cultivation of Lands Order of January 1917 powers were given to committees to inspect land, to waive restrictive covenants, to issue directions as to cultivation, to enter on and cultivate land, to cause land to be properly manured, and if necessary to take possession of land which was improperly cultivated.

It was not anticipated that owners or occupiers of land would obstruct committees or their officers in inspecting land and buildings, but in case the necessary permission was refused the Executive Committees were empowered, under paragraph 5 of Regulation 2 M, to give the necessary authority to their representatives. In fact, although it cannot be pretended that the committees or their officers were usually welcome visitors, very little trouble occurred in connexion with inspections.

A second type of question, arising out of restrictive covenants in farm agreements and leases, in practice called for much more attention. The committees were directed in the first instance

to secure the voluntary sanction of the owner to the changes
in cultivation proposed. If the landlord refused to modify the
covenant, committees were to have an inspection made by
a farmer and local valuer, after giving notice of their intention
to the owner. If satisfied that a modification of any covenant
was necessary, the committees were directed to make a Cultivation Order specifying the exact way in which the land was
to be cultivated in the interests of food production, so that
the tenant might be protected from the penalty attaching to
breach of covenant. If no agreement as to the compensation
payable for the breach of covenant could be come to, it was
explained that the case should be referred to the Defence of
the Realm (Losses) Commission, the body created for the
settlement of claims for direct and substantial losses arising
out of interference with property because of the operation of
Orders and Regulations made under the Defence of the Realm
Acts.

The power to issue directions indicating the crops which an
occupier might, or might not, grow on his land was one frequently
made use of by committees. During the war, while it was of
course objected to and sometimes greatly objected to (as in
the case of mustard growers, whose area of this profitable crop
was strictly limited) interference with the farmer's free choice of
the crops he might grow raised comparatively little protest; but
references to it in connexion with legislation after the Armistice
showed how very unpopular this particular power was. It is
not difficult to understand the unpopularity, and the mere
fact that, while freely used, it was comparatively little heard of
during the war, is equally creditable to the judgment of the
Executive Committees and to the attitude of farmers.

Under the power to enter on and cultivate land a large
amount of very badly managed land was ultimately dealt with
by the committees, as we shall subsequently see. The committees had powers to recover—under the terms of the Agricultural Holdings Act 1908 in default of agreement—the value to
the occupier of any improvements executed by them on land
entered on for purposes of cultivation. Where the management

of the occupier of land was hopelessly bad, committees were authorized not only to take possession of the land, but of buildings and equipment, and to farm the holding themselves, or to arrange that some neighbouring farmer should do so on their behalf. In all cases in which the committee entered upon farms, careful estimates of the probable cost were called for before action was taken.

Even in circumstances in which it was not considered desirable for the committees to interfere with the farmer's ordinary tillage operations, it was often possible to increase the food supply by requiring the use of more manure on crops. Committees were therefore authorized to undertake manuring ; they were further authorized to supply fertilizers at cost price and to defer payment for a time where this course was deemed necessary, so that the occupier might realize the crop before being called upon to pay for the manure used.

As it was usually undesirable that tenants, whose cultivation had been so bad as to lead committees to enter upon possession of their land, should remain nominally responsible, an alteration was made in Regulation 2 M which enabled the Board to serve a notice on incapable tenants determining their tenancies. On the application of the landlord the Board were also empowered to make an Order enabling him to determine a tenancy.

The power to determine tenancies was not delegated to Agricultural Executive Committees. When a committee came to the conclusion that a tenancy should be terminated, full particulars were supplied to the Department who, after inquiry, decided whether the tenant should, or should not, be dispossessed.

Survey for 1917 Harvest.

The immediate business when the Executive Committees began their work in January 1917 was preparation for the 1917 harvest, and their first duty was to make a rapid survey of the existing position in each county. Just before the Executives were set up, the War Agricultural Committee of Essex had

initiated a survey of their county, and for the purpose had
enlisted the aid of the Essex Agricultural Valuers Association.
The object of this survey was to classify the cultivated area
into three groups, (*a*) land well farmed, (*b*) land indifferently
farmed and capable of improvement, (*c*) derelict land. Each
of these groups included, as sub-classes, types of land requiring
different treatment, so that the committee might readily gauge
the total requirements in the way of labour, manure, &c., called
for by the cultivated land of the county.

The attention of the Executive Committees was directed to
the Essex Survey and arrangements were made to provide
necessary maps from the Ordnance Survey Offices. The committees made tentative arrangements for these surveys even
before their own organization was complete. Thus while the
Board's circular letter enclosing and explaining the new
Cultivation of Lands Order, from which the Executives derived
their authority, was dated 23rd January, by the 30th of the
month the West Sussex Agricultural Executive Committee had
submitted a return showing that reports had already reached
them on 123,111 acres in that county ; and that 95,165 acres
had been classed as satisfactory, 27,911 as unsatisfactory, and
34 as derelict. From the whole area about 4,000 acres of
permanent grass land suitable for oat-growing was reported,
and in addition 360 acres suitable for potatoes. Labour was
very deficient ; without an immediate increase even the 1916
cropping could not be maintained, 1,417 skilled men and 240
women being required at once.

Similar reports followed, and within the next few weeks
demands for labour, machinery, seed, and manure came in
rapidly.

Early Organization of Food Production Department.

Meantime the organization of the Food Production Department was being built up. The President of the Board replaced
the Agricultural Consultative Committee created in 1914 by
a new committee, ' The Advisory Committee on Food Production ', of which he himself was Chairman. This committee

included several of the prominent agriculturists who were formerly members of the Consultative Committee, together with others who were in a position to assist the Food Production movement, or were directly concerned in the Department's administrative work.   But although certain of its members were responsible for the administration of the Food Production Orders, and for the work on which the Agricultural Executive Committees were engaged, this Advisory Committee was—as the name indicates—a reviewing body, in no way charged with the executive work of the Department.   It met at regular intervals throughout the next eighteen months, and was of much value in representing the general agricultural opinion of the country. The non-official members were able to view the proceedings of the Department, and of the local Executive Committees, from an outside vantage point, and their frequent conferences with the official members responsible for directions to farmers (in effect compulsory though every effort was made to camouflage the compulsion) were of much assistance, and contributed to the success of the Department in avoiding frequent resort to legal proceedings.

Until the end of January the work of the Department had fallen on part of the existing staff of two of the Board's pre-war Divisions, which had been reduced by recruiting for the Army to a degree that barely admitted of the disposal of the work required of them before the new policy was inaugurated.   At this time the offices were transferred to 72 Victoria Street, S.W. 1., which henceforward formed the head-quarters of the movement.   Additional staff was secured without delay, and by the end of the month Commissioners had been appointed for fifteen of the new Food Production areas.   Some of these were the Board's existing Small-Holdings Commissioners ;   others were experienced local land agents.   The Commissioners acted not only as the Department's representatives on local committees ; but were required, through weekly reports, to keep head-quarters informed of all matters bearing on the welfare of agriculture.   Additions were also made to the technical staff of the Department.   By arrangement with the Governing Bodies of Universities and Research Institutes, the services of the chief authorities on different branches of agricultural science were secured, some as whole-time, others as part-time officers. As the programme developed, the assistance of these experts was of the greatest value.

The Executive Committees had not been many weeks at work when their demands discovered certain flaws in the powers and resources of the Food Production Department. The functions originally assigned to the Department were: the organization of the committees and the settling of their lines of work; the ascertaining of the need for labour, machinery, manures, and seeds in each district; the distribution of the available supplies; the provision of technical guidance in the treatment of badly managed land, and the regular reporting to the President of the Board of all circumstances affecting the state of the industry. But, except in the case of seed, the Department itself was not responsible for the supplies required by committees. All business relating to the supply and distribution of fertilizers and feeding stuffs had been transferred to the Ministry of Food on its formation in December 1916.[1] Questions relating to recruiting, to soldier and prisoner labour, and to machinery, were dealt with by a separate Branch of the Board, as was also women's labour. Thus in February 1917 the Food Production Department was receiving the most urgent demands for labour and machinery which were not at its disposal; and its efforts to secure seed—for the provision of which it was responsible —was, in the case of potatoes, made almost impossible by the Orders of the Food Controller. The lack of machinery and implements was due to transport difficulties. Purchases had been made in America as soon as the new policy was formulated, but deliveries could not be secured. The other chief difficulty— the supply of labour—may have been due to lack of sufficiently close contact between the Board and recruiting authorities. This was the explanation suggested in the Debate on the Address in the House of Commons when Parliament met early in February. Whatever the causes may have been it was clear that Executive

---

[1] The supply of fertilizers was entrusted to the Ministry of Munitions, and the distribution to the Food Production Department, in March 1917: the Ministry of Food controlled feeding stuffs throughout the war.

Committees were not getting what they asked for, and echoes of these difficulties were heard in the Debate above referred to. This Debate proved how strongly all parties were stirred by the dangers of the food situation. Conservatives (though not all) were prepared to plough their pastures, while Liberals and Labour members (again not all) were prepared to harrow their economic principles, if only they could mend the food situation. Enthusiasm for corn and potatoes had not risen so high at St. Stephen's since 1846. Food Production became the demand of the hour. And it was time. Seven days before, on 1st February 1917, the enemy's unrestricted submarine campaign had begun, and already Government were aware of the devastating powers of the submarine when employed to sink at sight. Reference has been made on p. 135 to the limitations which the Kaiser's order respecting neutral shipping had placed on German submarines ; and it was, of course, known that losses would become heavy if unrestricted warfare were resorted to, but the precise effect could not be estimated either by our enemies or by ourselves. A fortnight's experience taught us more than months of discussion, and by the middle of February the outlook for the future, made gloomy by harvest failures in the autumn, was made almost desperate by the sinkings of the submarine.

Enlargement of Department's Scope and Powers.

The activities of the Food Production Department became of first-class importance. The Cabinet decided to reorganize it on a much enlarged scale, and to turn it into an independent Department under a Director-General, responsible to the President of the Board of Agriculture and Fisheries, but otherwise unrelated to the Board. Sir Arthur Lee, K.C.B. (now Lord Lee of Fareham) was appointed Director-General. No selection could have been happier. He believed firmly in the possibility (then widely questioned) of adding largely to the output of England and Wales. He brought extraordinary persistence and energy to bear on the baffling tasks which confronted the Department, and in the competition for men, machinery, and supplies which characterized the following months he championed the cause of Food Production as few others could have done.

The new Director-General began work on February 19th, and immediately afterwards the responsibility for supplying labour and machinery was transferred to the Department. All questions relating to recruiting, to soldier and prisoner labour, and to the employment of women were from about 1st March dealt with at 72 Victoria Street. The Ministry of Munitions took over control of the actual manufacture of fertilizers; but the distribution of supplies was entrusted to the Food Production Department. For a time machinery was secured by various methods. Ultimately it was procured by the Ministry of Munitions to the order of the Department.

Scotch Procedure.

The procedure adopted in Scotland under the Defence of the Realm Regulations 2 L and 2 M presented certain differences from that followed in the case of England and Wales; but as the action taken to increase food supply in Scotland is described in another volume in this Series, it will be unnecessary to refer to the subject here.

Irish Procedure.

In Ireland the procedure adopted for stimulating food production differed from that followed in Great Britain. By Order in Council a special Regulation (2 P, see Appendix, p. 356) was applied to Ireland for the harvest of 1917, which, with certain exceptions, required occupiers who held grass land only to convert one-tenth of their holdings into tillage. In cases in which part of the holding was already arable, the tillage area was required to be increased by an amount equal to one-tenth of the whole area of the holding; it was not necessary, however, to till more than half of the arable land of the holding. Grass land which had been in rye-grass and clover for one or two years only was classed as tillage land. Regulation 2 L was modified, in the case of Ireland, so as to empower the Department of Agriculture and Technical Instruction to enter upon any land the occupier of which had neither broken up nor made preparation to break up grass, as required by the Compulsory Tillage Order, before the 28th day of February. The Department might either cultivate the land of defaulters themselves, or arrange for its cultivation.

Holdings of less than ten acres in extent were exempted ; also holdings the occupiers of which could prove to the satisfaction of the Department that tillage would not result in the production of more food.

In February 1917 the Department of Agriculture and Technical Instruction issued a memorandum drawing attention to the urgent need for increasing cultivation. They referred to the assistance given them in making their plans by a representative committee of Irish agriculturists ; they outlined their schemes for increasing the food supply, and they appealed to organized bodies, such as the County Committees of Agriculture and co-operative societies, and also to the clergy and the press, for support.

The Irish schemes were :

(*A*) Applicable to holdings of over £10 annual valuation.

(*B*) Applicable to holdings up to £10 valuation, including rural and urban allotments.

In *Scheme A* prices for the chief crops of 1917 were announced, viz. : wheat 60*s.* per 504 lb., oats 38*s.* 6*d.* per 336 lb.,[1] and the following minimum prices for potatoes (main crop only) in quantities of not less than six tons, 115*s.* per ton from the 15th September 1917 to the 31st January 1918 ; 120*s.* in February and March 1918 ; and 130*s.* for the rest of the season.

The Department prohibited the export of ' seed ' potatoes, and of seed oats until satisfied that the supplies were sufficient for the needs of all Irish cultivators ; and in conference with traders they arranged a scale of prices for seed. The agreed prices were £9 5*s.* per ton for the leading main crop potato planted in Ireland, £18 13*s.* 4*d.* per ton for white oats, and £17 6*s.* 8*d.* per ton for black oats, all free on rail. Steps were

---

[1] The Corn Production Act, 1917, increased these prices to 60*s.* per quarter of 480 lb. and 38*s.* 6*d.* per quarter of 312 lb. respectively.

also taken to secure for Ireland a share of the restricted quantities of manure then available.

By arrangement with the Ministry of Munitions agricultural implements and machines were secured priority as war material, both in manufacture and transport, and certain Irish implement manufacturers engaged on munitions work were specially assisted to increase their output of agricultural machinery. Through conferences with Irish manufacturers, the Department ascertained that the stocks of ordinary farm implements and machines were sufficient to meet the requirements of the extra tillage ordered in 1917. Similar inquiries satisfied the Department that both horse and manual labour were sufficient for the work contemplated. The special labour difficulties which prevented the extension of tillage in England and Wales were non-existent in most parts of Ireland.

The County Committees of Agriculture (which had been in existence for sixteen years) were entrusted with the local administration of the scheme. As in England and Wales, small Executives were set up, and these with the assistance of other local bodies, such as agricultural societies, co-operative societies, or cow-testing associations, undertook the local distribution of seed, manure, and implements. The Department gave county committees authority to deal with urgent applications for loans for the purchase of implements, up to a limit of £12 10s. in the case of individual occupiers. For loans of greater amount application had to be made direct to the Department.

In view of the large number of occupiers who were without experience in tillage farming, the whole attention of the educational staffs of county committees was concentrated on food production work. Additions to the existing staffs were authorized.

We shall return to the effects produced on the harvest by the Irish Compulsory Tillage Order on p. 190; in the meantime we may note the steps taken to deal with defaulters. At the beginning of March a return made by the Royal Irish Constabulary showed that 8,811 occupiers of land had not complied with the Order. Through their Inspectors, the

Department got into touch with these occupiers at once, and the great majority agreed to do what was required. In 230 cases, however, the Department were compelled to exercise the powers conferred on them by Regulation 2 P. Special measures to secure cultivation were taken in twenty of these cases. Because of the lateness of the season the remaining occupiers were not compelled to plough in the spring of 1917, but they were required to give an undertaking that after mowing the grass, or pasturing the land throughout the summer, they would break up their quota before the end of the year. In addition to the cases first reported by the constabulary, a number of occupiers, who had but partially complied with the Tillage Order, were subsequently discovered by the Department's Inspectors. These defaulters were dealt with in the same way as the others.

Under *Scheme B* assistance was provided for occupiers of land of £10, or under, annual valuation (including rural and urban allotment holders), by the Local Government Board for Ireland, who in consultation with the Department of Agriculture arranged loans for the purchase of seed and manure.

Rural and urban district councils were authorized to raise funds, on the security of the rates, with which to buy seeds and artificial manures in bulk, and to sell these to cultivators on easy terms. The Department undertook to find the seeds and manures indented for by local authorities, and to inspect the seeds both at the place of dispatch and at the place of distribution, so as to ensure good quality.

The assistance of County Committees of Agriculture and the services of instructors were available for small holders as well as for the occupiers of larger areas.

Land for allotments was acquired under the provisions of Regulation 2 L of the Defence of the Realm Act, as in Britain.

This scheme was adopted by 149 councils in rural districts, who provided some forty thousand applicants with seeds and manures; and also by 28 urban district councils who provided allotments. As a result of the scheme about 6,000 tons of potatoes, 2,000 tons of oats, 3,000 tons of manures, and

500 packages of vegetable seeds, of a total value of £117,000, were distributed to small growers. In a few cases loans were made to rural district councils, who purchased seeds and manures direct, instead of through the Department.

The Supply of Labour.

We may now turn from the consideration of the special administrative steps taken to increase production in 1917 to a survey of the agricultural conditions of the year, and especially of the labour supply as it affected the progress of the farmer's work.

The first important decision in connexion with the provision of agricultural labour for the 1917 harvest was announced in a circular letter addressed by the Board of Agriculture and Fisheries to War Agricultural Committees on the 5th October 1916. The letter quoted an Army Council Order which had been forwarded to General Officers Commanding-in-Chief, Districts, and to Officers Commanding Recruiting Areas. This order referred to what was generally known as the Substitution Scheme. With the object of safeguarding food supplies it was directed that unless the Man Power Board otherwise decided, or the military situation required reversal of the order, no more men were to be called to the colours from farms until the 1st January 1917, and no more men required for maintaining milk production until the 1st April 1917 'except in return for men released from the colours for work at agriculture'.

Military representatives before Tribunals were directed to pay particular attention to the official list of certified occupations, and to the scale of labour agreed upon between the Army Council and the Board of Agriculture and Fisheries as being required on farms.

This scale (known as the Bath Agreement) was one skilled able-bodied man or lad (wherever possible not of military age) for each of the following :

each team of horses employed in cultivation ;

every twenty cows in milk, where the assistance of women or boys was available ;

every fifty stall or yard stock, where auxiliary feeding was
  resorted to, and the assistance of women or boys was
  available ;

every 200 sheep, exclusive of lambs, on enclosed land ;

every 800 sheep on hill pastures.

The Army Council Order pointed out that ' it is obvious
this scale cannot be undeviatingly followed ' ; it was, however,
given as a guide to the selection of the men ' required under
present conditions to preserve the farming industry '.

The Board's letter announced that before the New Year
a census of men of military age employed on farms would be
taken, that no guarantee as to the permanence of the above
scale could be given, and that Army requirements would
necessitate revision during January for ordinary farms, and
during April for dairy farms. It then stated that :

' The President of the Board accordingly thinks it his duty
to urge in the clearest possible manner that farmers should
strain every nerve to prepare for changes that may become
necessary during January and April 1917.'

The letter concluded with the words : ' The maintenance
of our food supplies remains an important factor in the successful
prosecution of the war, and farmers will continue to render
good service to the State by facing their acknowledged difficulties with determination and courage.'

It was no doubt necessary, in the circumstances, to make it
clear that food production was essential for the successful
prosecution of the war ; but farmers were not impressed with
the degree of importance attributed to their efforts, while they
were very much alarmed by the prospect of a further reduction
of labour in January. Before January, as we have already seen,
there was a change in policy ; but the circular of the 5th October
and the weather of the following weeks did not assist seed
sowing, and again any chance of equalling the first wheat
crop of the war disappeared.

When on the 1st January 1917 the Food Production Department began its work, the land was sodden with rain, farm work
was in arrears, labour was everywhere deficient, and the out-

look for an increase in the area under any tillage crop was a poor one.

The first object of the new President was to gain time, as, in terms of the letter of the 5th October, quoted above, the respite given to farm workers not engaged in milk production expired on the 1st January. In this object Lord Ernle succeeded, and on the 22nd of December a communication was sent to War Agricultural Committees informing them that men employed in agriculture would not be called up until there was time to review the situation more fully.

On the 24th of January the War Office issued for publication a letter on the subject of the recruiting of agricultural workers over the joint signatures of the President of the Board of Agriculture and Fisheries and the Secretary of State for War. This letter stated that the number of men engaged in agriculture who had been released for service by the Tribunals—which since October had been dealing with exemptions—amounted to 60,000, but that it had been decided to call up 30,000 only, and that these men would be replaced by an equal number of substitutes. The substitutes would be men unsuited for military service, not necessarily skilled agricultural workers, but if possible accustomed to take charge of horses. Further, the War Department undertook to return from the colours those trained men who had been employed in steam cultivation before the war as soon as they could be traced, and to send out as many soldiers as possible to assist in spring cultivation and sowing. Thus, it was pointed out, agriculturists would have at command during the spring months of 1917 a greater supply of labour than they had had in the previous eight months.

This letter did a good deal to restore the spirits of farmers. The skilful way in which the gravity of both the military, and of the food, situation was brought out, the difficulties balanced, and the conclusion drawn that both sides must surrender something, made farmers feel that at last Government really intended to put food production almost on a level with military service in the competition for men.

Through the coming spring it was the business of the

Food Production Department to convince farmers that the spirit of this communication was being kept in the letter. The number of particular cases which appeared to farmers to show that the policy laid down in January was being departed from was considerable; it could not have been otherwise under the Tribunal system of the time, but on the whole confidence was maintained. The general policy adopted by the Food Production Department in dealing with labour questions was to ensure that the arrangements made with the Military Authorities were explicitly set before farmers through the Agricultural Executive Committees, and that any alleged contravention of those arrangements was investigated at once. If for any reason there had been a violation of some point covered by a general arrangement this was followed up, and as a rule amends were made. If, on the other hand, there were good reasons for any action, of which a farmer or Agricultural Executive Committee had complained, explanations were made.

In illustration of the first method of dealing with labour difficulties a memorandum dated 28th February may be instanced. This memorandum stated that henceforth all questions relating to the respective claims of the Army and Agriculture to man-power would be dealt with by the Food Production Department—which, it will be recalled, in the first few weeks of its existence was only concerned with the distribution of labour. The number of farm workers then required by the Army was next stated; the arrangements for consultation between Recruiting Officers and Executive Committees were referred to; the conditions applicable to holders of Exemption Certificates, and to Classes B and C on the recruiting lists, were given; and the procedure to be adopted in connexion with the Proclamation of the 30th January 1917, which called up lads of eighteen for service, was explained.

A second important circular was issued by the Department on the 20th March explaining the terms of the Military Service Acts, and dealing with men engaged in certified occupations, methods of securing exemptions, appeals from decisions of

Tribunals, and the powers of the Army Council and Military representative in connexion with exemptions.

Many of the difficulties arising in connexion with the working out of the arrangements made between the Military Authorities and the Department could be adjusted locally by interviews between the Commissioner for the district, the officials employed by the Agricultural Executive Committees, and the representatives of the Army. In other cases, when serious flaws were discovered in the working of the arrangements, further negotiations at head-quarters were opened up.

The War Office had issued instructions to recruiting officers to consult representatives of the county committees before deciding upon the men who should be called up in the different recruiting areas. In the early spring of 1917 those instructions were not being systematically followed. On April 2nd a deputation of the Federation of War Agricultural Committees waited on the Prime Minister and this difficulty was referred to. As a result the whole subject of agriculture and recruiting was again discussed by the War Office and the Food Production Department, and fresh instructions were sent to recruiting officers by the War Office. The exact effect of these instructions on the agricultural position was explained in a memorandum sent out by the Food Production Department on the 5th of May to Agricultural Executive Committees, and also to Agricultural Representatives before Local and Appeal Tribunals.

When Tribunals refused exemption to a farmer, or a farm manager, the Agricultural Representative before a Local Tribunal was directed to lay the case before the county Executive Committee immediately. If the Executive considered the recruit's services essential for the proper working of the farm, they notified the Area Commander. If the latter agreed, the calling-up notice was cancelled. If the Area Commander did not agree he was directed to submit the case to the War Office, the calling-up notice meantime being suspended until the question had been decided. If some man, other than the farmer or manager, was called up and the Agricultural Representative was satisfied that he was absolutely necessary, notification was to be sent to the Executive Committee, who were directed to find a substitute. At the same time notice was to be given to the Recruiting Officer, so that the calling-up notice might be suspended for three weeks, in order to enable work to proceed while a substitute was being sought for.

In spite of these arrangements difficulties continued and farmers were unwilling to undertake further commitments for cultivation in 1918. The subject was therefore brought before the War Cabinet, on whose decision it was agreed between the Department and Army Council that ' as from the 14th of June 1917 no man who was on the 1st of June 1917 and is still employed whole time on farm work of national importance, shall be posted for service with the colours or called up for medical examination or re-examination except with the consent of the Agricultural Executive Committee for the county '. This decision gave farmers a sense of security which greatly aided subsequent attempts to increase the food supply.

Side by side with the efforts made to retain men indispensable on the farm, the Department explored every possible source of additional labour, and assisted in giving effect to the schemes of others having the same object.

As already stated, the Army Council had decided to supply men unsuited for foreign service for work on the land. About 11,500 men were provided in the spring of 1917 and they were formed into Agricultural Companies. In addition 12,500 men in the Home Defence Force were granted furlough until the 30th April, in order to help with spring sowing. These men began to arrive at the Distribution Centres early in March, and were sent out as quickly as possible. Unfortunately only one man in eight was a skilled ploughman and most of them knew nothing of farm work. At this season the need for casual labour is comparatively small, and ploughmen only were in demand. On this being represented to the War Office, an order was issued, on March 12th, requiring all skilled ploughmen in the Home Forces to be given furlough, and in this way a great deal of most valuable help was given. By the first week in April about 40,000 soldiers were at work on the land. In the middle of May 18,000 of these soldiers—the skilled ploughmen in Category A—had to return to military service; the furlough of the others was extended until the 25th June. The Army Council later in the year released 17,000 men for harvest work.

In February 1917 the Ministry of National Service made an effort to secure volunteers for agricultural labour from among workers in less important industries. A number of men came forward, but relatively few were suited for farm work, and no important aid was got from these volunteers in 1917. A second scheme promoted by the Ministry was of much greater value. Arrangements were made for the formation of corps of schoolboys to undertake harvesting work. With the co-operation of Agricultural Executive Committees, camps were established in suitable centres. In this way nearly 5,000 strong and active lads were distributed over the country to those places in which help was most needed, and very useful assistance was given by them to many farmers.

During 1917 there was a further development of women's activities and, appealed to by organizations set up by the Ministry of National Service and the Board of Agriculture, many more women volunteered their assistance. Early in the year the Women's Land Army was formed; but as this movement was chiefly associated with the work of 1918, reference to it may be deferred until we describe the work of that season.

It will also be convenient to defer consideration of the steps taken to supply machinery for cultivation, although very considerable help was given in this way, especially by steam ploughs and tractors in the spring of 1917.

Manure Supply.

The supplies of nitrogenous manures were satisfactory, phosphatic manures were scarce, and potash was very scarce.

Government resolved to popularize the use of sulphate of ammonia, and in February an arrangement was made by the Ministry of Food which enabled farmers in any part of the United Kingdom to purchase sulphate of ammonia at £16 per ton. This caused a great demand, but unfortunately the early arrangements for distribution were faulty and there were many complaints. At this stage responsibility for the distribution of supplies was transferred to the Food Production Department. The arrangements for distribution were revised, and in the months March to May some 90,000 tons of sulphate of ammonia were supplied to farmers at the fixed price. The total sales in the fertilizers' year 1st June to 31st May amounted to 150,000 tons as against 75,000 tons in the preceding year.

The supplies of superphosphate in this season were smaller than in any war year, and the total consumption of dissolved phosphates was over 30 per cent. below the normal requirement. Every effort was made to provide rock phosphate ; but, partly from lack of transport and partly from sinkings, the shortage, especially in the spring months, was marked. The Department could do little to help the position. An occasional transference of rock phosphate from localities where it was less required to those in which it was urgently wanted was arranged ; and three cargoes (13,500 tons) of foreign superphosphate were secured to help to meet unfulfilled demands at the end of the season. A further reference to this purchase of superphosphate is made on p. 297.

Basic slag manufacturers suffered from labour shortage. After control was taken over by the Ministry of Munitions it was found possible to give some assistance to this industry.

The potash shortage was not relieved. At the beginning of the year supplies from Abyssinia were anticipated, and orders were placed ; but unforeseen difficulties prevented shipments. Flue dust, as a source of potash, was investigated by one of the Department's technical officers, and a process approved by him was taken up by the Ministry of Munitions ; but the quantities of potash supplied by flue dust in this season were immaterial.

Seed Supply.

The difficulty experienced in providing ' seed ' potatoes for small growers is alluded to on p. 195. Fortunately, in other respects the position was satisfactory. The Food Production

Department encouraged the sowing of spring wheat, and, in order to avoid any shortage of seed, members of the National Association of British and Irish Millers were requested to reserve, temporarily, any suitable spring wheats which came into their possession. A number of millers notified the Department that they held stocks, and to them farmers requiring seed were referred for supplies.

Much of the seed of root crops and vegetables imported by the colonies and by certain other countries is grown in the south and south-east of England. Steps were taken to safeguard home requirements and to ensure that the seed, for which export licences were issued by the authorities responsible, should go to those countries most likely to assist the Allies' food supply.

The Weather in Season 1917.

The arrangements made for the supply of skilled soldier ploughmen in spring, and for other labour in summer and at harvest, were of peculiar value because of the weather experienced during 1917. The additional help enabled farmers to grow and to gather in fair crops; without timely assistance the harvest of the year would undoubtedly have been very deficient.

Until the middle of April the season was remarkably cold and backward, and in one sense there was little scarcity of labour, since it was almost impossible to employ labour on the land.

The first fortnight of the year was wet, the soil was sodden with rain, and little out-door work was possible; then the weather turned cold, the land was frozen and there was no ploughing or sowing until the last week in February, when a certain amount of progress was made in the earlier districts. The improved conditions did not last, and throughout March, except for a short period in the middle of the month, ploughing and sowing were impossible over the greater part of the country. At the end of this month, when the sowing of cereal crops should be completed in the south and east of England, and ought to be in progress in later districts, a small percentage only of the spring corn crops had been sown.

In the first fortnight of April the temperature fell instead of rising, and remained from 7° to 10° below the normal, while much rain or snow fell. In the third week of April, however, conditions began to improve and the last ten days of the month were very favourable, with no rain and average warmth. Directly the weather permitted field work to proceed there was a period of intense activity on farms, and aided by soldier ploughmen the land was speedily ploughed and sown with cereals ; but not until about the middle of May was the work completed, a fortnight or three weeks later than usual. The preparation of the land for cereals was easy, because of the mellowing effects of the spring frosts, and thus much less time was occupied in getting oats and barley sown than in an average year ; but potato cultivation, which involves much more labour, was greatly delayed by the difficulty of securing planters. A relatively small area was planted at the proper time in April, and not until the beginning of June was the work completed.

Even a farmer in war-time could scarcely have found fault with the weather of May 1917. The first half of the month was dry so that sowing proceeded without hindrance, and then warm rains fell freely, freshening the bare pastures and helping the late corn to establish itself before the heat of midsummer. The rain continued into the first week of June, then came a fortnight of hot dry weather in which every crop grew rapidly. The dry weather continued too long and by midsummer rain was much needed ; fortunately the last few days of the month were cool and wet, and by 1st July, in spite of the difficulties in spring, the promise of the crops was on the whole satisfactory. Potatoes and barley were specially good, wheat was fair, and oats moderate.

Grasses and clovers had been late in starting growth, because of the cold spring, and much of the rotation hay crop was in the field when rain set in late in June ; hence the harvest was rather protracted, and without the help given him by women and soldiers, the farmer must have lost much of this crop. The season for securing meadow hay was favourable, and the weather of July, which was generally warm and dry,

enabled cereal crops to maintain the favourable start made in
May and June ; thus when harvest came in sight the prospects
were much better than could have been hoped for at the
beginning of May.   Then a change came in the character of this,
hitherto favourable, summer.   The last days of July and the
first ten days of August were very wet.   High winds prevailed
and the rapidly grown and weak-strawed corn crops went down.
A fortnight of good weather followed, in which the greater part
of the corn of the south was cut with difficulty, because so much
laid ;   and then a very wet week increased the troubles of the
farmer.   September was fine for the most part, except in the
south-west of England, where rain led to some loss of crop by
sprouting.   On the whole, however, the harvest was ultimately
secured in good condition, and from every district came reports
of the valuable assistance which farmers had received from the
organized labour of women, soldiers, and schoolboys.   Labour
difficulties and wet weather prolonged the potato harvest ;
but, except in the south-west, where there was some disease,
this crop was secured in good condition.

Harvest Figures.

    When the Agricultural Returns for the year were published
the effects of the food production campaign of the preceding
spring months were apparent.   The most noteworthy result
was the increase in the area being cultivated for other crops
than grass.   It will be remembered that in 1916 this area had
fallen by no less than 148,000 acres as compared with 1915.
The food production campaign not only arrested the backward
movement, but brought about a large increase in tillage.   In
1917 some 975,000 more acres than in 1916 were under the
plough.   The chief contributor to the increase was Ireland
with 638,000 acres.   In England and Wales the increase was
286,000 and in Scotland 49,000 acres.   The large addition in
Ireland was due to the Compulsory Tillage Order, which had
been introduced in the winter months and operated throughout
the spring, so that much additional land was in readiness for
oat sowing and potato planting.

In the other countries, where compulsion could be applied only by the service of an Order applicable to a particular piece of land, the local committees rarely resorted to compulsory measures in the spring of 1917, and the increase was due either to a patriotic response to appeals for more ploughing, or to ' peaceful persuasion ' applied by members of committees to individual occupiers. Even if a general Order requiring an increase in the tillage area had been applicable to British conditions (which it was not), it would have been useless because of the absence of labour. Some dislocation of labour on Irish farms had occurred, but the population employed in agriculture was substantially what it had been before the war, and a ten per cent. increase in the tillage area was not a heavy addition to the Irish farmer's task.

A second striking change in 1917 was that in the total area of cultivated land. When the Returns had been completed it was found that, in spite of the increase in tillage, the total area under cultivation was much less than in the preceding year. In England and Wales there was an increase of 8,000 and in Scotland of 1,000 acres, but in Ireland there was an apparent loss of 359,000 acres. It is impossible that so large an area should have reverted to waste, or to mountain grazing, in the course of a year ; it must therefore be inferred either that the Returns were incomplete, or that the Compulsory Tillage Order resulted in a more accurate classification than in previous years. Whatever the explanation, it would appear that the actual increase in the tillage area in 1917, as compared with the preceding year, must have been somewhat greater than the official figures indicate.

The total reduction in the grass area in 1917 was returned as being 1,325,000 acres. In England and Wales permanent grass was reduced by 188,000 and temporary grass by 90,000 acres ; in Scotland there was a reduction of 56,000 acres in permanent grass, but an increase of 8,000 in temporary. In Britain, therefore, for the first time since the outbreak of war, a substantial area of permanent grass had been broken up ; and much of this work had been accomplished in March, April, and

May at the instance of the Agricultural Executive Committees, aided by the tractors and the soldier ploughmen then supplied through the Food Production Department.

In Ireland the area under permanent grass showed an apparent reduction of 355,000 and the temporary grass of 642,000 acres ; but for the reasons indicated above these figures must be accepted with reserve. It is, however, clear that the greater part of the extra tillage obtained by means of the Compulsory Tillage Order was secured by ploughing out grass previously classed as ' temporary '.

The areas under wheat, barley, oats, and potatoes in each country and in the United Kingdom in 1917, and the quantities grown, are shown in Table XVII.

TABLE XVII

HARVEST OF 1917 COMPARED WITH AVERAGE HARVEST OF 1904–13
FIGURES THOUSANDS OF ACRES OR TONS
(For Areas and Yields of 1904–13 see p. 112)

| Country | Crop | 1917 | | 1917 ± 1904–13 | |
		Area	Yield	Acres	Tons
England and Wales .	Wheat	1,918	1,568	+ 229	+ 100
Scotland . . .	,,	61	67	+ 10	+ 10
Ireland . . .	,,	124	122	+ 84	+ 83
United Kingdom .	,,	2,103	1,757	+ 323	+ 193
England and Wales .	Barley	1,460	1,052	− 50	− 140
Scotland . . .	,,	159	138	− 40	− 33
Ireland . . .	,,	177	169	+ 13	+ 16
United Kingdom .	,,	1,796	1,359	− 77	− 157
England and Wales .	Oats	2,259	1,471	+ 162	− 13
Scotland . . .	,,	1,041	809	+ 85	+ 159
Ireland . . .	,,	1,464	1,352	+ 404	+ 446
United Kingdom .	,,	4,764	3,632	+ 651	+ 592
England and Wales .	Potatoes	508	3,341	+ 76	+ 698
Scotland . . .	,,	148	1,110	+ 5	+ 184
Ireland . . .	,,	709	4,153	+ 112	+ 1,130
United Kingdom .	,,	1,365	8,604	+ 193	+ 2,012

As compared with the harvests of 1904–13 it will be observed that there was in the United Kingdom an increase in wheat, oats, and potatoes, and a decrease in barley. The net increase in the quantity of corn was 628,000 tons, and in potatoes it was 2,012,000 tons. The contributions of the different countries were :

England and Wales	— 53,000 tons corn	+ 698,000 tons potatoes
Scotland	+136,000 ,, ,,	+ 184,000 ,, ,,
Ireland	+545,000 ,, ,,	+ 1,130,000 ,, ,,

Thus as regards increase in production the honours were Ireland's, with Scotland a fair second.

When we compare the areas cultivated with those of the pre-war period, we get the following figures :

England and Wales	+341,000 acres corn	+ 76,000 acres potatoes
Scotland	+ 55,000 ,, ,,	+ 5,000 ,, ,,
Ireland	+501,000 ,, ,,	+112,000 ,, ,,

It is evident from a comparison of these figures that the results of the year's work were not in proportion to the efforts expended in cultivation.

England and Wales had a very poor corn harvest, while both Scotland and Ireland had satisfactory crops. The potato crop in all three countries, and especially in Scotland, was a good one.

Ireland, as compared with the other countries, was specially favoured in the matter of labour ; but this circumstance does not fully account for the difference in the yield of crops in 1917. Nor is it altogether a question of the local weather, though the season was markedly more favourable to the Scotch farmer, for example, than to his English neighbour. The long duration of frost in spring made the English seed time relatively later than in Scotland. Late-sown cereals in England have a poor chance of success ; in Scotland, though work in the spring of 1917 was backward, oats and barley were sown much nearer the usual dates, and the chances of success were, therefore, greater than in the southern country.

But for a full explanation of the results of the harvest of 1917 a wider view is required. It must be sought in the systems of husbandry followed in the different parts of the kingdom, and reference may again be made to the characteristic rotations of the three countries. (See pp. 21–24.)

The four-course rotation of England with its single year of
clover, or clover and rye-grass, and still more the five-course—
in which three corn crops are grown to one of clover—provide no
reserve for the ploughman ; the area under clover cannot be
reduced without injuring fertility, the root crop cannot be curtailed except at the expense of the condition of the soil. On the
other hand the two or three years leys characteristic of Scotland
may be ploughed a year earlier than customary, not without
some loss of fertility, but with far less harmful results than
those which follow the omission of clover in England. The
long leys characteristic of Ireland may be shortened with even
less loss of fertility than would follow the curtailing of Scotch
leys. Thus it was that Scotch and Irish farmers were, in 1917,
dealing with soils in much better condition than their English
neighbours. To use an expressive agricultural term, the soil
of England had been ' scourged ' for the harvest of 1915, and
had been very badly farmed in 1916. At the end of that
season the condition of English tillage land was deplorable,
and this, combined with the late spring of 1917, accounted for
the poor yield of the corn crops in the third war harvest.

The redeeming feature of the harvest of 1917 was the
potato crop. Never since the Black Autumn of 1846 had the
potato been the object of so much interest as it was in April,
May, and June 1917.

Had the shade of William Cobbett visited any household
in England in those months, his surprise at the esteem in which
a dish of potatoes was held would have equalled—if not surpassed—his delight at the general disappearance of his ' accursed
root ' ; and in the autumn months, when from the produce of
fields, gardens, and allotments the public were once more
distending themselves to a normal circumference, he would
have found no supporters for his dictum that the absence of
potato cultivation is ' a certain sign that the working people
do not live like hogs ! '

Although planted much later than usual the crops in all
three countries were very satisfactory and went far towards
compensating for the poor corn harvest of England. A very

considerable proportion of the grass land broken in the late spring of 1917 was planted with potatoes with most satisfactory results.

Allotment Cultivation.

During 1917 the allotment movement made great progress throughout the country. Returns collected from 1,161 towns showed that during this year 19,812 acres of land were provided by urban authorities and let in 273,822 plots, for which there were 301,359 applicants. The season, as has just been noted, was a good one for potatoes, and this enabled the allotment holder to make a success of his land. Moreover the weather was particularly favourable for the successful cultivation of newly broken land by inexperienced growers; the long spring frosts mellowed the soil so that even the tyro had little difficulty in getting a suitable tilth, and the genial summer weather made vegetable gardening as simple as it was delightful to tens of thousands of eager ' plotters '.

Through the Horticultural Division of the Food Production Department instruction was organized, and potato-spraying and fruit-preserving campaigns were directed. The Local Organization Division assisted in the provision of land and the Supplies Division in the provision of ' seed ' potatoes and artificial manures.

' Seed ' Potatoes for the 1917 Allotments.

Arrangements for land and supplies were, indeed, begun before the Food Production Department had been set up. As soon as Regulation 2 L and the consequent Orders were gazetted in December 1916, preparations for helping the allotment cultivator were made.

Because of the failure of the potato crop in 1916 it was obvious that many allotment holders would be unable to obtain ' seed ' unless special measures were taken. The Irish scheme (*Scheme B*) has already been alluded to, and reference may now be made to the similar arrangements adopted in England and Wales.

Early in November 1916 information received through the

official Crop Reporters indicated a deficiency of about 330,000 tons in the British potato crop; on this estimate the total crop would have amounted to 3,200,000 tons; later reports reduced this estimate to 3,036,000 tons, the figure accepted for use in the Agricultural Returns. This figure, arrived at by the same method as in former years, was probably much too high. When the deficiency was first pointed out, the Boards of Trade and Agriculture, through two of their officers, made a special inquiry, with the result that on 10th November the probable British crop was estimated at 2,500,000 tons only. A census of stocks was immediately arranged by the Board of Trade, and the returns pointed to the total crop having been about 2,600,000 tons. The subsequent difficulties of the Food Ministry and the War Office in obtaining supplies support the view that the estimate of the Agricultural Returns for 1916 was, in fact, too high and that the British crop of 1916 was probably no more than 2,600,000 tons.

The deficiency was especially marked in Scotland, from which, with Northern Ireland, the best 'seed' potatoes are obtained, and in November 1916 the provision of next year's supplies engaged attention at the Board of Agriculture. It was recognized that large growers, aware of the position, would be able to arrange for their own requirements, but that, unless special measures were taken to secure 'seed' for cottagers and allotment holders, many of their small plots must remain unplanted. Authority was, therefore, obtained for the expenditure of a sum sufficient to purchase the quantity of potatoes which it was estimated would be required.

In the spring of 1916 the Agricultural Instruction Committee of the county of Somerset had arranged for the purchase of 'seed' potatoes in Scotland and their distribution to small growers in Somerset. The methods adopted were very successful. In a letter dated 10th December 1916 the Board drew the attention of War Agricultural Committees to this scheme and advised similar action in other counties. In the first few weeks of December, however, the price of Scotch 'seed' potatoes advanced rapidly; and it was obvious that unless local authorities took common action, further difficulties would arise. The Board therefore arranged through the Scotch Board of Agriculture for the formation of a representative committee of Scotch potato merchants, who would purchase ' seed ' and arrange for its transmission to English counties, and the War Agricultural Committees were asked not to attempt direct purchase, but to ascertain the local demand and to forward their bulk requirements to the Board. Many, but not all, of the committees took this advice. At this stage the scheme for supplying ' seed ' potatoes was taken over by the newly formed Food Production Department, who notified county committees of the conditions on which ' seed ' would be purchased, and made suggestions for their distribution through trade or voluntary agencies. Where the former method was adopted the committee was recommended to select local traders, and to make arrangements with them for the sale of the tubers on suitable terms to small-holders. Where voluntary agents were made use of, it was requested that consignees, to whom potatoes in four-ton lots might be sent, should be nominated for areas of a convenient size. These consignees would be required to arrange for the distribution of such potatoes as were required locally, and for reconsigning the balance to neighbouring villages. Consignees were responsible for collecting cash payments for ' seed ', but might give credit to the extent of one-third of the total value to Registered Societies of Small Holders affiliated to the Agricultural Organization Society. No more than 5 cwt. would be allowed to any one grower, and only cottagers and allotment holders could be supplied.

A list of the prices for ' seed ' potatoes fixed by the Food Controller in the ' Seed Potatoes (Growers' Prices) Order, 1917 ', was sent to War Agricultural Committees ; and on these prices orders were accepted from small-holders and forwarded to the Food Production Department. It was not possible to secure any indication of the quantity of potatoes required until the prices for ' seed ' potatoes were announced, and valuable time was lost in December and January ; but as soon as the Ministry of Food issued the Order above referred to, a committee of potato buyers was set up in Edinburgh to effect purchases. This committee gave the Department valuable assistance ; but though they worked hard to secure supplies, few purchases were made.

The prices in the first 'Growers' Prices Order' had been fixed with reference to the controlled price of table potatoes. During January it was realized that this price was too low, and on 1st February revised prices for cooking potatoes were adopted. The result was that all 'seed' potatoes were held up, or sold for cooking. Moreover dealers, disregarding the 'Seed Potatoes (Growers' Prices) Order', were paying higher prices than were fixed by it.

By the middle of February the Food Production Department had orders in hand for 11,000 tons of 'seed' potatoes at the prices allowed by the 'Growers' Prices Order' of January, but no one would sell at these prices !

Later the controlled price of 'seed' was revised and purchases were made, but the stocks were then so small that in spite of the efforts made by the committee of buyers in Scotland little more than half the quantity required could be obtained from that source. Moreover, the weather was so bad that potatoes could not be transported in safety and one or two consignments were, in fact, injured by frost.

When the Food Production Department sent out the conditions on which 'seed' potatoes would be supplied to War Agricultural Committees, it was understood that Ireland had a very considerable quantity of potatoes to spare and that, were it necessary, 30,000 to 50,000 tons might be obtained from Ulster. Unfortunately, however, the Irish Department were themselves unable to purchase the 'seed' required for their own allotment-holders at the prices they were then prepared to offer, and until their requirements were met the Vice-President of the Department would not sanction the shipping of Irish potatoes to England. Ultimately, through the good offices of the Chief Secretary, Irish potatoes were released ; and, though it was then near the end of March, the weather had so delayed cultivation that the supplies still required to meet the demands of English allotment holders were delivered in time for planting.

The end of the season found many large growers without 'seed', and when the needs of cottagers had been met about 4,000 tons were provided for farmers.

The demand in April was extraordinary, and among applicants for potatoes were some county authorities who in the first instance had elected to purchase their own supplies, leading seedsmen, and latest of all, Kentish hop growers who had been compelled to grub hop plantations and could not procure potatoes for planting on the land thereby released for food production. It was the beginning of May before 'seed' potatoes could be obtained for the last group; but the favourable season which followed enabled the growers to raise satisfactory crops.

The Improvement of Tillage.

The main business of the Food Production Department from March 1917 onwards was preparation for the harvest of 1918, and the crops grown in 1917 assisted this work in two different ways : they afforded an opportunity for cleaning the land, and they provided experience in the management of newly broken pastures.

Labour difficulties and the large area of white straw crops grown in 1915 resulted in badly cultivated green crops in 1916, and in the autumn of that year the land intended for next year's corn was in very poor condition; with results which we have already noted in describing the 1917 harvest. In the summer months of 1917 a great effort was made by the Executive Committees to secure proper cultivation for the root crops, and, as the result of constant supervision and the provision of casual labour, much was done to improve the chances of the 1918 crop before a bushel of seed was sown. It is not possible to separate out the effect of the improvement brought about by Executive Committees in the summer tillage of green crops in 1917 from the other influences affecting the 1918 harvest; but it may be stated with some degree of confidence that this thorough summer tillage had no small bearing on the success achieved in growing corn in the following year.

Crops on Newly Broken Grass Land.

The experience gained in the management of newly broken land in 1917 was also very valuable. No subject was more discussed in the earlier years of the war than the prospects of a corn crop grown on newly ploughed pasture. Very little experience had been gained in recent years, and it was not easy to rebut the assertions of authorities, even of those—and they were numerous—whose knowledge of farming had been gained during week-ends, or who were known to be more familiar with the pen than with the plough. Special attention, therefore, was given to the experiences of those farmers who broke up land in 1917.

A circular letter containing a number of questions on which information was desired was addressed to farmers, and over 300 replies were received from all parts of England and Wales. The successes and failures were classified, and a pamphlet was issued summarizing the experience gained, and directing attention to essential points. The information was issued in August 1917 so that it might be available before any part of the 1918 crop was sown.

Reports from 38 counties were discussed. The successes numbered 231, the failures 55, while in 34 cases the crops were fair only. In view of the inexperience of most of those who broke up old pastures, of the labour difficulties, and of the character of the season, the results were distinctly encouraging. Most of the failures were attributed to wireworm attacks; but inspection showed that in many of these cases the damage was due to the rapid drying out of the land, because of imperfect consolidation after ploughing. Successes were recorded with a number of crops—oats, wheat, barley, beans, peas, potatoes, mangolds, mustard, rape, turnips, and linseed; but the first-named crop was grown in by far the greater number of cases.

From the information collected it was possible to draw up

hints for the guidance of farmers breaking up grass land ; these technical points need not be referred to ; the following extract from the pamphlet on the subject sums up their bearing on the work and outlook for the harvest of 1918.

' The essence of the experience of 1917 is contained in the Yorkshireman's maxim, " Tread the turf well or else you will have trouble ; " [1] but everyone who has had long experience of tillage land knows how variable are the problems presented by the ploughed field, and how impossible it is to give directions for the successful management of all the types of soil which the British farmer ploughs, in all the " samples " of weather with which the British climate can be credited. Grass land must be broken up, and to this task the farmer is expected to give all his skill and knowledge in the coming year. He must not, as in the case of the Welsh critic, wait until the corn is laid before he comes to the conclusion " what absolute fools the Authorities are ; " [2] he must be guided by his experience, and then, like the Cumbrian farmer who, although vexed by the agents of the Government, ultimately triumphed by the exercise of " practical common sense ", he will, it may be predicted, in four cases out of five, grow a satisfactory crop in 1918 ; since, fortunately for the country, " practical common sense " is not monopolised by the farmers of Cumberland ! '

Maximum and Minimum Prices.

The influence of price-control on the food supply in the later years of war is dealt with in another volume of this Series,[3] and no detailed examination of a subject which was prominently before agriculturists in 1917 and 1918 will here be attempted ; but it will be convenient at this stage, before passing on to describe the preparation for the 1918 harvest, if we refer briefly to the maximum and minimum prices fixed for the principal field crops ; and also to the farmer's attitude to price-control, in so far as this attitude affected the work of the Food Production Department.

We have seen that at an earlier period of the war the desirability of guaranteeing prices was a subject on which

[1] This and the following quotations were from reports included in the pamphlet.

[2] It should be explained that the ' Authorities ' whose advice led this Welshman astray were not connected with any Agricultural Department.

[3] *British Food Control*, by Sir William Beveridge, K.C.B.

agriculturists themselves were not in agreement; but it was
keenly demanded by the majority. In the second war year,
too, the rise in the prices of fertilizers and feeding stuffs had led
some to demand price-control.   But when those spokesmen for
agriculture who, in face of rising prices, were in 1916 loudly
calling ' wolf ' did get ' control ' at the end of the year, and
had time to ponder its bearing on the farmer's business, their
cry was changed to ' Help ! ' Unlike the boy in the fable, however, the fate of the alarmed spokesmen was not a particularly
hard one. Agriculturists in this country were treated by the
Orders of the Food Controller in a way that must have aroused
envy in the enemy countries. If we can forget the fate of our
cattle in the autumn of 1917 (and there were reasons for their
fate that did not appear at the time), and the fate of our potato-
clamps in May and June 1919, it may be asserted that farmers
had no very substantial grievances against the Ministry of Food.
The working of control in practice must often have led to
situations that were trying to individuals, but the industry
was not seriously interfered with.

A great effort was made to prevent those restrictions which
were found to be necessary from affecting the business of
agriculturists adversely; for nothing was farther from the
intentions of the authorities than that food production should
be directly, or indirectly, hindered by the measures called for
in the control of supplies and distribution. The Food Controller was constantly in consultation with the Agricultural
Departments, and although he alone was responsible for the
actual prices fixed, the prices were nearly always agreed, as
being reasonable under the circumstances, by the official
representatives of agriculture. Thus it may be observed that,
although the official representatives of consumer and producer
did not satisfy—could not be expected to satisfy—all their
clients, and at times did not satisfy each other, the great
majority of the farmers of the country were well enough
contented with the results. That this was the case is proved
by the attitude which farmers adopted, and by the energy
which they threw into the cultivation of the land in 1917–18.

It is by their actions that their attitude to the Government's control policy must be judged, not by the utterances of their spokesmen ; for, in the din of war, voices are apt to be high. Although, therefore, the criticism of controlled prices was often loud and prolonged, so that at times much apprehension existed lest control should seriously hinder production, it may now be concluded that nine-tenths of our farmers, appreciating the great difficulties of the situation, accepted without any particular resentment the prices which were settled for their produce ; they were satisfied that they were being fairly treated.

This general attitude of contentment—or if not of content-ment, at least of resignation—was no doubt promoted by the fact that some of the early measures of control, those relating to fertilizers for example, were taken in the interests of farmers. One of the first acts of the Food Controller had been to intervene between two competing groups of agriculturists. The object of the Seed Potatoes (Growers' Prices) Order of 19th January 1917 was to enable southern cultivators of potatoes to secure supplies of ' seed ' at reasonable rates from northern growers.

The decision of the Government to concede the long-standing demand for a guaranteed minimum price, too, had at first a very favourable effect on the attitude of agriculturists. The announcement of this policy was the central feature in the important statement made by the Prime Minister in the House of Commons on 23rd February 1917. In this speech Mr. Lloyd George made it clear that the Government were aware of the farmer's real difficulties ; he alluded to agricultural experience in the end of the nineteenth century, he showed how deeply these experiences had impressed themselves on the farmer's mind, and how very real the risks of breaking up grass land were, and he concluded with the statement,

' therefore there is only one way of ensuring immediate action on the part of the farmer, and that is by guaranteeing prices for a definite period of time—minimum prices. . . . These are the guarantees we propose to give. We propose that in the present year we shall guarantee :

' For wheat 60s. per quarter of 504 lb.,[1] that is the minimum; for 1918 and 1919, 55s. ; for 1920, 1921, and 1922, 45s. Then the guarantee comes to an end.

' For oats in 1917 we propose to guarantee 38s. 6d. per 336 lb.[1] That is higher than the minimum price we arranged with Ireland some months ago. The guarantee for 1918 and 1919 is 32s., and for the next three years 24s.

' Potatoes we simply propose to guarantee for this coming season at £6 per ton.

' The only guarantee we have given of the maximum is this, that if the State commandeers either potatoes or cereals, the prices will not be fixed without the consent of the Boards of Agriculture of England, Scotland, and Ireland, and, therefore, there will be an opportunity of consultation before the prices are fixed. Obviously you cannot limit the power of the State to commandeer for national purposes.' [2]

A few weeks later, on 5th April 1917, a Bill was introduced to give effect to the Government's agricultural policy, and while the crops of 1917 were ripening, the first of a series of measures intended to promote British agriculture was being warmly debated in Parliament.

An account of the Corn Production Act, 1917, may more fittingly be given in Chapter X than now ; for the discussion which it aroused led not so much to the success of the Food Production Campaign as to its ending. Although the public may have heard much of the Corn Production Acts, the effective work of the Food Production Department was done under the authority of the Defence of the Realm Acts ; and the ' boomerang ' legislation designed to promote corn growing is now of more practical interest to students of politics than to students of food production in war.

Nevertheless the first effect of the introduction of the Corn Production Bill was good. The principle of the guaranteed price was welcomed by most agriculturists ; if it did nothing more, it showed at least that Government appreciated the risks involved in breaking up grass land.

The prices named in the Corn Production Bill of 1917 bore

[1] By the Corn Production Act, 1917, these prices for wheat and oats were made payable per quarter of 480 lb. and 312 lb. respectively.

[2] *Parliamentary Debates, House of Commons*, vol. xc, 1917, col. 1606.

no relation to the actual market prices of the time. On 16th April 1917 the Food Controller fixed 78s. per 480 lb. wheat, 65s. per 400 lb. barley, and 55s. per 312 lb. oats as the maximum prices for the crops of 1916. On 14th August 1917, before any of the 1918 crop was sown, maximum prices for the 1917 crop were fixed, which, depending on the time of sale, rose from 73s. 6d. to 79s. 9d. per 504 lb. wheat, from 44s. 3d. to 48s. 6d. per 336 lb. oats, and in the case of barley remained at 62s. 9d. per 448 lb. throughout the season. On 31st August 1918 maximum grain prices for the 1918 crop were announced ; for wheat the price fixed was 75s. 6d. per 504 lb. until December, and thereafter 76s. 6d. ; for oats from 47s. 6d. after harvest to 52s. per 336 lb. in June 1919 ; for barley the price was fixed at 67s. during the entire season.

Throughout the whole period in which these prices were in operation the market demand kept the actual price which was received by the farmer for sound grain, at, or nearly at, the maximum ; and it was prices of the order indicated above that farmers expected to obtain later on, when, in the winter and spring of 1917–18, they were preparing their land and sowing crops for the 1918 harvest. They knew, of course, that by the Corn Production Act 1917 they were guaranteed only 60s. per 480 lb. for wheat, with 38s. 6d. per 312 lb. oats for the 1917 crops ; and 55s. per 480 lb. wheat, with 32s. per 312 lb. oats for the 1918 crop ; but from the condition of the markets farmers were warranted in thinking it was the maximum, not the minimum, prices that directly concerned them.

The case with potatoes was different. Of this crop the country may easily produce more in a good season than the public will take. It is expensive to grow, and the consequences of a glut are serious for the grower. While therefore the maxima of £6 10s. per ton for sound cooking potatoes sold before 15th April 1918, and of £7 10s. for potatoes sold after 14th May, announced by the Food Controller, may not have attracted the speculator, most experienced potato growers were reassured by the minimum price of £6 per ton for the 1917 crop, which had been guaranteed by the Prime Minister in his speech of 23rd

February, and there can be no question that this guarantee substantially increased potato planting in 1917.

On 9th January 1918 arrangements for the 1918 crop were announced by the Food Ministry; the main feature of these arrangements was that, after 1st November 1918, the whole crop was to be taken over by the Food Controller. The prices first announced were held to be unsatisfactory, and ultimately the prices for different districts were fixed by a Commission which took evidence locally from representatives of potato growers.

There were many awkward points to settle in handling the 1918 crop, and complaints were loud, and often justifiable; but the real grievances of farmers were not due to the prices fixed, or even to the prices first announced; they arose out of the difficulties involved in taking over and marketing the crop. The quantity was very large; in the spring of 1919 consumers' demands were not pressing, and there was much wastage in the stored tubers before the whole crop could be disposed of. The farmers who got their potatoes to market early in the season were fortunate, those who could not secure delivery suffered. The results were inevitable; they were part of the price that must be paid for the control and purchase by Government of the potato crop in any year when, as in 1918, the total yield is very large.

CHAPTER IX

THE HARVEST OF 1918

The First Programme for 1918. The Revised Programme. Local Organization. County Surveys. Compensation for Occupiers. Credit Facilities for Farmers. Work of the Divisions of the Food Production Department. Progress of the Programme. The Weather. Critics. Harvest Difficulties. Harvest Figures. Losses and Gains in 1918. Reduction in the Milk Supply. Reduction in the Meat Supply. Gain from the Crops grown on Newly Ploughed Grass Land. Results of the Plough Policy.

THE months of January and February 1917 were mainly devoted by the Food Production Department to preparations for the harvest of the current year, but early in March work on the programme for the 1918 campaign was begun. It was decided to attempt a very large addition to the tillage area—the largest that it would be possible to accomplish, assuming good weather to favour the effort. It was recognized from the outset, however, that the possibility of carrying out the full programme was small, for it postulated a degree of luck that in our climate does not often favour the farmer. On the other hand, it was determined that, in the event of the weather being very favourable, progress should not be delayed by lack of land, labour, and machinery, if by careful planning and strenuous efforts this could be avoided.

It was known that enough land suitable for cultivation existed, because less than fifty years before it had been tilled ; the problem was to locate the grass land, which could best be spared, in the time at disposal. The Agricultural Executive Committees had already shown their capacity ; but the members were greatly over-worked, and the organization must be strengthened. The tractor had been shown to be a machine with great possibilities for certain purposes ; but, like many other munitions, the types available left a good deal to be desired, and the numbers then available were totally inadequate. It was impossible to find skilled agricultural labour that was

not already utilized. Of about a million farmers and their men
who had tilled the land of England and Wales in 1914, some
250,000 of the strongest were already in military service ; and,
in addition, many casual labourers, formerly employed on farms,
had turned to other work where higher wages were being paid.
It was necessary both to find a large number of additional men
and to estimate the extent to which additional work could be got
from the men and horses remaining on farms. Again, extended
cultivation would call for the provision of more manure; and
supplies of certain kinds were insufficient to meet the pre-
war needs of the area already tilled. Schemes for economizing
manure and for obtaining further supplies had, therefore, to be
worked out. Precautions had also to be taken against shortage
of seed, of ordinary cultivating implements, and of such
requisites as binder-twine for harvesting, or copper sulphate for
spraying.

The First Programme for 1918.

These and similar subjects bearing on the cultivation of
the land of the country were very carefully considered, and in
April 1917 a programme for the 1918 harvest was placed before
the Cabinet. When the preliminary estimates were being
framed it was not known to what extent Scotland and Ireland
might be able to increase their cultivation. The programme
assumed that 3,000,000 acres of permanent grass land must be
broken up in the United Kingdom ; if the other countries could
produce no more corn in 1918 than in 1916, then 3,000,000 acres
must be sought for in England and Wales. This area was
approximately three-fourths of the total extent of the land
converted from tillage to grass in the preceding half-century.

The task, it was recognized, was a gigantic one under
the conditions then prevailing ; it was with the greatest
difficulty that farmers had been able to carry on in 1916, but that
season had been unfavourable, and good weather would make a
great difference. The careful calculations which had been made
showed that under certain conditions the task was possible, and
in war the possible must be attempted ; the Cabinet were,

therefore, informed that if the following conditions were fulfilled, and the requisites were provided, the programme would
be put in hand immediately :

1. That farmers should be allowed to retain the full number
of skilled workers to which they were entitled under
the Bath agreement (see p. 180) and also either the 40,000
soldiers at the time lent to them by the Army, or equally
useful men.

2. That an additional 80,000 men should be made available
from the Home Forces, or other sources.

3. That the Women's Land Army should be brought up to
a strength of 25,000, and that the part-time services of
all women locally available should be utilized.

4. That 5,000 tractors (in addition to some 500 then at the
disposal of the Department) should be provided, with the
necessary supplies of fuel.

5. That 60,000 horses should be borrowed from the Home
Army, or otherwise provided.

6. That not less than 50,000 tons of rock phosphate should be
imported monthly.

7. That as a precaution against short supplies of seed wheat
at the beginning of the autumn sowing season, 100,000
quarters of seed from the 1916 crop should be reserved.

These were the minimal requirements, and it was explained
that if arrangements were delayed, or supplies reduced, the
programme must be correspondingly curtailed.

In making up this preliminary programme it was estimated
that of the 3,000,000 acres permanent grass to be ploughed up,
the farmers themselves could plough 800,000, assuming their
labour not to be further depleted by recruiting. This would
leave 2,200,000 acres to be dealt with by the special labour and
machinery which it was proposed to place at the disposal of
the Agricultural Executive Committees. It was hoped that
tractors would be secured sufficiently soon to enable them to
plough 1,000,000 acres ; the balance would be broken up by
soldier ploughmen with horse teams. At the time horses were
being lent out to farmers in charge of competent ploughmen

drawn from the Army or the police force, and a large extension of
the system was proposed.

From a speech made by the Prime Minister at the Guildhall
on 27th April 1917 it was known that Government approved the
Department's proposals in principle ; but the finding of the
necessary labour was a difficult task, and it was not until two
months afterwards that the Cabinet decided to release 50,000
men from the Army for work on the land. These new workers
were promised at the rate of 5,000 per week, beginning on
7th July.

Instead of the immediate increase in the labour supply
for which the Department asked, there was at first a reduction.
Included among the 40,000 soldiers working on the land when
the programme was framed, there were 18,000 skilled ploughmen
who had been temporarily liberated from the Army for spring
cultivation. It was hoped that these invaluable workers could
have been retained ; but this was not possible. On 10th May
notices recalling them were issued, and ten days later all had
returned to the colours.

As soon as it was known that the Cabinet had approved the
proposals of the Department in principle, the Executive Committees were informed of the areas which each would be expected
to find. A rough apportionment of the total area of 3,000,000
acres had been prepared, and this was communicated to them.
As might have been anticipated, the very large programme met
a somewhat varied reception ; but most of the committees
immediately set about looking for suitable land for ploughing.

The Revised Programme.

As the weeks of May passed and the labour position became
worse instead of better, it was obvious that a modification of the
programme would be necessary, and a complete revision was
undertaken. It was now impracticable to secure any great
addition to the wheat area from grass land ploughed out in the
summer months, and the whole of the arrangements which had
been made had to be reconsidered.

Moreover, while it was no longer possible, even with the

best of weather, to add 3,000,000 acres to the tillage land of England and Wales, the need for so great an increase was less, for it was now known that Ireland would largely increase the area under grain and potatoes, and that in Scotland, too, it would be possible to plough a substantial quantity of permanent grass.

The new programme drawn up for England and Wales, at this stage, aimed therefore at securing a total area of about 8,300,000 acres of corn in 1918, being an increase of 2,600,000 acres on the area grown in 1916. It was estimated that to provide land for this purpose, and for an increase in the potato crop of about 170,000 acres, it would be necessary in the two seasons 1917 and 1918 to plough up 2,050,000 acres of permanent grass, and also to plough 645,000 acres more temporary grass than was customary ; this work must be completed not later than the end of April 1918.

Having settled the demand for the whole country, each county was considered in turn, and a statement was prepared and circulated on June 14th, showing (1) the total area of corn at which the Executive Committee must aim, (2) the area of grass land which the Department estimated it was necessary to plough, in order to secure enough land for grain, and (3) the percentage of the whole arable area of the county which should carry corn crops in 1918. Committees were informed that it would be necessary to plough up a substantial area of temporary grass and also that, should it be quite impossible to plough the area of permanent grass indicated, the balance must be found by breaking up additional temporary grass. At the same time the objections to further reduction in the area then under clovers were emphasized.

The principal factors taken into account in fixing the quota for a particular county were : the area then under cultivation and the usual rotations ; the area cultivated forty years before ; the character of the local soils and climate ; the total area of grass land in relation to the labour available for breaking up ; the area fallowed or under roots in 1914 ; the suitability of the county for growing particular crops ; the character of the live stock kept, and the provision necessary for dairy cows.

After the county tasks had been settled in June, no change was made in the programme, and on the whole the allocations were well received. Although some committees were disposed to look beyond the county boundaries and to assert that their neighbours had been dealt with more leniently by the Department than were they themselves, most Executives were far too busy to concern themselves with their neighbours' tasks and they loyally strove to accomplish their own.

Local Organization.

In view of the heavy programme contemplated for the following year, the organization of the local Executives set up in the previous January and February required strengthening. The immediate requirements of the spring months—labour, manure supply, the selection of land for ploughing—kept members of the Executive Committees incessantly at work throughout February, March, and April 1917, and it was now obvious that the sub-committees originally contemplated must be set up without further delay, so that some relief might be given to the members of the Executives. The formation of at least three county sub-committees, to consist of not more than two members of the Executive Committee with a suitable number of co-opted members, was therefore suggested by the Department. These sub-committees were required to deal with Labour, Machinery, and Supplies respectively. Each sub-committee was authorized to employ a whole-time official, a Labour Officer, a Machinery Officer, and a Supplies Clerk. In most cases these appointments were made before the harvest of 1917 began. If considered necessary the Executives were also authorized to set up sub-committees for such other purposes as the supervision of the Survey or Finance.

Since a close examination of the condition of the farms in every parish was required, it was also necessary to make greater calls on the district sub-committees than had been the case in the spring months. Until the preparation for the 1918 crop began those district sub-committees which had been formed were given relatively little work ; in May 1917, however, each Executive Committee was advised to subdivide the county into districts of convenient size, as a rule coinciding with the existing Rural Districts, and to appoint a district sub-committee of not less than four or more than seven members, who should be experienced local agriculturists, willing to give up a considerable amount of time to the public service. Secretaries were to be employed, who, like the members, must be expected to give up a large share of their time to the work; meetings should be held at least once a fortnight and preferably at weekly-intervals. It was suggested to the district sub-committees that they should appoint a correspondent in each parish, and many such appointments were made.

These district sub-committees with their parish correspondents formed the ultimate link in the chain connecting the Food Production Department with the farmers of the country, and the general character of the work requiring the attention of those engaged in the Food Production Campaign of 1918 is indicated by the following list of matters to which the district sub-committees were directed to give attention.

1. Any land within the district not being used so as to contribute adequately to the food supply of the country was to be reported to the county Executive, so that steps might be taken for improvement.
2. Grass land that should be ploughed in the national interest must be scheduled for tillage.
3. Labour shortage should be ascertained, and demands formulated for woman, soldier, or prisoner labour, as the circumstances might require. Action should be taken in consultation with representatives of the National Service Department, or of women's organizations.
4. When seed, manure, or other supplies were difficult to procure, information should be sent to the Executive Committee, with a view to the provision of supplies from the different sources of these materials.
5. Everything must be done to facilitate the work of the

tractors, steam tackle, horse teams, and gangs of prisoners organized throughout the country by the Food Production Department.

6. Farmers in need of credit for extending cultivation should be informed of the special facilities offered by banks under Government guarantee.

7. Measures should be taken to organize the repression of pests destructive to food, such as rabbits, rats, rooks, wood pigeons, and sparrows.

8. Obstructions to the drainage of land, such as badly cleaned watercourses, or improperly managed mill-dams and locks, should be reported.

9. Everything should be done to assist allotment cultivators. Endeavours must be made to provide land. Co-operative action for the purchase of seed, manure, and other supplies should be encouraged, and care should be taken that allotment ground was properly cultivated.

It was the duty of the county Executive Committee to notify district sub-committees without delay of the instructions issued from time to time by the Food Production Department, and to ensure that the district committees acted on such instructions as were applicable to their particular areas. While the Executive Committees could not delegate to sub-committees the special powers conferred on them by Orders issued under the authority of the Defence of the Realm Acts, it was possible to use the district sub-committees for much of the action necessary in increasing the food supply, and Executives making use of sub-committees were thus able to relieve themselves of the detailed supervision of local efforts. It was of course impossible to expect uniformity of action throughout the length and breadth of the country. Sub-committees varied much in their efficiency, and the Executive Committees had to take this fact into consideration in deciding how much of the work could safely be entrusted to them.

County Surveys.

In no direction were the services of the district sub-committees of more general value than in the important work of the Survey. The selection of suitable grass land for breaking up for the 1918 harvest necessarily called for local knowledge, and the detailed character of the work demanded many local assistants. Assertions have frequently been made imputing lack of skill in the selection of land for ploughing. The value of these statements will be apparent when the results of the work have been described. Meantime a description of the methods adopted may be given.

In selecting land for breaking up for the 1917 harvest the committees gained a good deal of experience ; but when the survey for 1918 began not all of them organized the work with equal skill. The following details refer to a Midland county, where the survey was very carefully carried out. In spite of this its committee did not escape severe criticism ; but, if the critics of this survey, and of other similar surveys in England and Wales, had been set the task described below, it may be alleged with some confidence that they would not have improved on the work. In the great majority of cases the farmers and surveyors who were employed were the most skilful men available, but, busy as the nation was in 1917, there were enough onlookers left in every parish in England to furnish critics !

The Executive Committee of County X, like other committees, was informed in a letter dated June 14th of the area of grass land which it should attempt to find and break up for the 1918 harvest. Before the end of August between three and four thousand holdings extending to over 400,000 acres had been inspected field by field ; notes had been written on every farm ; every grass field had been classified ; every addition made to the arable land since 1916 had been noted ; farmers' requirements with respect to labour, fertilizers, &c., had been tabulated, and specific recommendations for cropping in 1918 had been made. The Executive Committee was thus supplied with a table showing, for each of eighteen districts in the county : all the tillage crops being grown in 1917 arranged separately under ten headings, the area of grass land that should certainly be ploughed, the further area that might be ploughed if necessary, and the area that should not, under any circumstances, be broken up. The committee was also provided with maps on which every field needing attention was indicated ; and with descriptive notes on the general condition of agriculture in each district surveyed. The whole of the work was done voluntarily by some seventy parties of local surveyors and farmers who co-operated with the officer in charge of the survey.

This very fine piece of work was due to the organizing ability of the member of the Land Valuation Staff to whom the Executive Committee entrusted the making of the arrangements for the survey. If every detail had not been thought out in advance the results above indicated would have been impossible.

For the purposes of the actual survey each district within this county was broken up into groups of two or three parishes, and a Survey Party of two or three agriculturists was set up. The area allocated to a party depended to some extent on the complexity of the work. Where fields were small, and close attention was required, a party might deal with from three to five thousand acres ; under opposite conditions ten to twelve thousand acres might be undertaken.

A schedule of Notes and Instructions was drawn up for the use of survey parties. Particulars of the area of the entire county and of the land required for corn growing in 1918 were furnished, and the approximate proportion of corn required on an average farm was indicated, so that surveyors might know precisely what was expected of them. Suggestions were made as to the selection of grass for ploughing, and the main considerations to be kept in view were indicated. Note books were provided, with instructions for the filling in of details in a methodical way calculated to reduce the work of classification, and ruled forms were enclosed with examples of the way in which they were to be filled up. The forms were ruled both for use in the detailed inspection of farms, and as required for summarizing the information collected in the survey party's area. The descriptive notes furnished by the surveyors were of much use in making arrangements for labour and other requisites for successful cultivation at a later period.

Each survey party was provided with 6″ Ordnance Survey maps. These maps, as published, do not show the areas of individual fields, and this information and also the field numbers of the 25″ Ordnance Survey maps were inserted on the 6″ sheets at the county head-quarters before issue. As the survey number of each field reported on was recorded, it was possible for committees to ascertain the exact position of any field in the county that formed the subject of correspondence in the course of their subsequent work.

All the Executive Committees in England and Wales, adopting methods similar to those described above, though not always with the same care in the organization of the work, carried out surveys of the farms within their areas, and before the end of the year most counties knew how much grass land could be cultivated without difficulty if labour were available ; and also what the additional area was that might be brought under the plough should the necessity arise.

The survey parties employed in different parts of the country, consisting as they did for the most part of local farmers and tenant right valuers, held widely different views on the subject of ploughing up old grass land. In one or two arable districts grass, however good, met with little leniency if it could be shown that without it the farmer would still have at his disposal as much pasture as his neighbours thought he required ; but in the great majority of cases surveyors were extremely reluctant to schedule for ploughing any grass that could reasonably be called ' good '. By far the larger proportion of the land scheduled for ploughing had not been many years in grass and represented the least successful of the pastures formed in the forty years before the war. It is not possible to estimate the actual contributions which these pastures were then making to the food supply, but it may safely be assumed that their average contributions were well below the average production of the grass land of the country, and therefore considerably less than 72 lb. meat or 133 gallons milk per acre.[1] In most cases the Executive Committees themselves settled the quality of the

[1] Cf. p. 75.

pastures that should be ploughed ; but in one or two counties
where good pastures were exceptionally common, and difficulty
was therefore experienced in finding the quota on poor land,
representatives of the Food Production Department inspected
a number of test cases and assisted the local committees
in fixing the standard to be aimed at in selecting land for
ploughing.

Compensation for Occupiers.

It was properly held by committees that in so far as their
action depreciated the value of farms, or caused pecuniary loss
to occupiers, there should be compensation. It would have been
quite impossible to have spread the risks uniformly over the
entire number of owners and occupiers. In a great many cases
it was obvious that no losses would be sustained, but in others
it was equally clear that the risks were considerable ; moreover,
the breaking of grass land might contravene the contract of
tenancy. This position had been foreseen, and the protection
of tenants, as well as the payment of compensation for losses, had
been reckoned with in framing the Food Production Scheme.

To make the position plain to landowners and farmers
and to ensure that the efforts of Executive Committees were
not hindered by doubts on the part of surveying parties, or by
obstruction on the part of occupiers whose land was scheduled
for ploughing up, a letter addressed to the Land Union on this
subject was published by the Board of Agriculture and Fisheries
in April 1917. This communication stated that where, for the
purpose of increasing the food supply, an Executive Committee
decided to break up grass land and served a notice on the
occupier requiring him to plough, the occupier was protected
from any consequence of the nonfulfilment of his agreement ;
while the landowner, if he thought it desirable, could bring a
claim for compensation before the Defence of the Realm
(Losses) Commission.[1]

----

[1] This procedure was modified by the Corn Production (Amendment) Act, 1918 ;
see p. 281.

During the summer months as the survey progressed a certain number of occupiers, knowing that in the opinion of surveyors their land should be ploughed, broke up grass that had been scheduled for ploughing, without being directed to do so by Executive Committees. In such cases there was neither protection for any breach of contract that might have occurred, nor against any subsequent loss that might be sustained. It was undesirable that persons inspired by patriotic motives and ignorant of the law on the subject should be placed in a worse position than their less active neighbours ; in August, therefore, the Food Production Department sent the following instructions to Executive Committees :

' In order to safeguard the claims (on the Losses Commission) of both landlords and tenants where such loss (from breaking up grass) is incurred the Agricultural Executive Committee should, in every case in which grass land is broken up, make an Order for the purpose under Paragraph 1 (e) of Regulation 2 M. Such an Order should be made in cases where both parties consent to the breaking up, as well as in cases where the landlord or tenant objects to the breaking up. The making of such an Order in every case will prevent those who break up land voluntarily from being put in a worse pecuniary position than those who object to doing so, except under compulsion.'

Credit Facilities for Farmers.

Injustice to occupiers of land might be caused by other circumstances than compulsion to break up grass which was being more profitably employed in stock-raising than in growing corn. Although farmers as a whole had much improved their financial position since 1915, some of them were short of capital, and Executive Committees would reasonably have objected to issue compulsory notices, if there were no method by which the recipient of an Order could raise the capital required for the successful cultivation of tillage crops. With the sanction of the Treasury, therefore, the Directors of the leading Joint Stock Banks were approached and they agreed that, in return for a Government guarantee, special credit facilities should be offered by their country branches when capital was required for increasing food production. Under this scheme a farmer requiring assistance in the purchase of seed, fertilizers, or of any other commodity necessary for improving the output of his land was directed to apply to the Executive Committee of his county, giving full particulars ; if, after inquiry, the committee were satisfied that aid should be given, the specific purposes for which credit was required were stated by them, and the banks gave loans at 5 per cent. per annum for a period not exceeding nine months.

No very considerable amount of credit was, in fact, provided under this scheme. Farmers short of capital were usually reluctant to let committees know their affairs. The scheme gave a good deal of trouble to committees ; those who most pressed for advances were not likely to be the most dependable members of the community, and even where their security was adequate their transactions wanted watching ; the machinery or stock purchased with the money advanced was not always of a kind essential for increasing the food supply. The value of this particular scheme, therefore, was indirect rather than direct ; it enabled committees to require farmers to do things which, without the power to offer credit, would not have been demanded. The scheme undoubtedly oiled the committee ' machine ', and though the quantity of ' lubricant ' used was small, and did not altogether prevent friction, there is no question that it was necessary ; and the assistance given by the Joint Stock Banks was much appreciated by the Food Production Department.

Work of the Divisions of the Food Production Department.

At head-quarters, as in the counties, while the Department awaited the decision of the Cabinet respecting the programme of work to be undertaken in 1918, the organization was modified to meet changing demands ; and a brief reference to the Divisions responsible for different branches of the Department's work may conveniently be made at this stage.[1] In addition to a Secretariat there were six Divisions—Local Organization, Labour, Cultivation, Supplies, Horticultural, and Technical.

[1] Further particulars respecting the work of each Division will be found in the Report of the War Cabinet for 1918.

Correspondence with the Agricultural Executive Committees on all questions of policy, on the constitution of committees and sub-committees, on the appointment of local officers, on the interpretation of Orders, on the provision of credit for farmers, and on the drainage of land, was undertaken by the *Local Organization Division*.

The Department's district Commissioners were attached to this Division. Frequent conferences were held with the Commissioners, and each week they reported to head-quarters the chief features in the agricultural position. These reports were edited, classified, and circulated; thus Commissioners knew what was happening in other districts, and any useful suggestion arising out of the work of one Executive Committee could be brought to the notice of others without delay. The reports kept the Department fully informed as to what was taking place in the counties. Frequent references were made to such subjects as: the effect of the weather on crops; changes in the labour situation; the localities in which certain supplies were short; the progress of the survey; the rate at which grass land was being ploughed; the views of committees on badly managed farms; difficulties caused by recruiting; unsatisfied demands for threshing or harvesting machinery; demands for land for allotments.

The work of the *Labour Division* has already been illustrated. In addition to the many questions arising out of recruiting and the provision of soldier labour, schemes were prepared for prisoners' camps, for the utilization of casual labour in harvesting and for training men for farm work. In association with the Cultivation Division about forty schools for training soldier ploughmen were established, and the selected men who were sent to these schools soon became useful. A scheme which gained rapidly in popularity was that for supplying prisoner labour. When this scheme was first announced farmers were disposed to give the German prisoner a wide berth. But the men placed at the disposal of the Food Production Department were nearly all industrious land-workers, who, once they had settled down in their new surroundings, quickly created a

demand ; so that later the only complaint about prisoners was
that there were not enough of them available. Prisoners were
organized in gangs for several kinds of work, and while in all
kinds they gave satisfaction, the services of the ploughmen
sent out with horses and tillage implements were specially
appreciated.

While prisoners of war rapidly established themselves in
favour, it was impossible to make much use of conscientious
objectors : the feeling against them in country districts was
strong and efforts to place them on farms met with small success.

Questions affecting the retention of agricultural labour
occupied much of the time of the Labour Division. The
arrangements made with the Military Authorities in the summer
of 1917 were greatly appreciated, and the progress in carrying
out the tillage programme made between November 1917 and
April 1918 was largely due to the sense of security which
farmers felt as the result of these arrangements.

All questions relating to women labour were dealt with by
the *Women's Branch* of the Labour Division. The organization of women workers has been referred to in previous chapters.
A notable step was taken when the Women's Branch of the
Board of Agriculture was formed in January 1917. In the
following March this Branch was transferred to the Food
Production Department, and shortly afterwards preparations
for the harvest of 1918 were begun.

Women workers of two classes were recruited : (1) village
women willing to give whole or part-time aid, but unable to
leave their homes ; (2) members of the Women's Land Army,
whole-time workers prepared to go wherever they were sent.

Women belonging to the first class had always taken part
in field work. The 1911 census showed that there were then
some 70,000 women agricultural workers ; but a great extension
was both possible and necessary, and means were required
to stimulate activity. For this purpose Women's County
Committees had already been set up and voluntary helpers
acted as village registrars. Renewed attention was now given
to the recruitment of village women. Group Leaders, having

some knowledge of agriculture, were appointed in charge of gangs of women workers, and measures were taken to stimulate patriotic action. Large numbers came forward, and from returns collected it may be estimated that no fewer than 230,000 village women assisted with the crops of 1918 in England and Wales.

The recruiting of women for the Land Army was begun by the National Service Department early in 1917 ; later, recruiting was shared between the Ministry of Labour and the Food Production Department. For the purposes of this scheme the Women's War Agricultural Committees, in their respective counties, set up two sub-committees, one of which selected recruits while the other organized training centres and provided dépôts in which members of the Land Army could stay when not out at work. The training courses, which had been provided by certain agricultural colleges early in the war, no longer sufficed for the numerous recruits now requiring an introduction to farm work, and ultimately about six hundred training centres were arranged on farms where accommodation could be provided. The terms offered by Government at this time, to recruits accepted by committees, included a month's free training, an outfit, a minimum wage of 18s. weekly, and maintenance in the dépôts while unemployed. The Land Army was very popular, and when recruits were called for there was a great rush of applicants, but many were unsuitable, and the first 7,000 women who were accepted were picked from no fewer than 47,000 candidates.

As in the case of the men's committees, a great deal of voluntary assistance was given by members of Selection and Training sub-committees and by village registrars. It was estimated that in 1918 some 13,000 women were assisting the Food Production movement in this way.

While the farmer and his wife, especially the latter, were at first disposed to eye the land girl in her long mud-proof boots and knee-breeches with a certain hesitancy, the novelty soon wore off, and everywhere members of the Land Army were welcomed ; perhaps nowhere more warmly than in London streets, when, headed by grave seniors from the Food Production

Department, they took part in some Saturday Recruiting Rally, carrying their accoutrements, and bearing in their arms trophies from the land. Not only were the Land Army women themselves very good workers, but their example did much to stimulate village women to activity, and the exertions of Hodge himself, as he toiled through the sweltering days of mid-August or the murky gloom of mid-September 1918, were, unquestionably, lightened and perhaps brightened by their presence !

The *Cultivation Division*, which was responsible for the provision and working of tractors, farm implements, and, in the later months, of horses, had a most difficult task. For a few months in 1917 the tractors were run direct from head-quarters. At the outset it was not possible for members of committees to give assistance of equal value to the Department, in dealing with mechanical cultivation, to that which they gave in other branches of work. Tractors were novelties of which few committee members had then had experience; thus reliance had to be placed on local motor engineers, and it was a difficult matter to secure that combination of farming and mechanical skill which was essential in using these new machines successfully. In August 1917, however, it was possible to abandon the plan of working the tractor scheme entirely from head-quarters. The Executive Committees then set up Machinery sub-committees to control the distribution of the machines and implements provided for each county ; local Supervisors were employed to look after Tractor Units—which at full strength consisted of eleven tractors—and the supervisors were made responsible to the County Machinery Officer. The duties of the county staff were exclusively agricultural. The machinery officer decided the kind of land which should, or should not, be worked by tractors and he was responsible for the contracts made with farmers for the execution of work. The supervisors carried out the details of these contracts, saw that the tractor drivers did their work properly, and that each machine was supplied with fuel, lubricants, and spare parts. The Department, on the other hand, supplied the mechanical staff; it had in each county a Tractor Representative—a local motor engineer—who was responsible for the upkeep of the tractors and for providing the machinery officer with the implements required for the work he had in hand. The tractor representative had also to supply mechanics to keep machines in proper repair.

This scheme for the control of tractors was in operation during almost the whole period in which preparation was being made for the harvest of 1918, and, though the best that could be devised in 1917, it was not satisfactory. It was costly, and the responsibility was too much divided. The committees were apt to regard tractor cultivation as exclusively the Department's affair, and for this attitude there was some reason. At a later stage, therefore, and before the 1918 crops were harvested, a new scheme was introduced with the object of placing the control directly under Executive Committees, and also of lessening the cost of working. The Tractor Units, instead of being managed by local supervisors, were let out to Engineer Contractors who, at fixed rates, operated the machines under the directions of the tractor representative. This officer was now made responsible to the committees instead of to head-quarters. The change effected a great economy ; but it would not have been possible to have adopted it in the first instance when tractors were in the experimental stage. Even at the end of 1918 difficulty was experienced in a number of counties in getting engineer contractors to come forward and undertake the work.

From 1st October 1917 onwards a record was kept of all cultivation done by tractor implements, and from that date until the end of the tillage season the work of the tractors equalled the ploughing of some 480,000 acres. The whole of the tillage carried out by tractors for the preparation of the land for the 1918 crops would have been equivalent to the ploughing of about 600,000 acres.

Tractors gave valuable aid in the late spring and summer cultivation of 1918, and they were specially useful in the harvest field, where they contributed materially to the rapid ingathering, and thus (as the weather experienced in September proved) to the safety, of the crops of the south and east of England.

In the spring of 1917 the tractor was a new, untried, and rather distrusted implement, and although by the end of 1918 it was familiar and was eagerly sought after by farmers in every county, its rapid introduction and progress in favour had been secured as the result of an immense amount of effort, and at a high cost. It was otherwise with steam tackle. The steam plough had proved its value and capacity long before the war, and when the Food Production Department was set up immediate steps were taken to develop its usefulness. As the result of a special inquiry the position of every set of steam tackle plying for hire was located. It was found that nearly half of the 500 sets traced in England were idle, some were out of repair, but in most cases ploughing engines were laid up because the engine-drivers had left for the army or munition factories.

The Steam Cultivation Development Association was asked to help, and their Chairman joined the Department as a voluntary worker, rendering in this capacity much valuable aid. Many of the missing engine-drivers were tracked and 300 were released from military service. Repairs were effected, and soon almost every set of tackle in the country was again at work. Long hours were arranged and the owners consented to keep the machinery at work throughout the winter (when engines are usually laid up) so that advantage might be taken of every possible day when the soil was dry enough to cultivate. The result was that, at little outlay to the State, a great increase in tillage was secured. The total area ploughed and cultivated by steam tackle in preparation for the 1918 harvest was about 1,200,000 acres, or about three times as much as would otherwise have been tilled by steam power.

A scheme for providing steam tackle to would-be purchasers on the instalment plan was prepared and put in force.

Action was also required for the purpose of organizing the effective use of steam threshing machinery. The largely increased area under corn, and the fact that corn was being grown in new districts, made it necessary not only to secure additional sets of threshing tackle, but to ensure that facilities for threshing were provided in localities in which they were then non-existent.

Many thousands of new field implements, ploughs, cultivators, harrows, rollers, self-binding reapers, &c., had also to be procured by the Cultivation Division. The requirements had to be anticipated months in advance, and estimating was most difficult ; it was only possible to assume that the programme, as formulated, would be carried out, and to order the implements required, after making allowances for the extra work that might be expected from implements already in the country. A census of the latter was taken at an early stage ; but difficulties, inherent in the rapid enumeration and classification of farm implements, made it but an indifferent guide.

In association with the Labour Division, the Cultivation Division worked out plans for providing horses. The demands of the Army had left some farmers short of horses, but in most arable districts the shortage was not serious, and the demand for horse labour arose largely from grass farms, unprovided with either horses or implements. To meet such cases gangs of ploughmen with horses and implements were placed at the disposal of Executive Committees, who contracted to plough grass land and undertake other classes of tillage at rates approved by the Department. Comparable rates were fixed for horse and tractor cultivation so that equally full use might be made of both. As soon as prisoner ploughmen were available, use was made of them in connexion with the horse gangs, and in the later stages of the war most of the gang labour was supplied by prisoners. In addition to the horses sent out with the labour gangs, many animals were lent to individual farmers with, or without, soldier ploughmen. In all, about 5,000 horses were at work by the end of 1917, and about 11,000 six months later. Many more horses could have been provided if there had been a larger number of skilled soldier ploughmen available and if harness could have been secured.

A central dépôt for tractors, implements, harness, and stores of all descriptions was established at Willesden, in carriage sheds belonging to the L. & N. W. Railway Co., and from this extensive store machinery, spare parts, and all the materials required for the work supervised by the Cultivation Division were sent to every part of the country.

The chief work of the *Supplies Division* of the Food Production Department in 1918 was the distribution of artificial manures and the supply of seed.

In Chapter VII some account has been given of the work of the Fertilizers Committee of 1916, and the efforts then made to get farmers to use sulphate of ammonia in sufficient quantities have been referred to. The experience of 1917 increased the popularity of this manure, and the high prices of corn stimulated the demand ; thus in 1918 it was very freely purchased. As in the previous year, arrangements were made to sell it at a uniform price in all parts of the country ; and, to equalize buying and thus reduce the storage difficulties which manufacturers had hitherto experienced, a sliding scale of prices was introduced —the prices being lowest in seasons in which the manure was least in demand. The arrangements in 1918 worked well, and it may be estimated from the sales effected that about 230,000 tons of sulphate of ammonia were applied to the 1918 crops, as compared with about 150,000 tons in 1917 and 75,000 tons in 1916. This additional use of nitrogenous manure undoubtedly added largely to the grain output of 1918.

In the quantity of superphosphate available there was also an improvement. The amount provided by the exertions of the Fertilizers Branch of the Ministry of Munitions was estimated at about 770,000 tons, rather more than the pre-war quantity. As the area under tillage had increased and nitrogenous manure was freely applied, a great deal more superphosphate would no doubt have been desirable. An insufficient use of superphosphate cannot, however, have much affected the corn crops of 1918 ; the results of a deficiency would tell on the root crops of that year, and on grain in subsequent seasons.

During this year arrangements were made through the Ministry of Munitions to extract potash from flue dust, and a certain quantity of potash from this source became available. The total amount provided was very small in comparison with the country's requirements ; and, though no estimate of the loss is possible, the harvest of 1918 must have been prejudiced by a deficiency of potash. It was remarked after harvest that some of the grain crops did not thresh out in accordance with expectations. Experiences of this sort are of a kind that might be expected to result from ill-balanced manuring.

As in the previous year, steps were taken to secure seed potatoes for small growers, and, in addition, certain varieties immune from wart disease were provided for growing in localities affected by this troublesome disease. In all about 22,500 tons of potatoes were distributed.

Similar action was taken with respect to both wheat and oats; of the former 24,000 and of the latter 27,000 quarters were provided for sowing. In neither case was the whole quantity used in this country; a small proportion of the wheat was supplied to the French Government, and about 3,000 quarters of oats were taken by the War Office for sowing on Army farms in France.

Land for allotments was provided by the Local Organization Division and seed by the Supplies Division; the *Horticultural Division* was set up to afford allotment holders and other small growers advice on the management of their land, and to organize the movement. County and District Horticultural Committees were established, and many local correspondents of the Division, known as Horticultural Representatives, were appointed.

The Village War Food Societies started in 1916 were, under the name of Food Production Societies, greatly increased in number. Schemes for preventing potato disease by spraying, and for preserving fruit, both on the large and on the domestic scale, were undertaken; and, with the object of utilizing waste from allotments, measures were adopted for increasing rabbit and poultry keeping. To assist allotment-holders and cottage gardeners in selling their produce, marketing organizations were set up in a number of counties.

In the early part of 1917 local authorities had been very active in securing land for allotments under the powers conferred by Regulation 2 L of the Defence of the Realm Acts, but in the autumn of this year enterprise slackened. Inspectors were, therefore, appointed by the Horticultural Division to visit local authorities and represent to them the need for acquiring fresh land. As a result some 8,500 acres, providing for 125,000 allotments, were secured for cultivation in 1918.

Inquiries addressed by the Division to local authorities, and investigations made by Inspectors, brought to light much interesting information respecting the growth of the allotment movement during the war. Replies received from 6,230 authorities out of 8,500 to whom questions were addressed, showed that in 1918 these authorities were providing 890,000 allotments with a total area of 130,000 acres. Many of the rural authorities provided allotments of considerable size ; but the typical war allotment was the one-fortieth acre plot provided in the urban areas. In the case of sixty-nine of the eighty-one county boroughs of England and Wales 222,000 allotments had been formed since the outbreak of war, in addition to about 60,000 previously cultivated. Adding the allotments provided by private persons, it was estimated by the Horticultural Division that in 1918 there existed about 1,400,000 allotments, of which 830,000 had come into existence since the outbreak of war.

The work of the *Technical Division* of the Department will be referred to in Chapter X (see p. 282).

Progress of the Programme.

While the organization of work at head-quarters and in the counties was proceeding rapidly during the autumn months of 1917, the programme itself was making little progress.

In October 1917 a return was submitted by all Executive Committees giving the area of land that had been surveyed, the quantity of grass scheduled for breaking up, and the area which farmers had already tilled, or had promised to break up. The returns showed that the work of survey parties was well advanced, and that much land had been inspected and classified ; but in other respects the position at this time was far from satisfactory. Although six months had passed since the programme for 1918 had been drawn up, very little increase had been secured in the area under tillage. The Cabinet had dealt with the Department's demands for labour and other requisites on 27th June. It had then been decided that, from the 5th July onwards, regular weekly contingents of the men to be provided from the Home Forces would be sent out for work on the land. But in spite of the most strenuous efforts to secure this promised help long delays occurred. If the agreed time-table had been adhered to, all of the 43,000 men expected would have been available by the end of August; the number actually at work, or in the dépôts, in the middle of November was 26,000. Moreover, the men provided were relatively inefficient. It had been promised that 21,500 skilled ploughmen, or at least men accustomed to work with horses, would be supplied. In fact it was found that, of the 13,000 nominally skilled men who had arrived before November, 2,500 only could plough. The best that the Department could do was to establish ploughing schools for training those men who could be trusted with horses ; but this involved a further loss of time. As there were so few skilled ploughmen, it was impossible to make much use of the horse teams, by means of which it had been hoped that a large area of grass land would have been broken up before November 1917.

Nor was the position with respect to tractors and implements any better. Experience in the spring of 1917 showed how difficult it was to obtain tractors from America ; thus when the 1918 programme was first drawn up it was resolved to attempt to manufacture tractors in this country at a rate which would place between five and six thousand at the disposal of the Department by the end of the year. For a time it appeared likely that, with the consent of Mr. Henry Ford which had generously been given, the Ministry of Munitions would be able to manufacture Fordson tractors on a large scale ; but unexpected difficulties led to the abandonment of this project. Orders were then placed with British firms for tractors ; the rate at which they could be supplied, however, did not materially add to the Department's resources. A large order was also cabled to America as soon as it was known that the Ministry of

Munitions could not undertake the manufacture of tractors ; but in spite of much effort to expedite delivery the total number of machines at the Department's disposal in November was 1,500 only, or nearly 4,000 less than the number for which the original programme had stipulated.

These delays in obtaining the labour and machinery required for carrying out the 1918 programme had serious consequences for the Department's work ; not only because of the loss of time, but because of the effects of delay on Executive Committees and farmers. For months members of committees, with many voluntary assistants, had been surveying land, and labour and machinery had been promised to farmers for the additional tillage which they were being urged to undertake. Naturally enough, when the promises were not fulfilled, not only was nothing done by those farmers who required additional help before increasing their corn area, but their neighbours, whose own resources would have enabled them to extend their cultivation, adopted a ' wait and see ' attitude. After harvest began almost every one had a sufficient excuse for delaying the ploughing of grass land ; for not only had the crops to be secured, but directly the fields were cleared the cultivation of stubbles provided work for every ploughman in the country. Although, therefore, both the Department and the Executive Committees had made every possible preparation for adding largely to the area under corn in 1918, the outlook in November 1917 was dismal. Organization, however carefully thought out, and an ambitious programme on paper, could not cultivate land nor sow corn, and the season was passing rapidly. Operations were not going 'according to plan'. Moreover, the need for carrying out the full programme was greater than ever. What then was to be done ? Assuming that events now took a more favourable turn, by what means could the lost time be made good ?

In the earlier months of the year Executive Committees had been instructed to keep agricultural considerations carefully in mind when selecting land for ploughing. Thus the grass which had been scheduled was usually of a kind which it was obviously desirable to convert into tillage. The ploughing of this grass land involved neither much risk of financial loss, nor of crop failure because of the character of the turf or the soil. In the course of the work many of those farmers who happened to occupy grass land of a kind which survey parties thought too good, or too heavy, to plough were not required to increase their cultivation. Some Executives had quite definitely instructed the survey parties not to schedule grass with the object of making each occupier ' do his bit '. In the circumstances of November 1917 this policy—a very proper one when regarded solely from the farmer's point of view—was re-examined. On the one hand it was clear that, if departed from, there would be an increased risk of failure in the corn crops sown on the new land in 1918, and that some labour diverted from the existing tillage to the new corn land might be lost. Moreover, there would be a loss of summer grazing and, in not a few cases, a loss of profit. On the other hand it was recognized : That in the event of real scarcity and shortage of bread-stuffs, a successful grain crop on three acres out of four broken up would mean approximately a seven-fold increase in essential food from the whole area ploughed ; that, from the point of view of transport, whereas a fleet of forty vessels of 5,000 tons (40 cub. ft.) could carry to this country the meat produced on a million acres of the kind of grass land which would be ploughed, it would require almost two hundred vessels to carry the corn likely to be grown on the same land after tillage ; that from the point of view of the stock owner himself the risk of a short supply of winter fodder was much greater than the risk of a shortage in summer grazing, and that if losses were incurred as the result of ploughing pastures, compensation was payable ; that for two years at least newly broken grass land would not require summer cleaning, and that the extra acres would enable a greater quantity of the existing tillage land—then in bad condition—to be summer fallowed or sown with roots ; finally, that since the prospects of securing sufficient supplies of phosphates and potash were remote, the only reserves of fertility then available were those accumulated in pastures. It was therefore decided that there must be no relaxation in the effort to secure the completion of the programme. But the season of the year for breaking up heavy clay soils was now past ; the scarcity of ploughmen was such that, on those farms on which grass suitable for cultivation had already been scheduled, nothing could be done for want of labour ; the finding of labour was much more difficult than the finding of land. It was therefore agreed that where farmers had the necessary labour, and also occupied grass land on which there was a reasonable prospect of growing a crop, they must accept a certain risk ; they must even sacrifice good grass land, if allowed to retain enough to carry dairy cows and other essential stock through the summer months.

It was this change in policy which gave rise to so much criticism of the Agricultural Executive Committees who, in the following summer, were charged with ignorance and recklessness. The charges were absurd. The results secured testify to the high merit of the committees' work. But if the increase of 1918 had not been realized the charges would still have been absurd, and have reflected only on the committees' critics. No praise can be too high for the Agricultural Executive Committees and for the many competent farmers and surveyors whom they enlisted to assist them in finding land for tillage. They were not responsible for the policy, and they were given a most difficult and in many cases a distasteful task ; we shall presently learn how successful they were; meanwhile let us record and remember the fact that Executive Committees, their sub-committees, and those who assisted them on the surveys served their country faithfully, and their fellow countrymen extraordinarily well, in the crisis of the war.

At this stage, after the position had been surveyed by the Department, a conference of the Chairmen of Executive Committees was called, the position of the programme and the difficulties of securing soldier labour and machinery were explained to them ; it was shown that the food situation was quite as uncertain as it had been earlier in the year, and each county was urged to increase the area of arable land. After the conference a report was sent to the Cabinet, drawing attention to the position of the programme, showing how it had suffered because of delays in supplying the requisites originally asked for, and pointing out the need for accelerating deliveries. Above everything else the necessity for additional skilled ploughmen was urged. There were now barely a hundred days left in which to add to the tillage crops of 1918, and so far the increase secured was of small account. To enable the Department to overtake the arrears it was urged that 4,500 additional ploughmen should be provided at once, and 4,000 more before the busy spring season set in. A request was also made for 31,000 extra unskilled men. The Cabinet dealt with these demands on the 13th December 1917, and decided that from prisoners' camps and other sources 8,000 ploughmen and 20,000 unskilled men should be found.

Furlough for three months was given, in December, to 1,500 ploughmen serving overseas. The first camp for German prisoner ploughmen was opened on the 1st February 1918, and by the 15th March seventy-four camps had been established and 2,650 prisoners were at work. At this date about 7,000 of the 28,000 men promised in December had been received ; the ploughing season was almost over and urgent requisitions for more men were being sent in by Executive Committees. Everywhere farmers, who were not only willing but anxious to take advantage of the fine weather and break up grass land for corn growing, were clamouring for more men. It was under these conditions that the tillage programme for 1918 was being carried through, when in April there came the imperative demand that farmers, in their turn, should provide 30,000 more men for the Army.

The rate of delivery of tractors, too, continued to be much below what had been asked for. In January, when at one time it was hoped that 5,000 would be available, some 1,650 only were at work, and in the month of March the average number available was no more than 2,240.

The Weather.

But if the exigencies of war prevented the Department from securing the labour and machinery which had been asked for, at this stage the maligned British climate came to our aid, and, from the time when in the gloomy November of 1917 the Department decided that increased difficulties must be met by increased efforts, the sun literally shone on food producers. The weather of the year, as we shall afterwards see, was by no means always at its best; but the currents of the upper air arranged their movements so as to facilitate the spring ploughing campaign, in a way that the weather seldom does in England.

The Department then reaped the reward of the carefully designed programme and the carefully planned organization. Though the additional labour and machinery were far below what had been aimed at, farmers now made the fullest use of their existing resources. On each fine spring day every fit man was at the plough, and almost every countryman, fit or unfit, was at work on the land. The activity was amazing, and many hundreds of thousands of acres of grass land were broken up, tilled, and sown in February and March 1918.

The change in the weather began early in November; until the end of the first week of that month it had been by no means favourable. The first part of October had been cold and wet, the end of the month was also wet, and wheat sowing was much delayed. About the 7th November, however, the land was sufficiently dry to permit of sowing, and for five weeks it remained in good condition. The mangold crop was safely secured, and much wheat was sown before Christmas. In the dry, cold month which followed not much work was possible on the land; but the soil benefited from frost and did not lose condition in the one wet week experienced about the middle of January. From the last week in January until the end of March conditions were ideal; there was little rain, much sunshine, and seldom enough frost to check the plough. In this period corn was sown on most of the existing tillage land, and, as above noted, a great deal of grass land was ploughed and sown with oats. April was less favourable, and cold weather in the middle of the month checked the growth of the young corn and grass; but conditions for work on the land were fair, and with the aid of soldiers and women the month closed with spring cultivation well advanced. Though skilled labour was everywhere in urgent demand, the favourable weather conditions, and the organized casual labour now available, resulted in the farmer's position being better than in either 1916 or 1917.

It was in the latter half of April that the labour event of the year occurred—the call up of more men from the land for military service. The actual effect on the 1918 harvest was not considerable, in spite of the gloomy forebodings of agriculturists, but the action of the National Service Department had a great influence on the food production programme. This subject will be referred to in Chapter X.

May was again a favourable month ; the latter half was both warm and dry—in many districts, indeed, too dry for late sown spring crops. June was dry and cool, even cold, and growth was checked. As the month passed the prospects for a good harvest seemed none too favourable ; the wheat crop promised well, but oats and barley had suffered from drought, the hay crop was poor, and roots were starting badly. From April onwards, wherever the cereal crops on newly broken grass land were checked by cold dry winds, there had been reports of crop failures. Investigation showed that, as in 1917, some of these failures were due to improper cultivation and to an insufficient consolidation of the land before sowing ; but it was soon discovered that leatherjackets (the grubs of crane flies) were much more common than usual, and as the season progressed many reports of severe damage by this pest, and by wireworms, were received.

Critics.

The crops sown on newly broken grass land were being watched with great interest throughout this period, and every failure attracted attention. Now came the opportunity of those who had persistently opposed the ploughing up of grass land. A great agitation was raised and for weeks the public were informed of the follies of ' Government ' and ' Committee farming ' by those eminent authorities who from the railway, or the roadside, had followed the progress of the plough ; or who, during week-end visits to the country, had learned to repeat the sapient onlooker's motto, ' bushels, not acres '. Panegyrics on grass land and laments for 'good food' destroyed by the myrmidons of the Food Production Department filled the correspondence columns of country newspapers. If Gulliver could have beguiled his travels with these midsummer diatribes, a new 'Voyage to the Country of the Houyhnhnms' would doubtless have enriched the annals of the Great War. It was indeed grievous to read the tales told of soft green corn disappearing into the brown earth in the tracks of the wireworm and the leatherjacket, of ploughed paddocks now bare of sustenance for man or beast, of rascally committees who had stolen some common from the cow, of innocent children left milkless.

Here, for example, is a forceful paragraph from one of these aspen pens :

'Thousands of acres of our finest old pastures—a short year ago the pride and glory of our farms and fruitful sources of our food supply to man and beast—are to-day, as the result of coercive and untimely methods of tillage, and the miserable supply of skilled farm labour, with the ravages of inevitable grub and worm attendant upon inefficient cultivation, simply wretched wastes, filled with thistles, charlock, wind-grass—in fact with anything but the crops of corn our charlatan "farmer" foolishly hoped to see ! '

But the drought passed and the crops grew, and the real damage to food production which followed this clamour was done, not in parched fields by wireworms and leatherjackets, but 'in another place' as, in our next chapter, we shall see.

Harvest Difficulties.

There was heavy rain in the middle of July, which added somewhat to the subsequent difficulties of harvesting, but until the end of August the weather was favourable, and the fine harvest of the south and south-east of England was almost completed by the end of the month. With the magnificent crops of the north and west, however, farmers had a melancholy experience. September and October were very wet months, as bad as they possibly could be for harvesting, and the cut grain remained for weeks in sodden fields ; very little corn was secured during September, and harvest was not completed until the end of October. The losses were heavy, but when the harvest was over it was found that they were much less than had been feared, and though many individual farmers suffered, the country did not lose the benefit of the efforts that had been made to increase production.

Of all the arduous days in this great adventure of 1918, the closing weeks contained the most arduous for the farmers of the north, the west, and the midlands. It was only by taking advantage of every favourable hour that they and their men, aided by women, soldiers, prisoners-of-war, tractors, self-binding reapers, and all the resources [1] at the disposal of the Food Production Department, succeeded in saving the crop. The ingathering of the farmer's corn during fitful intervals in the rain and mist of autumn was a finer feat even than the ploughing and sowing of the great extra area in the sunshine of spring. In spite of the weather, and of influenza, which in many districts attacked nearly every labourer, the work was at last completed, and the experiences of these weeks in the autumn of 1918 should serve to comfort those fearful agriculturists who dread attempts to grow corn in the British climate. Four-fifths, and more, of the largest harvest of modern times was saved in one of the worst seasons possible, and in face of labour difficulties that it may be hoped will never occur again.

Harvest Figures.

It will not be necessary to describe the methods adopted in Scotland and Ireland to increase the production of corn in 1918. In the former country the methods resembled those employed in England, and are described in another volume of this Series. In Ireland the same procedure was followed as in the previous year, with the exception that the Compulsory Tillage Order specified an increase of 5 per cent. in 1918 as compared with 10 per cent. in 1917. We may now, therefore, turn to an examination of the results secured in each country and in the United Kingdom as a whole.

When the official Returns collected by the three Departments of Agriculture had been compiled, it was found that during the year 4th June 1917 to 4th June 1918 the total area of cultivated land in the United Kingdom had fallen by 70,000 acres. A part

[1] These resources in the autumn of 1918 included about 120,000 landworkers (of whom 70,000 were soldiers and 30,000 prisoners of war), 11,000 horses, 4,000 tractors, and many thousands of harvesting and cultivating implements.

of the large area not accounted for in Ireland in the preceding year had been recovered, so that the cultivated area of Ireland was returned at 38,000 acres more than in 1917; but as in the previous year the Irish returns cannot have been so complete as they were until 1916, and over 300,000 acres in that country would appear to have escaped classification.

In England and Wales there was the notable reduction of 94,000 acres in the area of cultivated land, and in Scotland of 15,000 acres. A small part of this loss may be attributed to the land taken up by the Air Ministry and War Office; the greater part was due, no doubt, to the reversion of high-lying cultivated grass land to hill pasture. Even before the war the normal losses in some years reached a high figure; thus, for example, in 1913 a loss of 68,000 acres of cultivated land had been recorded in Great Britain.

These losses in the total area available for cultivation in 1918 did not, however, prevent a large increase in the area under tillage. Excluding temporary grasses, clovers, and sainfoin, this area had increased during the year by no less than 1,989,000 acres. Toward the total England and Wales contributed 1,557,000, Scotland 227,000, and Ireland 203,000 acres.

In the period 1904–13 the United Kingdom had, in addition to grass, 12,910,000 acres under cultivation; in 1918 this area had increased to 15,700,000 acres, or by 21·6 per cent.

These additions to the tillage area enabled farmers in 1918 to grow 920,000 acres and 1,015,000 tons more wheat, 1,564,000 acres and 1,421,000 tons more oats, and 338,000 acres and 2,631,000 tons more potatoes than in the years 1904–13. In the case of barley, although the area was reduced by 38,000 acres, the yield was increased by 24,000 tons.

The actual contributions made by each of the countries to these satisfactory totals is shown in Table XVIII.

Summarizing the figures for each country it will be seen that in 1918, as compared with 1904–13, the increments in area and yield of corn were:

England and Wales	.	.	.	1,683,000 acres	1,479,000 tons
Scotland	.	.	.	.	274,000 ,,	300,000 ,,
Ireland .	.	.	.	.	658,000 ,,	681,000 ,,

TABLE XVIII

HARVEST OF 1918 COMPARED WITH AVERAGE HARVEST OF 1904–13

FIGURES THOUSANDS OF ACRES OR TONS

(For Areas and Yields of 1904–13, see p. 112)

Country	Crop	1918		1918+1904–13	
		Area	Yield	Acres	Tons
England and Wales .	Wheat	2,557	2,339	+ 868	+ 871
Scotland . . .	,,	79	88	+ 28	+ 31
Ireland . . .	,,	157	152	+ 117	+ 113
United Kingdom . .	,,	2,793	2,579	+ 920	+1,015
England and Wales .	Barley	1,571	1,228	+ 61	+ 36
Scotland . . .	,,	155	133	− 44	− 38
Ireland . . .	,,	185	179	+ 21	+ 26
United Kingdom . .	,,	1,911	1,540	− 38	+ 24
England and Wales .	Oats	2,851	2,056	+ 754	+ 572
Scotland . . .	,,	1,246	957	+ 290	+ 307
Ireland . . .	,,	1,580	1,448	+ 520	+ 542
United Kingdom . .	,,	5,677	4,461	+1,564	+1,421
England and Wales .	Potatoes	634	4,209	+ 202	+1,566
Scotland . . .	,,	169	1,151	+ 26	+ 225
Ireland . . .	,,	702	3,863	+ 105	+ 840
United Kingdom . .	,,	1,505	9,223	+ 333	+2,631

Note. In the case of England and Wales 142,000 acres growing 620,000 qrs. of ' mixed corn ', which was separately recorded for the first time in 1918, have been added to barley and oats ; half to each crop. In the case of Scotland the produce of 4,000 acres mixed corn has been similarly divided.

When the Food Production Campaign was first under discussion, the programme aimed at securing 3,000,000 acres more tillage in 1918 than in 1916. The Returns for 1918 show the extent to which this aim was realized. The increase, over 1916, secured in the cultivated area, other than grass, was :

England and Wales	.	.	.	1,843,000 acres
Scotland	.	.	.	276,000 ,,
Ireland .	.	.	.	841,000 ,,
		Total		2,960,000[1] ,,

The precise source of these extra acres cannot be ascertained, because of the quantity of land which is unaccounted for—the cultivated area in 1918 was less by 420,000 acres than in 1916—

[1] It should be noted that this extra area was not secured by the method originally contemplated ; cf. p. 208.

but the total reduction in the grass area between 1916 and 1918 which can be traced in the Agricultural Returns was 3,381,000 acres, viz. 1,929,000 acres in England and Wales, 290,000 acres in Scotland, and 1,162,000 acres [1] in Ireland. The reduction fell mainly on the area under permanent grass. A comparison of the reduction in permanent and temporary grass in the different countries is of interest, as indicating the main sources of the extra land found for corn and potatoes. The reductions between 1916 and 1918 were :

England and Wales	1,435,000 acres permanent grass	494,000 acres temp. grass.
Scotland . .	164,000 ,, ,, ,,	126,000 ,, ,,
Ireland (including loss) .	543,000 ,, ,, ,,	619,000 ,, ,,
	2,142,000	1,239,000

It will thus be seen that while Ireland found more than half the extra tillage land cultivated in 1918 by ploughing temporary pastures, and Scotland found more than two-fifths of its increase from the same source, England and Wales were only able to find one-fourth. Three-fourths of the additional land required in England and Wales had to be provided by ploughing out permanent pastures. It was this fact that made the task of the English Agricultural Executive Committees such a difficult one. For not only were owners and occupiers very much more reluctant to plough permanent than temporary grass land, but in the case of the former the labour and implements necessary for cultivation were often not available locally.

The results secured in the 1918 harvest clearly indicate the influence which the system of husbandry adopted in each country has had both on the total output and on the flexibility of production. The effects are brought out by the figures in Table XIX, in which the total yield, and the increase in yield, of wheat, of all three cereals, and of potatoes, are shown per thousand acres of cultivated land.

In 1918 an average thousand acres of land in England and Wales, Scotland and Ireland respectively, produced 86·3, 18·4, and 10·3 tons of wheat. This represented an increase of 59·3

[1] It appears to be probable that the actual reduction in Ireland was about three-fourths of this figure ; one-fourth being due to incomplete returns.

per cent. over the pre-war level in England and Wales, of 54·4 per cent. in Scotland, and of 390·3 per cent. in Ireland; it was relatively an easy task to increase the very small wheat crops of Scotland and Ireland. The English crop of 1918 was the chief factor in the supply, for it will be seen that one thousand acres of cultivated land in England and Wales contributed as large an amount to the loaf as 4,690 acres in Scotland and as 8,180 acres in Ireland.

TABLE XIX

TOTAL CROPS OF WHEAT; OF WHEAT, BARLEY, AND OATS; AND OF POTATOES IN HARVEST OF 1918
With Increase over Average Crops of 1904–13, and
Percentage Increase over Crops 1904–13
Per Thousand Acres of Cultivated Land

	England and Wales	Scotland	Ireland	U.K.
Wheat crop of 1918, tons . .	86·3	18·4	10·3	55·3
Increase over 1904–13, tons . .	28·4	6·5	7·6	21·8
Percentage increase over 1904–13 .	59·3	54·4	390·3	64·9
Wheat, barley, and oat crops of 1918, tons	207·0	244·0	120·7	183·7
Increase over 1904–13, tons . .	54·5	62·7	46·2	52·7
Percentage increase . . .	35·4	33·0	62·0	40·2
Potato crop of 1918, tons . .	155·2	240·5	268·8	197·7
Increase over 1904–13, tons . .	57·4	47·0	57·0	56·4
Percentage increase . . .	59·6	24·3	27·8	39·9

Per thousand acres of cultivated land Scotland grew most corn in 1918, and the actual though not the percentage increase was the largest in any of the countries. Scotch systems of husbandry are both productive and elastic. The large percentage increase secured in Ireland indicates the possibilities of the extension of corn-growing in that country. Similarly the percentage rise in the production of potatoes in England shows how readily the crop might be increased if the demand arose. But until the cost of transport and marketing can be reduced there is little scope for the activities of the English potato grower; a crop as large as that of 1918 would fail to find a market under post-war conditions.

Losses and Gains in 1918.

The information given above about the crops of the 1918 harvest must now be supplemented by an attempt to estimate the losses and gains in the crops grown in 1918, and the live-stock products of the year June 1918 to May 1919, which resulted from the land ploughed up between January 1917 and April 1918.

We shall first refer to the effect of the ploughing of the pastures on live-stock farming, and then to the crops grown on the newly ploughed land.

Reduction in the Milk Supply.

The most important of the animal products affected by the plough policy was milk. Special efforts were made both by the Food Production Department and by the Executive Committees to avoid any action likely to prejudice the supply of winter milk. Even in the case of summer milk, of which there was no shortage, care was taken not to schedule land for ploughing if required for cows. The quantity of food produced per acre of grass land in the form of milk being relatively high, the objections to ploughing were greater than in the case of meat.

The extent of the reduction in the output of milk during the war was considered by the committee on the *Production and Distribution of Milk* of which Lord Astor was chairman. This committee in their Final Report [1] estimated the total production of milk in the United Kingdom in 1909–13 at 1,895 million gallons (about one hundred million gallons more than the figure adopted by the Food (War) Committee in 1917); the corresponding estimate for 1918 was 1,505 million gallons. The loss in production was attributed by Lord Astor's Committee mainly to (1) scarcity and high prices of feeding stuffs, (2) deterioration in the quality of feeding stuffs, (3) the decreased efficiency of milkers. It was noted that these causes operated chiefly on the supply of winter milk. The total number of cows in milk had not decreased, but there was evidence that in those districts which specialized in winter milk there were fewer cows. Purchased feeding stuffs and the products of arable land are

[1] (Cmd. 483), H.M. Stationery Office, London, 1919.

largely used by producers of winter milk, and thus the cost per
gallon of winter milk had risen to a much greater extent than
the cost of producing summer milk in grazing districts.

The committee did not attribute any part of the loss to the
ploughing up of grass land ; and, as one of the chief aims of the
plough policy was to secure a larger quantity of winter fodders
for cows and other live stock, it would be difficult to show that
the shortage of winter milk was a result of this policy. But, in
spite of the care taken not to interfere with the milk supply, it
may be admitted that, in districts producing butter or cheese, the
ploughing of grass land is likely to have resulted in some decrease.
We shall therefore assume (although this is almost certainly an
over-estimate) that the ploughing of pastures resulted in a loss,
between June 1918 and May 1919, of one-fifth of the amount
of the loss estimated by Lord Astor's Committee for 1918 ; in
round figures eighty million gallons. From the conclusions
reached in Chapter IV, it may be shown that this quantity of
milk would represent the production of about 650,000 acres of
cow pasturage of average quality.

Reduction in the Meat Supply.

The total reduction in the grass area between 1916 and 1918
was, as we have already seen, 3,381,000 acres, but all of this was
not land which had been ploughed. The total increase recorded
in the ploughed area was 2,960,000 acres ; but this figure must
represent less than the actual area of grass ploughed, for in
1918 a considerable area of cultivated land was diverted to
other purposes or unaccounted for. The exact area ploughed
must lie somewhere between the two figures, and if we place it
at 3,150,000 acres,[1] and deduct 650,000 acres for cow pastures,
there would have been a reduction of 2,500,000 acres in the grass
land used in meat production.

If we were further to assume that the meat-producing
pastures ploughed during the war were of average quality, the
figures given in Chapter IV show that, under normal conditions
of stock-rearing and fattening, a reduction of 2,500,000 acres

[1] This is an outside figure, taken so that the loss of meat may not be understated.
The area of grass land ploughed was probably between 3,000,000 and 3,050,000 acres.

of pasture would have decreased the meat supply by nearly 75,000 tons. But the conditions were not normal.

The figures quoted on p. 67 relating to the production of meat during the war, which were based on returns collected by the Ministry of Food, estimate the production of beef and mutton in the period June 1918 to May 1919 at 829,000 tons. Taking the writer's estimate of 1,000,000 tons for the pre-war production, there would thus have been a reduction of 171,000 tons in 1918–19. If we analyse this figure with the object of ascertaining the actual effect on the meat supply of the reduction of 2,500,000 acres of grass in 1918, we find it impossible to agree that the ploughing of pasture land could have reduced the meat supply of 1918–19 by as much as 75,000 tons. Because of drought there was a scarcity of grass in the summer of 1918, but from the end of July onwards there was no lack of grass, and in the autumn months there was much more than the available stock could consume. The production of meat in the quarter ending December was 238,000 tons, in the following quarter it was 211,000 tons ; thus it was at the period of the year when stock depend mainly on the products of arable land and concentrated feeding stuffs that the meat supply was most reduced. The loss of meat in 1918–19 was no doubt to some extent due to the shortage of grass in the summer of 1918, but the reduction was mainly brought about by other causes. The premature slaughter of cattle in the autumn of 1917 reduced the average size of cattle in 1918, and labour difficulties, coupled with a bad lambing season, reduced the flocks. Again, there were the demands of the War Office for hay for Army horses, and of the Board of Trade for forage for town horses. Above all there was the shortage of concentrated feeding stuffs, which not only directly affected the meat situation by lessening the total quantity of food available for stock, but decreased the output of both beef and mutton by upsetting the farmer's plans, and leaving him without the means of ' finishing ' his stock in the usual way, or maintaining them in the spring of 1919 when roots were very scarce.

The increase of corn at the expense of the area under roots no doubt accentuated the difficulties of the stockowner in the

spring of 1919. But it should be observed that this change was
not entirely, or even mainly, due to the policy of the Food Production Department. It has already been pointed out that the
effects of the war on labour and prices resulted in an increase
of corn at the expense of roots, and one of the main objects
of the plough policy was to counteract this undesirable tendency
by adding to the total area of arable land, so that the normal
balance of British rotations might be restored.

If the conditions of the time be taken into account, it
is obvious that the 2,500,000 acres of pasture—pasture, be it
noted, of less than average quality—of which cattle and sheep
were robbed by the plough in 1918, could not have reduced the
production of meat by as much as 75,000 tons; it is very unlikely
that the reduction amounted to one-half of this figure, but,
so that there may be no understatement, the loss will be put
at 60,000 tons of beef and mutton.

In setting out these estimates of the losses that resulted
from the ploughing of grass land, the advantages which stock
derived from the increase in the area of arable land have not
been taken into account.

When the Food Production policy was framed, it was
believed to be likely that on balance there would be some
reduction in live-stock products; but, as events shaped themselves, it may well be questioned whether, if the country had
pursued to the end the agricultural policy which was followed
in the earlier years of the war, and there had been no ploughing
campaign, the public would have had at their disposal between
January 1917 and the signing of the Peace Treaty a single
pound more meat or a single gallon more milk than they actually
obtained.

Gain from the Crops grown on Newly Ploughed Grass Land.[1]

Even in the late summer of 1918, when fine crops were in
prospect, doubt was occasionally expressed as to whether any
substantial return would be secured from newly broken grass
land, and it was frequently stated that, if the loss of pasture

---

[1] The technical experience gained in breaking up grass land in 1918 is summarized
in an article by C. Bryner Jones, C.B.E., in the *Journal R. A. S. E.* for 1919.

were taken into account, the gain from the ploughing campaign would be found to be very small.

It is not possible to separate the yield obtained from the newly broken grass land from that of the other crops grown during the year, since in the official Returns they are recorded together ; but, as the result of an inquiry made in England and Wales before harvest, a fair estimate of the yield secured from new tillage land may be made.

In August 1918 a circular letter was addressed to each of the sixty-one Executive Committees requesting them to furnish the Department with particulars of the crops sown or planted on, and of the yields anticipated from, the grass land broken up for the harvest of that year. It was recommended that parishes should be selected in the proportion of one parish for each 5,000 acres of grass land broken up in the county, and a request was made that all crops, good and bad, in the sample parishes should be reported on. In reporting the results, the committees were asked to send notes on cultivation, and comments suggesting reasons either for specially good crops or for failures.

Inspections of the growing crops were made by expert agriculturists just before harvest, and completed forms were subsequently returned from all, save four, counties. Of the latter, two were English and two Welsh; one only of the four was of considerable size, and, though no details were submitted, it was reported in this case that ' the result of the ploughing-out scheme may be described as thoroughly satisfactory, good crops have been obtained and the yield (on newly broken grass) has been above the average '.

On the whole the returns showed evidence of care in compilation; and the committees of Monmouth, Durham, Gloucestershire, and Kent sent in particularly valuable reports.

The reports were prepared and the estimates made before the wet weather of September and October set in, which in many of the northern and western counties led to serious losses of grain. These losses were, of course, felt by crops grown on both newly ploughed grass and old tillage land, but the wet weather did most harm to the extraordinarily fine long-strawed crops, which had been grown on the new arable land in many of those counties which usually complete their harvest after the month of August. Reference to the losses in harvesting will be made later; for the present, attention may be confined to the yields estimated at the special inspection made before harvest.

The area of permanent grass land ploughed in England and Wales between the 4th June 1917 and the 4th June 1918 was about 1,246,000 acres.[1] The reports received referred to 77,765 acres, and included particulars of the following crops:

Wheat	14,391 acres	Beans . . .	1,251 acres
Barley	5,224 ,,	Peas	1,096 ,,
Oats . . .	45,217 ,,	Linseed and flax . .	224 ,,
Dredge corn . . .	495 ,,	Mustard . . .	257 ,,
Rye	1,283 ,,	Buckwheat . . .	48 ,,
Potatoes . . .	2,791 ,,		
Turnips and mangolds .	321 ,,		72,598 ,,

The returns relating to the remaining area of about 5,000 acres were rejected after scrutiny, either because they were incomplete or inaccurate.

The returns which were analysed [2] referred to 8,795 fields situated in more than six hundred parishes. These totals give an average of thirteen parishes per county, and are equivalent to fourteen fields for each parish in England and Wales. In the case of the three principal cereal crops the samples were sufficiently large to justify the ' raising ' of the figures to the county areas; thus a ' weighted ' average yield of wheat, barley, and oats for England and Wales may be given.

In the case of all other crops the average yields of the areas actually reported on are referred to here.

In comparing the average figures given below with the averages as stated in the Agricultural Returns, it must be remembered that while the latter refer to crops actually harvested, the figures in this special return refer to all crops sown.

[1] For reasons given on p. 245 the exact area cannot be ascertained. It should be noted that the figures here given are for one year; those on p. 242 are for two years.

[2] By J. A. Venn, M.A., Statistician to the Food Production Department, on whose figures this summary is based.

Thus if oats had been sown and failed completely, and the land were resown with barley, the barley would be included in the barley average in the ordinary way; but the land on which the oats failed would also be included as having been sown with oats.

To take a concrete case, 1,122 acres of oats were sown in Hertfordshire and the average crop was 30 bushels per acre only; of these 1,122 acres, 226 acres failed completely and were resown with barley, producing—with 61 acres originally sown with barley—a crop of 26·2 bushels per acre. But if the oat crop had been estimated by the Crop Reporters collecting data for the Agricultural Returns, they would have found 896 acres of oats only, and the average oat crop would have been put down at 37·5, not at 30, bushels per acre.

If additions are made to the figures of the reports received to represent the probable areas in the four counties sending in no returns, it may be estimated that the 1,246,000 acres of permanent grass land broken up for the harvest of 1918 were sown with the following crops :

Oats . . .	850,000 acres	Peas . . . 15,000 acres
Wheat . . .	205,000 ,,	Rye . . . 14,000 ,,
Barley . . .	75,000 ,,	Dredge (mixed) corn 8,000 ,,
Potatoes . . .	32,000 ,,	Unclassified and fal-
Turnips and mangolds	5,000 ,,	low . . . 28,000 ,,
Beans . . .	14,000 ,,	1,246,000 ,,

The following statement gives the estimated yield for each of the three cereals, wheat, barley, and oats, grown on newly broken grass in 1918, as compared with the average yield in the preceeding ten years, as given in the Agricultural Returns.

	Wheat	Barley	Oats	Three cereals
Acreage reported on . . .	14,391	5,224	45,217	64,832
Yield 1918, bushels . . .	31·3	28·8	40·7	—
Ten-year average of E. and W., bushels	31·4	32·4	40·4	—
Per cent. 1918 to ten-year average .	99·7	89	101·7	100

It may be pointed out that after all losses due to the selection of unsuitable land, imperfect cultivation, and insect pests—but not losses due to bad harvest weather—have been taken into account, the estimated average yield of the three cereals from the new tillage land in 1918 was exactly equal to the average yield on arable land in England and Wales in the preceding ten years. Wheat on the new land was almost exactly an average crop, barley was under- and oats over-average.

The following notes on each crop bring out the chief points disclosed by the inquiry.

Wheat was reported as having been grown on newly broken land in every county except Cumberland, Westmorland, and Radnor. The highest yield estimated was 80 bushels per acre on an 8-acre field in Gloucestershire, the second best 70 bushels on 16 acres in Northamptonshire.

By those counties which were estimated to grow over 5,000 acres, the best and worst yields per acre reported were :

Best				Worst			
Cornwall	.	.	. 38·5 bush.	Sussex	.	.	. 18·3 bush.
Monmouth	.	.	. 37·9 ,,	Buckingham	.	.	19·3 ,,
Essex	.	.	. 36·9 ,,	Huntingdon	.	.	23·8 ,,
Wiltshire	.	.	. 35·9 ,,	Kent .	.	.	24·3 ,,

These figures may be compared with the best and worst yields secured in English counties in the preceding ten years.

Best				Worst			
Lancashire	.	.	. 36·1 bush.	Huntingdon	.	.	28·2 bush.
Northumberland	.	. 35·5 ,,	Devonshire	.	.	28·5 ,,
Kent	.	.	. 34·9 ,,	Monmouth	.	.	28·9 ,,
Durham	.	.	. 34·0 ,,	Gloucester	.	.	29·2 ,,

The largest areas of wheat reported on as having been grown on newly broken grass land were : Gloucestershire 2,052 acres, Wiltshire 1,061 acres, Monmouth 1,059 acres. On the basis of these figures the estimated total area of wheat on newly broken land in these three counties would have been, Gloucestershire 12,100, Wiltshire 10,000, and Monmouth 10,200 acres.

From the reports sent in, it is estimated that over 10,000 acres of newly ploughed grass land were sown with wheat in the following counties, in addition to the three above mentioned; Somerset (16,500), Cornwall (14,900), Sussex (11,800), Northampton (10,100).

Barley. Little importance can be attached to the yield estimated for barley. In a great many cases this crop was sown either on land ploughed up too late to be sown with oats, or on fields in which wheat or oats had been sown and had either partially or totally failed.

It is estimated that 2,500 acres, or more, were sown with barley in the following counties, with the results indicated: Leicester (5,600 ac., 25·2 bush.), Northampton (4,100 ac., 28·6 bush.), Wiltshire (3,400 ac., 27·1 bush.), Hereford (3,100 ac., 26·6 bush.), Stafford (2,800 ac., 32·9 bush.), Kent (2,500 ac., 22·8 bush.).

Oats. It is estimated that the total area of newly ploughed grass land sown with oats was more than four times as great as that sown with wheat. This crop, when it got a good start, was a very fine one; but, in not a few cases, bad preparation of the soil, or insect attacks, caused failures; thus the 'average' crop in this case does not represent the ordinary crops grown in 1918, but the result of combining the production of very good and of very bad crops and total failures. There were, in fact, very few 'average' crops to be seen.

In the case of those counties in which it is estimated that 5,000 acres or more of newly broken grass land were sown with oats, the best and worst yields were as follows:

	Best				*Worst*		
Pembroke	.	.	.	57·9 bush.	Radnor	. . .	25·7 bush.
Cumberland	.	.	.	50·1 ,,	Surrey	. . .	27·4 ,,
Dorset	.	.	.	49·7 ,,	Leicester	. . .	29·3 ,,
Stafford	.	.	.	48·5 ,,	Northamptonshire	.	30·1 ,,
Warwick	.	.	.	48·3 ,,	Oxford	. . .	30·1 ,,
Cornwall	.	.	.	48·3 ,,	Kent	. . .	31·4 ,,

These figures may be compared with the best and worst yields secured in English or Welsh counties on the average of the preceding ten years:

	Best			*Worst*	
Cambs. and Isle of Ely	.	53·3 bush.	Monmouth	. . .	33·1 bush.
Lincoln	. . .	48·6 ,,	Cheshire	. . .	33·2 ,,
Norfolk	. . .	46·3 ,,	Warwick	. . .	34·1 ,,
Pembroke	. .	44·6 ,,	Derby	. . .	36·7 ,,

The largest areas of oats reported on were in the counties of the West Riding of Yorkshire (4,300 ac., 38 bush.), Lincoln (3,396 ac., 43·1 bush.), Durham (2,917 ac., 41·6 bush.), Wiltshire (2,267 ac., 43·5 bush.), Devonshire (2,125 ac., 41·9 bush.), and Norfolk (2,052 ac., 38·3 bush.). From the reports sent in it has been estimated that 25,000 acres, or over, were grown in the following counties : West Riding of Yorkshire (56,200), Lancashire (47,000), Devonshire (46,100), North Riding of Yorkshire (36,200), Cumberland (31,000), Sussex (28,900).

The highest estimates of yield were 100 bushels per acre on 20 acres in the Holland Division of Lincolnshire, 96 bushels on 13 acres in the North Riding of Yorkshire, 90 bushels on 12 acres in Worcestershire, 90 bushels on 25 acres in Cumberland. There were references to occasional crops of 70 bushels per acre in the reports from most counties.

So far as could be ascertained from the reports sent in, the area on which the oat crop was a total failure and the ground was either resown, or fallowed, amounted to about 12,000 acres, and it is further estimated that a partial failure—that is a crop of 24 bushels per acre or less—occurred on an additional 85,000 acres. The failures were chiefly in the dry Home Counties, and to the fact that they were not infrequently close to London may be attributed the attention which they got from the public in the months of May and June 1918.

Potatoes. The average yield for the 2,791 acres on which reports were sent in was 7·1 tons, as against 6·2 tons per acre for England and Wales in the preceding ten years. One 19-acre field in the Holland Division of Lincolnshire was estimated to yield 18 tons per acre. The poorest crops were reported from Warwickshire, Gloucestershire, and some of the Welsh counties.

Beans. This crop was grown mainly in East Anglia. The average yield was 27·5 bushels from the 1,251 acres reported on. The ten-year average was 29·4 bushels. The best county yield was 43·2 bushels estimated on 128 acres grown in the Holland Division of Lincolnshire.

Peas. The average yield was estimated at 26·9 bushels ; in the preceding ten years it had been 25·7 bushels. Lincolnshire grew 426 acres and Kent 321 acres out of the total area of 1,096 acres reported on.

Dredge Corn. This crop consists of barley and oats mixed, with, frequently, peas or vetches in addition. It is cultivated almost exclusively in the south-west of England—Wiltshire (172 acres) reported the largest area. The total area reported was 495 acres and the yield was estimated at 36·3 bushels.

Rye. The area reported on was 1,283 acres. The estimated yield was 17·7 bushels per acre only; this is accounted ·for by the large proportion (767 acres) reported from Norfolk, where it was grown on very poor dry soils. Suffolk reported 316 acres. The best yield in any county was estimated at 34·7 bushels in the East Riding of Yorkshire.

Mangolds. Small areas were reported on from all parts of England. The total area reported on was 200 acres. The crops were good.

Swedes and Turnips. The area reported on was 121 acres. The crops were promising at the date of the report.

Mustard. The area under this crop was restricted by a Cultivation Order, otherwise it would have been largely grown on newly broken grass land, as it is nearly always very successful. The reports related to 257 acres and the crop was in all cases satisfactory. It was grown almost exclusively in East Anglia; Cambridgeshire, with 108 acres, reporting the largest quantity.

Flax and Linseed. Flax for ' line ' was reported on 152 acres, and a seed crop was reported from 72 acres, chiefly in East Anglia. The average seed crop was estimated at 18·5 bushels.

Buckwheat. In the Isle of Ely 48 acres of this crop were estimated to produce 20 bushels of seed per acre. It was doubtless grown in small areas in several other counties, but was not reported on.

Results of the Plough Policy.

During the summer of 1918 it was frequently stated that as compared with the crops on old tillage land, the yield of fields recently ploughed out of grass would be small. This view proved to be incorrect. Taking the country as a whole the average yield of the principal crop—oats—grown on the newly tilled area was little less than on the old tillage land. In the dry south-east it was considerably less, but elsewhere the best crops in the district were usually to be found growing after grass. Although, as already stated, the figures obtained in the inquiry of August 1918 are not directly comparable with those subsequently published in the Agricultural Returns, they suffice to show that there was no very substantial difference between the average yield of new and old tillage land.

A closer examination of the figures available for oats, much the most important of the crops in question, will make this point clear. At the end of the year the yield of oats in England and Wales was officially returned at 41·3 bushels per acre harvested. The August estimate for the new land was 40·7 bushels per acre sown, but on some 12,000 of the 850,000 acres sown the crop was a total failure; the crop harvested, therefore, works out at the same figure for the new land as for the whole area under oats. Thus the reduction to be made for new land is approximately the amount by which the August estimate was affected by the subsequent rains of September and October.

A special inquiry made by the official Crop Reporters indicated that, as a result of bad harvesting conditions, 7 per cent. of the wheat crop would be unfit for milling and 15 per cent. of the barley unfit for brewing. No estimate was made in the case of oats, but the quantity of lost and seriously damaged grain is not likely to have exceeded 15 per cent. Damaged grain had a special value to the stock-feeder in the winter of 1918–19; very little of it, therefore, was wasted, and it is improbable that the total loss from bad weather over the whole country exceeded 10 per cent. Thus if the August inquiry had been postponed until after harvest the result would have been likely to point to an oat crop of not less than 37 bushels per acre as having been secured from newly broken grass land.

Apart from the special inquiry made in August, numerous inspections were made on behalf of the Food Production Department, and all the evidence available went to show that new tillage land made a large contribution to the harvest of the year; but it should be observed that the assistance given to the harvest of 1918 was not confined to the grain and other crops actually grown on the area recently added.

Of the total wheat crop of England and Wales about 7·4 per cent. and of the oat crop about 31·5 per cent. was grown on the additional land provided by the ploughing campaign; but, as we have already seen, the total wheat crop of 1918 exceeded the 1904–13 average by 59·3 per cent., and the oat crop was increased by 38·5 per cent. A cursory examination of the figures might lead to the conclusion that it was the weather of 1918 that was mainly responsible for the great harvest of the year. But this conclusion will not bear examination; for while it is, undoubtedly, the case that without the fine dry weather experienced in the winter and spring a substantial increase could not have been obtained, it is also the case that, without the special effort which was made, no approach to the actual increase secured in 1918 would have been possible. An analysis of the harvest results shows that, except in the case of potatoes, the season was not an unusually good one for spring crops. The oat and barley crops, taken all over, were little better than average. The success of the year was made either with autumn or early sown spring cereals, and chiefly with autumn sown wheat; and both the large addition to the wheat acreage and the early sowing in spring resulted from the action taken by the organization called for by the plough policy.

It was because farmers knew that ploughed grass land would be available for oat-sowing in spring that so large an area was spared for the wheat crop in autumn; and it was because farmers were spurred to action by the Executive Committees that not an hour was lost when weather conditions were favourable for tillage operations in the spring.

Moreover, while the labour, machinery, and other resources which the committees had at their disposal were very much less than the Food Production Department had hoped to be able to provide, they were far greater than would have been available if no plough policy had been adopted. And although the committees' resources were mainly intended to increase the tillage area in winter and spring, they proved at other seasons to be quite invaluable in assisting with the cultivation of the old arable land. It was admitted, even by those who questioned the value of the additions made to the tillage area, that the committees were successful in securing a great improvement in the general standard of cultivation in many parts of the country.

While, therefore, grateful acknowledgement is clearly due to our uncertain climate for the weather provided until August

1918—gratitude tempered by a recollection of the worst harvest-weather within memory in September and October—it must be agreed that we owe most of the success of the harvest of 1918 to the exertions of farmers and their men and women.

And would these exertions have been forthcoming but for the Agricultural Executive Committees, the district sub-committees, and their officers ? And these again, what were they but the visible evidence in every parish in the country that Britain then had a plough policy ?

Thus when we ask why—as is shown by the diagram on p. 258—the harvest of 1918 stood out so clearly from its pre-decessors, we find the explanation suggested by that shrewd and friendly observer of English methods, Dr. W. H. Page, whose presence in this country was so valuable, and so much valued, in the war years. Writing of England, as he saw it in 1913, the American Ambassador remarked, ' You come to the conclusion after awhile that a man and a nation does what it does because of its organization rather than for any other reason. They have no eggs and butter organization, but they have admirable financial organization, and they do the banking of the world. They have shipping organizations and they do the shipping of the world. They insure cargoes, and they do the marine insurances of the world. . . . It 's your organization that does the trick.' It was not ' eggs and butter ' organization only that English farming lacked in 1913, and in the early years of war continual experiments in the organization of food produc-tion were made ; but not until Lord Ernle became President of the Board of Agriculture and Fisheries, and Lord Lee had been appointed Director General of Food Production, was a satisfactory organization worked out in England and Wales.

When suitable methods were adopted in England and Wales, and also in Scotland and Ireland, our ' organization did the trick'. This is the contribution made to our war lessons by the war's last harvest. And the 1918 harvest's material contribution ? This may be estimated at stocks of food and fodder, equivalent to some four million tons of shipping space, at a period when shipping was the gravest difficulty of the Allied Nations.

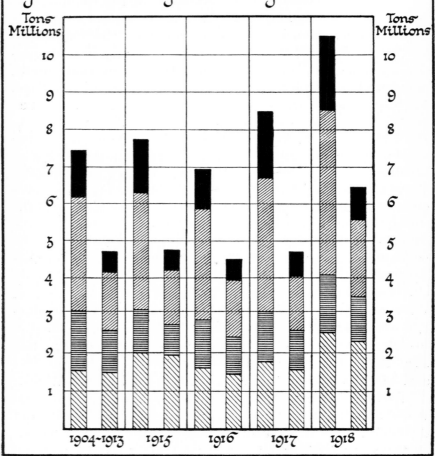

Produce of the United Kingdom (tall column) and of England & Wales (short column) in 1904~1913 and in successive War Harvests. The columns represent Wheat (base), Barley, Oats, and Potatoes (top). Cereals in millions of tons, Potatoes in five millions of tons.

CHAPTER X

THE END OF THE FOOD PRODUCTION CAMPAIGN

Food Situation in Winter and Early Spring of 1918. Tillage Programme for 1919. The Call for Recruits in April 1918. The Corn Production Act, 1917. The Corn Production (Amendment) Act, 1918. Lord Lee's Resignation. The Food Production Department ' Carry On '. Compensation Claims. Land Drainage. Scientific and Technical Work. Live-stock Questions. Artificial Manures. Lime. Insect and Fungus Pests. Seed Testing. Utilization of Straw. Reports on Farms. Departmental Conferences and Committees. Closing down.

Food Situation in Winter and Early Spring of 1918.

THERE was no improvement in the food position in the winter and early spring of 1918. The difficulties, indeed, were greater than they had been in the previous year. The heavy inroad made on live stock in the autumn of 1917 had reduced the meat supply, and our grain ships were for a time frost-bound on the farther side of the Atlantic. The submarine, though less destructive than in the previous year, had done its work too well, and it was now apparent that there would not be enough tonnage to transport American troops and munitions and also to bring in the foods and feeding stuffs that were wanted. Clearly, even if the submarine menace, which twice before in the course of the war was supposed to be ' well in hand ', had at last been effectively countered, every ton of food the country could grow was required to relieve the pressure on shipping.

Again, it was by no means certain, even if enough shipping for the transport of everything required in the following year could be provided, that the necessary grain would be forthcoming. Russia and Rumania, two of the chief wheat exporting countries, were completely shut off, and the long voyages to India and Australia made the surplus of those countries also quite beyond reach of the Allies, at any rate until a number of new ships had been built. For practical purposes Western Europe must depend on the American Continent for bread stuffs. The great trans-Atlantic harvests of 1915 had so far saved the Allies from grave difficulties, but there was no certainty that the poor crops of 1916 might not be repeated in 1918 and 1919. All three American wheat exporting countries had much extended the wheat acreage, but frosts in Canada, or drought in the United States or in Argentina, might prevent a corresponding increase in the crop.

Further, our experience in this country had shown that war increased the *per capita* consumption of bread stuffs, since the extra work which war entailed called for an extra supply of energy in the diet of the workers. Now that the United States had entered the war a similar experience would no doubt be met with there ; and though for the time being Americans were denying themselves wheaten flour, in order that the Allies might have bread, it would be unwise to frame plans on the assumption that this state of affairs could last if war were prolonged.

The testing weeks of late March and early April 1918 proved that military reverses were powerless to break the spirit of the Western Allies. Although the position was not appreciated by the public at the time, it would now appear that the greatest danger to which the Allied peoples were exposed after the United States entered the war was the risk of the war weariness which would have immediately followed on any serious food shortage. In this country we were peculiarly dependent upon a full supply of bread stuffs for the prevention of popular unrest. The success which our rationing schemes met with was largely due to the fact that it was possible to avoid bread rationing ; it was this that enabled the country to endure the food difficulties of 1918 with fortitude. Throughout all the months of war we in this country never experienced the effects produced on the morale of a war-weary people by a sudden reduction in the supply of food. But those who were watching the food position in Germany were provided with a sufficiently explicit warning of the danger that threatened us, by the experiences which that country went through in March and April 1917.

In the autumn of 1916 a considerable error was made by the German food authorities in estimating the harvest yield, and the mistake was not detected until February. About the same time it was realized that the civilian population had been exceeding the rations allocated for their use in the previous autumn. The double discovery created a crisis and a panic, and large reductions were made in the supplies provided for urban consumers. The effect produced in a few weeks was extraordinary, and almost before their watchful rulers realized what was happening the morale of the civilians of the towns had disappeared. The ' will to win ' of which we heard so much in 1915 had been evaporating throughout 1916, and in April 1917 it gave place to a demand for ' peace at any price ' by the starved population of German towns. Ample reserves of food had been set aside for the Army in the preceding autumn, and apparently it was only by drawing upon these military stores that complete collapse was prevented in Germany in the early summer of 1917.

While in this country those only who were specially concerned with food questions realized clearly how vulnerable an organ the stomach may be in a nation at war, our enemies' bitter experience had brought conviction to the entire population. The great hopes which German civilians, as well as their military rulers, based on their submarine campaign— hopes which the majority in this country, who believed that our people could long endure severe privation, regarded as quite exaggerated—depended on Germany's own experience of the influence of the stomach on the ' will to win '.

These considerations were fully discussed at the Food Production Department in the spring of 1918, and to those responsible for future policy the risks of shortage of food then appeared to be so great that, in spite of formidable difficulties which none realized more clearly than the staff of the Department, it was decided that an effort must be made to add a further million acres to the tillage land of England and Wales before April 1919.

Tillage Programme for 1919.

A detailed programme was then prepared in which estimates were framed of the additional labour, machinery, manures, &c., that would be required ; and an examination of the position in each county was made with the view of ascertaining how much extra land could be found.

It was recognized from the outset that it would be extremely difficult to get additional land scheduled for ploughing ; for committees had not secured all the extra tillage asked for in 1918, and for that year's harvest most of the land obviously suitable had already been taken. There were, it is true, considerable areas of very poor clay land in some of the corn-growing counties, which the late start in the previous summer had prevented the committees from tackling effectively. Provided labour were available there would be no opposition by farmers to the breaking up of such land. On the other hand, these poor clay soils required much tillage, the yield was uncertain, and in view of the great difficulty of providing labour it would have been risky, in the circumstances then existing, to have concentrated a considerable percentage of the Department's resources on land of this class.

It was decided, therefore, that an inroad must be made on grass occupying soils of suitable quality for tillage, even though the grass land itself were of distinctly higher quality than that which had been broken up in the previous season. This policy involved a re-survey of the land, and it was decided to introduce more uniformity of method in the different counties than had been possible in the previous year. Very great care was required to secure suitable grass for ploughing and at the same time to retain what was essential for live stock.

A preliminary examination of the data available showed that, given labour, the task of adding another million acres should certainly be possible; and that if the selection of land were wisely made the advantages to live stock would equal the disadvantages.

The circumstances in each county were then considered, and it was found that, after setting aside enough grass for dairy cattle and working horses, a levy in different counties of from

8 to 12 per cent. on the remaining grass land would provide what was required.   Starting from this basis, and taking into account all the information about the position in each county which was then at the Department's disposal, a ploughing task to be aimed at by each of the Executive Committees was settled for 1919.   If this task were carried out, it was shown that for the country as a whole from 94 to 95 per cent. of the grass land (permanent and temporary) at the disposal of farmers in 1918 would be available in 1919, and that in different counties the figures would vary between 90 and 97 per cent.   As com- pared with the position in the middle of the 'seventies, when 55 per cent. of the cultivated land of England was under grass, the year 1919 would have found 57 per cent. in grass.   In ten English counties only would the percentage of grass have been somewhat lower than it was forty years before the war.

Apart from questions of labour, and the other requisites for tillage, the task of finding land was therefore not an impossible one in view of the country's great need ; but it was known that opposition to more ploughing would be strenuous and that unless full powers under the Defence of the Realm Acts were retained, little extra grass land would, in fact, be broken up. In order that powers under the Defence of the Realm Acts might be retained fresh legislation was required, and was asked for.

It was estimated that to carry out the proposed programme, in addition to the labour already promised—but not fully available—and to such casual labour as the Department could organize, 24,000 permanent workers, chiefly men, would be required.   It would further have been necessary to expend about £2,300,000 on the purchase of machinery, implements, and fuel ; it was also essential that the importation of phos- phatic rock should be increased.

It was estimated that the extra crops which the programme aimed at would, in the event of an average harvest, provide food for about 1,550,000 persons, and further that it would effect a saving in shipping of some 850,000 tons of 40 cubic feet.

While this programme was under discussion the National Service Department took the action for recruiting farm workers referred to below, and it was clear that a further increase in the area under grain crops had been rendered impossible. Attention was therefore concentrated on the measures required to prevent the 1919 corn area falling below that of 1918.

Before the war about 51 per cent. of the arable land of England and Wales was annually under grain. The percentage began to rise on the outbreak of war; in 1918 the area rose to 60 per cent., and as a result the soil's fertility and condition were rapidly being injured. The process could not long go on if disaster were to be avoided, and in 1919 it was most desirable that there should be more temporary grass, more root crops, and more fallow than in 1918; otherwise, if the season were average, the yield of the harvest must fall, and if under average there would be a very sharp drop in production. Experience had long taught farmers the disastrous effects which a bad season produces on worn-out soils. Arable land now wanted rest from corn, and more winter food for live stock must also be provided. It was estimated in the spring of 1918 that, if no more grass land were broken up, the area under grain crops in England and Wales in 1919 must be between 500,000 and 600,000 acres less than in 1918,[1] and the ploughing of 550,000 acres—referred to in subsequent debates in Parliament as ' relief land '—was therefore proposed by the Department.

Although all necessary arrangements were made, and the organization of Agricultural Executive Committees was strengthened in order that they might undertake extra work, this programme for 1919 was not carried out. The reasons for the abandonment of the effort to add to the tillage area must be referred to in some detail, since the experience of the Department contains lessons for the country that should provide guidance in future emergencies.

The Call for Recruits in April 1918.

The military reverses of March 1918, and the urgent call for men for the Army which followed the German advance on

[1] A small area of grass land was broken up after April 1918, and when in the autumn of 1919 the Official Returns were published it was shown that the reduction in the area of grain was 488,000 acres; the forecast was therefore correct.

Amiens, led the Ministry of National Service to withdraw, by proclamation on 20th April, the exemptions which, in the previous summer, had been granted to farm workers between the ages of 18 and 23 in Grade 1 or Category A.

The President of the Board of Agriculture and Fisheries and the Director-General of the Department pointed out the disastrous effect which this proclamation would have on food production, and urged reconsideration. The arguments on both sides were examined by the Cabinet, who decided that in view of the imperative demands of the army 30,000 men must be provided by the agriculturists of England and Wales, and 5,500 by those of Scotland. Instead, however, of calling up all of the men automatically by age groups, it was decided that they would be selected with the assistance of Agricultural Executive Committees, so that the men taken for military service might be those who could be spared with least loss to food production.

During the preceding weeks Executive Committees had been writing and telegraphing to the Department, asking for the immediate supply of men long promised and now urgently required for work on the land. In the circumstances it would have been useless to consult the county committees as to the number of men who could be spared. The Food Production Department had, therefore, to undertake the allocation of the men between the counties of England and Wales. A committee of three members of the Department's staff was constituted, and they prepared county quotas from the information available. It was the worst task that could have fallen to the Department, for it meant the destruction of much of their work. Hitherto they had been engaged in carrying out a policy which they knew to be of direct value to the nation in the conduct of the war; now they were convinced that, in the event of war being prolonged, the consequences of their action would be severely felt in the following year, and might expose one or other of the Allied Nations to the peril which menaced Germany in April 1917. But there was no choice, and in the circumstances less harm would be done by action taken by the Department through the Executive Committees than by any other method of recruiting that could be adopted.

An examination of the figures collected by the Ministry of National Service showed that before April 1918 about 273,000 men between the ages of eighteen and forty-three had left the land for the Services or munition works. In addition, agriculture had lost older men attracted by higher wages to other industries. The number of these older men could not be ascertained. As compensation for the losses there were the workers supplied through the Department, and there was also some increase in the number of boys remaining on the land.

Using the figures available for each county, quotas were ascertained by two independent methods. In one a levy was made on the estimated number of men of military age remaining in each county; in the other method the minimum number of men who would be required to attend to the area under grass land and crops in each county in 1918 was calculated, and compared with the number estimated to be available; a quota by each method was then arrived at which represented an equivalent sacrifice by each county. The two quotas for each county were compared. In most instances they agreed more closely than might have been expected from the different methods by which they were prepared; but in a few there were wide discrepancies. For example, in one county the first method gave a quota of 2,900, the second of 1,350; while in the county next on the list the respective figures were 550 and 500. The discrepancies were carefully analysed in the light of the intimate knowledge of each county's position which the Department then had, final quotas were agreed upon, and the number of men demanded from each county was communicated to the Executive Committees.

The quotas were received by the committees with indignation and bewilderment. They had for weeks been pressing the Department to send them the men, who had long been promised, for the urgent work of spring cultivation. Here was the reply: a request addressed to them to find men for the Army! The commotion produced by the call for more men soon spread beyond the offices of the Department and its committees. Deputations from the counties hurried to London, and strong protests were made in both Houses of Parliament.   Towards the end of June the Cabinet reconsidered the subject, and on the 27th June ' calling up ' notices were suspended until after harvest.

The Agricultural Executive Committees, although they protested strongly, and pointed out, in no uncertain terms, the effect which renewed recruiting would have in their respective counties, made strenuous efforts to find the men asked for by the National Service Department ; but in England and Wales without success.   The number found before 27th June was 22,654.   After harvest the military position had so far improved that no more men were called up.   The fact that, in spite of the efforts made in May and June 1918, 75 per cent. only of the men demanded could be found, is in itself a proof of the farmer's labour difficulties at the time.

It was the danger of loss to the harvest that stirred up opposition, both among farmers and in Parliament, to the calling up of agriculturists for military service in May and June 1918 ; but the real risk lay in the effect on the preparations then being made for the subsequent harvest.   No one could tell at that time how long the war might last ; and, should it be extended, no risk to which the war-weary Allies were exposed was so great as the risk of food shortage.   But it was the immediate risk of some loss to the crops then growing, not the risk to the Food Production movement, that excited the public.   The possible loss to the coming harvest through the withdrawal of 30,000 skilled men from agriculture could be calculated.   And when the calculation was made—as it was immediately—there was no one fully informed of the position who would have questioned the wisdom of the proposals of the National Service Department, if it had been a harvesting question only.   That Department's difficulties at the time were immense.   The age for recruiting had been raised, and the country regretfully saw much unfit material absorbed into the Army.   The public indignation thus aroused was in its volume

far greater than the indignation of agriculturists. The situation
is indicated in two lines written (with apologies to a well-known
author) by an irate and witty medical critic of the recruiting
policy of this period :

> And the Young Men cheered in their thousands
> As the Grand Dads went to the War.

The fit young farm worker was the very best material left in
the country ; surely a percentage of them could be spared !
This appears to have been the argument that appealed to the
Cabinet, for in defending the action of the Government in the
House of Commons, the Prime Minister argued that it was
impossible to discriminate between essential industries. ' One
industry says, " If you take away the young men, then this
industry cannot produce coal." Agriculture says, " We cannot
produce the necessary corn." You go to another industry and
they say, " We cannot produce the necessary munitions." In
each case the protest is a perfectly *bona fide* one. It is made not
to protect particular men, but rather to increase or to maintain
the output. If you were to treat each case on its merits, it would
be difficult to answer it, but the aggregate result would be that
we should not get the men.' [1]

An unanswerable argument if the cases were parallel ; but
whereas the loss in the approaching harvest, like the loss in
munitions and coal, would be proportionate to the numbers
taken, there the similarity between the essential industries
ceased. Munition works, railways, and even coal mines were
under State control to an extent that was impossible in agriculture. The great increase secured in the 1918 harvest was
got by enlisting the co-operation of hundreds of thousands of
men living isolated lives on farms and in hamlets all over the
country. These men, persuaded in 1917 of the vital importance
of their work for the winning of the war, guaranteed the necessary labour and supplies by Government, and carefully shep-
herded by the Executive Committees, had made an unparalleled
effort. Now, at a time when the immense area which they had
ploughed had just been sown, when they were calling out for

[1] *H. C. Parliamentary Debates*, June 1918, vol. cvii, col. 1300.

the urgently needed labour which they had been promised, came the proclamation of the National Service Department. A great harvest was in front of them, they knew that it must save thousands of tons of shipping, they knew that many thousands of magnificent American troops were beyond the Atlantic awaiting transport, and yet the food, which they had been told was as precious as shells, must be sacrificed. It was in vain that the Food Production Department tried to rally them, to show that a very small proportion of their workers would be taken, that substitutes would be found, that the harvest was in no serious danger, and that an effort for 1919 was as important as it had been for 1918. The arithmetic that had convinced the Cabinet made no appeal to agriculturists. Nor is it altogether surprising that arithmetic failed to restore their confidence. A year earlier Lord Ernle had summoned them to the defence of a 'beleaguered city'; barely six months before the Prime Minister had called them into the fighting line, ' every sack of food you raise is worth ammunition, is worth a gun, to use in this great struggle, and we ask you to come into the fighting line with your food.' And they went. Farmers and their men took their places in the organized Food Production Campaign convinced that the 'home front' was a sector, and a most vulnerable sector, of the ' fronts ' occupied by our armies. Now they reflected bitterly that their place was far from the fighting line. They were not combatants. Were they even camp followers ?

At the time, perhaps, little change could be detected by the outside observer of the Food Production movement—the Department and the committees continued their work without interruption ; but those who were watching events from within knew that on the farms the men were no longer the same. A flaw revealed itself in what, until then, had been the main-spring of a carefully elaborated organization, the farmer's belief that he and his men were in ' the fighting line '.

After the Cabinet's decision had been taken on the subject, Lord Ernle pleaded the cause of the Army so strongly, and so steadfastly directed committees and farmers to do their duty by completing the county quotas, that agriculturists supposed him to be unaware of the real consequences of the Government's decision. This was a wholly incorrect view. He felt the blow keenly, and as he himself stated in the House of Commons, he recognized that it meant ' to a great extent the wrecking, or at all events the imperilling ' of all the work he had done in the past eighteen months. It always was Lord Ernle's custom to defend others when they were attacked (it was a practice, moreover, in which he had much experience, for during the past year there had scarcely been a working day in which he was not engaged in defending the deeds and misdeeds of the Food Production Department), and it was with characteristic altruism that he supported the demands of the National Service Department in May and June 1918 when their policy was so strongly criticized in Parliament.

In connexion with the criticisms of Lord Ernle's action, a statement made in the House of Lords in a debate on the disastrous results of the recruiting policy upon agriculture may be quoted. In this debate Lord Clinton stated that ' the President of the Board of Agriculture on more than one occasion placed the entire facts before the Government, and explained very fully the probable effects of the withdrawal of these men, not only on the coming harvest but on the general need of agriculture. . . . He went further and made it quite clear that the absence of these keymen would imperil not only the coming harvest but the whole programme of food production which had been laid down for the safeguarding of the nation's food supply.' [1]

Unfortunately for the progress of Food Production, the recruiting difficulty was not the only one experienced during the summer of 1918. On the same day (8th August) that the House of Lords condemned the effects of the recruiting policy on agriculture, Royal Assent was given to a Bill which they themselves had recently amended in a way destined to complete the work which the recruiting proclamation of the previous April had begun. To explain how this result came about, we

[1] *Parl. Deb. H. L.*, Fifth Series, vol. xxxi (1918), col. 676.

must return to events that occurred in the spring and summer of 1917.

The Corn Production Act, 1917.

As has been stated in a previous chapter, the Food Production Department, in beginning their work, derived their authority from Regulations framed under the Defence of the Realm Acts, especially from Regulation 2 M. The Corn Production legislation of 1917, although required because of the Food Production movement, was mainly designed for purposes other than those for which the Defence of the Realm Regulations had been framed. The latter conferred on the Food Production Department the powers which were required to extend arable cultivation; the purpose was to safeguard the country's food. The action taken was called for in the interests of the whole community; but this action affected the interests of labourers, of farmers, and of landowners, and for their protection fresh legislation was required.

An increase in the tillage area would necessitate longer hours of work and more effort from the labourer. His wages had been rising, but they were increasing at very unequal rates, while the cost of living was increasing everywhere, and more rapidly than wages rose. Even if justice did not already demand legislation in the interests of the farm-worker, common prudence required measures insuring him an adequate supply of food, and freedom from the vexation which hard bargaining would involve.

Again, it was obvious in the spring of 1917 that the action of the Food Production Department would expose occupiers and owners of land to financial risks. Provision for losses had been made by referring claims to the Defence of the Realm (Losses) Commission. But this Commission, in so far as it dealt with agriculture, had been created for adjudicating on the claims of farmers whose land had been acquired for camps, aerodromes, and other military purposes. Compensation was given as an ' act of grace ', and the procedure was not well adapted for dealing with agricultural claims arising out of the work of the Food Production Department. Agriculturists took up the wholly reasonable attitude that if their farming was to be dictated by the nation's needs, and not by ordinary business considerations, the nation should share the risks.

But here a further interest was involved. If the taxpayer were called upon to share risks, his representatives must share in the supervision of the work. Without some form of public control, public money must not be expended. Again, the taxpayer's representatives insisted that none of the money paid by way of guarantees for corn production should have the effect of increasing rents.

There were, therefore, several distinct interests—those of the labourer, the occupier, the owner of land, and the taxpayer—which called for attention in the spring of 1917, in order to ensure the satisfactory progress of the Government's policy for increasing the supply of food.

The justice of each claim for recognition could be proved; the common sense of the proposals was obvious; the nation was in dire need, inaction would expose it to greater dangers than it had ever before been required to face; here was the land in defence of which it was fighting desperately, untouched by the enemy, with stores of fertility waiting to be used. Nothing was wanted, except co-operation, to increase the stocks of food so urgently required. Could common action be secured? This was the problem to which the President of the Board of Agriculture and Fisheries addressed himself. A Bill was prepared the principal features of which were, in Part I guarantees of minimum prices for the corn grower, in Part II minimum wages for the farm labourer, and in Part IV control of cultivation on behalf of the community; Part III stipulated for no increase of rent to the landowner from any changes brought about through the Bill.

When on 24th April 1917 the President of the Board moved the second reading of the Corn Production Bill in the House of Commons, he was obliged to admit that it bristled with difficulties, that it had been impossible to omit controversial questions, and that, unless members accepted it as a necessary war measure, controversy could not be avoided.

A few weeks earlier a valuable report on Agricultural Reconstruction after the war, by a committee of which Lord Selborne was chairman, had been issued. This committee —one member dissenting—had recommended the guaranteeing of the prices of wheat and oats as a post-war policy; and certain members of the House of Commons—strongly opposed to guarantees—viewed the Corn Production Bill, not as a war measure, but as an attempt to commit the country to the policy of guaranteeing prices after the war. The President of the Board replied that the Bill was based on the report of Lord Milner's Committee (see p. 120) and that it was strictly a war measure; but that as the ploughing of grass land must affect the cultivation of farms for at least six years, it was impossible to make the guarantees proposed in the Bill lapse on the declaration of peace. But this explanation was not accepted, the Bill gave opportunities for argument which the House of Commons could not resist, and the debates were animated. It needed little parliamentary skill, indeed, to expose the weaknesses of the Corn Production Bill when its parts were considered independently. It could be shown, to the satisfaction of considerable groups of Members, that the guarantor of prices made an indifferent bargain, that the minimum wage was an interference with the laws of economics, or that the control of cultivation was a departure from sound business principles. Moreover, even if such objections were waived, it was argued that as there was no labour it was absurd to break up fresh land. Although the Second Reading was carried by a large majority, the further stages of the Bill were keenly debated.

The Financial Resolution was made the occasion of a further ' second reading ' discussion of principles, and most of the clauses had a troubled passage through the Committee stage. It was at this stage that, for the first time, a real danger to the tillage policy emerged. The experiences of the Food Production Department, and the changes made in the Bill itself, had shown by the summer of 1917 that Part IV could not replace the Regulations under the Defence of the Realm Acts without endangering the movement for increasing the home harvests. On 23rd July, therefore, the President of the Board moved as an amendment in Committee that: ' The powers conferred by this part (Part IV) of this Act shall not be exercisable as long as the powers exercisable by the Board of Agriculture and Fisheries with a view to maintaining the food supply of the country under the Defence of the Realm Regulations remain in force.' An attempt was made to amend this amendment by a provision that the powers of Part IV should be in substitution of the powers under the Defence of the Realm Regulations; but the Government amendment was insisted on, and with the above words included the Bill went to the House of Lords.

The Corn Production Bill was as strongly assailed in the Upper as it had been in the Lower House; but whereas the proposal to guarantee prices was the chief cause of criticism in the House of Commons, in the other House control of cultivation attracted most attention. The Lords discussed the Bill almost wholly as if it were a post-war measure. They took strong exception to the proposal to continue the powers under the Defence of the Realm Regulations in place of those contemplated by Part IV of the Bill, and would apparently have rejected the measure unless the amendment inserted in Committee by the President of the Board had been altered; for the Debate in the following year alludes to a ' bargain ' having been made at this stage. What the Official Report discloses is that the Government introduced an amendment in the House of Lords which provided that ' This part (Part IV) of this Act shall come into operation at the expiration of one year from the passing of this Act or at the termination of the present war whichever is the earlier.' This proposal did not satisfy the critics of the Bill, and the amendment finally adopted provided that the powers conferred under the Defence of the Realm Acts should lapse after a year and be replaced by the powers conferred by Part IV of the Corn Production Act. In the case of Ireland, however, Part IV came into operation at once, and the Department of Agriculture and Technical Instruction were permitted to retain as concurrent powers the authority granted to them by Regulation 2 P made under the Defence of the Realm Acts.

The Corn Production (Amendment) Act, 1918.

The parliamentary bargain did not at first cause apprehension to those responsible for the Food Production Campaign. It was hoped that long before the year was over the need for powers under the Defence of the Realm Acts would have ceased ; but these hopes were not realized. When, therefore, in the opening months of 1918 the food difficulties had increased rather than diminished, the Department prepared the programme for the harvest of 1919 mentioned above. For the success of this programme experience showed that powers under the Defence of the Realm Acts would be essential. It would not be possible to secure even 550,000 acres of permanent grass—the fresh land required to enable the 1918 corn area to be maintained—were these powers denied. It was, therefore, decided that an amendment to the Corn Production Act, 1917, would be necessary.

Meantime, however, events had hardened opposition to the plough policy. The Agricultural Executive Committees had done their work extraordinarily well. With very much less labour and machinery than they had originally been promised, they had carried through a substantial part of their programme, and, though the full measure of their success was not yet known, it was apparent that there would be a large increase in corn production. Naturally they had many critics ; they could not both secure more corn and please all occupiers of grass land. The committees were not disposed to accept excuses ; they carried persuasion almost to the point of compulsion in the case of one holding high office in one Government Department ; they soundly trounced the cultivation of another Government Department's Director-General ; the pages of Hansard show that members of both Houses of Parliament had unsuccessfully argued with them. Then in the early summer the campaign had been unfortunate in the weather ; drought and insect pests caused many failures on the newly broken grass land and, as already mentioned, although the committees' critics had enjoyed but a brief innings, they had hit out vigorously and they scored substantially before their arguments were disposed of.

Thus when, in a white sheet, the Parliamentary Secretary of the Board of Agriculture and Fisheries brought the Corn Production (Amendment) Bill before the House of Lords and confessed that the measure violated a bargain, it was not the straits of the Allied Armies, not the fact that German troops were again almost within range of Paris, not the absolute necessity of saving shipping so that American soldiers and munitions might be transported to Europe, that affected the course of the Debate. The real gravity of the situation, as it appeared to the majority in the House of Lords, was that Government should seek to set aside a parliamentary bargain, that as a result of the broken bargain more grass land might be ploughed than could be tilled effectively, and that the agricultural industry would still be controlled !

The amending Bill proposed that the operation of Part IV of the Corn Production Act, 1917, should be postponed in favour of the powers conferred by the Defence of the Realm Regulations. An appeal to reason and generosity was made by the Parliamentary Secretary, who summed up his opening argument in the following words : ' I have admitted at the very beginning that this Bill is a breach of faith, which I regret to bring forward ; I have claimed that successful as our efforts in the cause of food production have been it is necessary to maintain them at the highest pitch and that to this end we require the Defence of the Realm Regulations.' To this appeal, however, the attitude of the House was so hostile that the representative of the Board promised to submit fresh proposals. These proposals were brought forward and were further amended. Finally, an agreement was reached which permitted Agricultural Executive Committees to carry on their work under the powers conferred by the Defence of the Realm Regulations, and to continue the issue of those Orders which required negligent occupiers to improve their cultivation; but, if committees issued Orders requiring an occupier to plough up grass land, an appeal might henceforward be made to an arbitrator, to be appointed, in default of agreement, by the President of the Surveyors' Institution. The right of appeal was also allowed to tenants whose mismanaged land committees might wish to enter upon and farm. Certain other changes of a desirable kind were made with respect to payment of compensation; they will be referred to subsequently.

As was anticipated, these changes, following on the labour difficulties caused by calling up recruits for the Army, practically ended the efforts made in England and Wales to increase the area under corn; and when in August 1919 the Agricultural Returns for the year were available, it was found that, as foretold by the Food Production Department in the spring of 1918, the area under corn in England and Wales had fallen by about half a million acres.

Lord Lee's Resignation.

The refusal of Parliament to grant the Food Production Department powers, which they believed to be essential to the success of their work, led Lord Lee to resign the post of Director-General, which he had filled with such conspicuous success since February 1917.

To the energy, courage, and determination of Lord Lee the very large addition made to the tillage area was undoubtedly due. Without his driving force it would have been impossible to have obtained the labour and machinery which were essential, or to have secured so much extra tillage from the very limited resources which were placed at the Department's disposal.

His colleagues endeavoured to persuade him to remain, for they realized how much his loss would mean to the work in which they were engaged. Moreover, on personal grounds they deplored his departure; the scratch organization of January 1917 had now grown into a large and smooth-working department, and they recognized that its efficiency had resulted from his efforts. But though Lord Lee was ready to lead an advance he was not prepared to rest in a ' trench '; he was not to be dissuaded from his purpose and he left the Department in the middle of July.

The resignation of Lord Lee was a blow felt by every Agricultural Executive Committee ; for in the counties, as well as at the Food Production Department, the difficulties which he had surmounted in procuring for the committees the conditions and requisites for successful work were known and appreciated.

The debates in Parliament, too, had been profoundly discouraging to members of committees. There had been much criticism of their actions ; statements were made which proved that their efforts had not been appreciated, and that their successes were unknown. Outside the official spokesmen there had been few supporters of the Food Production movement, and although a certain number of critics had qualified their statements by explaining that they believed the errors which had been made were errors of policy, and were not the fault of the committees, these reservations made little difference. Indeed they made the position worse, by implying that the hard work of many months had been a waste of time.

Not a few of the hundreds of volunteer workers who, in the past year, had given all their energies to increasing the country's food supply, had themselves been doubtful of the wisdom of attempting the heavy task set them in 1917 ; but experience had shown what determination and energy could accomplish, and now in the fourth summer of the war they had the satisfaction of knowing that the land of England and Wales was being cared for in a way that would have done its occupiers credit in time of peace. The task of securing this result had not always been congenial, and though less than one-third of 1 per cent. of the hundred thousand Cultivation Orders, which the committees had served upon occupiers of land, had been disregarded, no small pressure had been required to secure action in a substantial number of cases. Members of committees knew, too, that their efforts had not always added to their local popularity, and that in every market town in the country some of their decisions had been adversely criticized. This was to be expected. But surely, they reasoned, Parliament should have known the importance and value of their work, and should have trusted them sufficiently to have continued their powers in this great crisis. Thus when it was known that their authority was to be challenged there came protests from nearly every committee in the country, and almost without exception the belief was expressed that if the question of whether grass land was, or was not, to be ploughed were submitted to arbitration, little extra tillage would be secured; and experience quickly proved this view to be correct.

The effect which the 'call up' of 30,000 men had on the rank and file was paralleled in the case of the leaders of the Food Production movement by the decision of Parliament. When, therefore, Sir Charles Fielding succeeded Lord Lee as Director-General of the Department, though there was no definite change in policy, the task of maintaining the area under corn which had been reached in 1918 was soon found to be impracticable, and attention was concentrated on getting what results were possible from the tillage land already secured.

The Food Production Department ' Carry On '.

Fortunately for the country, the risks accepted when the ebb in food production set in were not destined to affect the course of the war. On the very morning of the day on which the Corn Production (Amendment) Bill, 1918, became an Act, from the slopes fronting Hangard Wood and Demuin British troops began that final forward movement which was not stayed until the Rhine was crossed; and the rapid change in the military situation quickly relieved the anxieties which had prompted the Food Production policy.

In September and October the anxieties of the Department were of another kind. Reference has already been made to the atrocious harvest weather of this period. Not until well on in November were the difficulties in which it involved the

Executives at head-quarters and in the counties finally surmounted. The routine of organizing labour, finding machinery for harvesting and threshing, and thus assisting farmers to make the best of a very difficult situation continued throughout the autumn.

In preparation for the programme projected for 1919, improvements had already been effected in the organization, and full advantage of these improvements was secured in the difficult autumn of 1918. The changes made had been mainly in the direction of further decentralization. Until the summer of 1918 the Executive Officer in each county had associated with him certain other officers for the supervision of labour, tractors, and horses. The responsibilities of the Executive and other officers of the committees had not, in all cases, been clearly defined, and had differed to some extent in different counties. From 1st July 1918 counties were expected to employ a Chief Executive Officer in general charge, with men responsible for the different branches of work under him, and also a Deputy Executive as principal assistant. Similarly, district sub-committees were advised to employ a District Executive Officer, who would work under the Chief Executive Officer and act as the Executive Committee's representative for all purposes within the district, usually extending to from thirty to fifty parishes.

Changes were also introduced in connexion with the Tractor and Horse Schemes, which had hitherto been worked independently; in future the same staff was to control cultivation by both tractors and horses. Under the Chief Executive Officer the Tractor Representative and Horse Officer would respectively be responsible for the machinery and fuel, or for the horses, harness, and fodder required by the county; while the actual supervision of the working of both tractors and horses in any district would be under the control of the District Executive Officer. The Labour Officer, acting under the Chief Executive Officer, took charge of soldier, prisoner, and war volunteer labour. In most counties these arrangements were in force in the autumn of 1918.

Compensation Claims.

Changes were also made in connexion with compensation claims, because of the new legislation of the Corn Production (Amendment) Act. Hitherto compensation had been payable as an ' act of grace ' by the Defence of the Realm (Losses) Commission. The Act of 1918 entitled any person interested in land, in respect of which a notice for certain purposes had been served under Regulation 2 M, and who had suffered loss, to claim payment of compensation from the Board of Agriculture and Fisheries. If agreement were not reached between the claimant and an Executive Committee acting as agents for the Board, the compensation was to be settled by a single arbitrator. If the parties could not agree on an arbitrator, he was to be appointed by the President of the Surveyors' Institution. A claim might be made in respect of any loss provided for under Part IV of the Corn Production Act, 1917, which had not already been settled, whether the notice under Regulation 2 M had been served before or after the passing of the Act of 1918. Most of the notices issued by the committees were involved, including claims for loss in breaking up grass land, for failure of crop on land broken up under an Order, for loss sustained by determination of tenancies, and by any other action necessary in enforcing good cultivation. On the other hand, claims for loss of rent, or land, or buildings, or for the value of live or dead stock taken over in entering on land, were, as before, left for settlement by the Losses Commission.

An indication of the skill and care with which Executive Committees carried out their work when making Orders for the breaking up of grass land is afforded by the claims made by occupiers for loss in the cultivation of the subsequent crops. By the middle of 1921 claims had been lodged in respect of 122,000 acres in England and Wales. Scrutiny of the claims reduced the total area to 75,000 acres, or 4 per cent. of the land ploughed under compulsion. Allowing for claims to be submitted later, it is unlikely that the total area on which compensation will finally be payable will exceed 5 per cent.

of the area ploughed. A certain number of occupiers entitled to claim compensation no doubt refrained from doing so, but in view of the fact, that on land thoroughly suited for ploughing, leatherjackets, wireworms, frit flies, and other pests caused substantial and sometimes complete loss of the crops sown, the absurd character of the extravagant statements made in the summer of 1918 respecting the results of the Agricultural Executive Committees' work is clearly proved.

Land Drainage.

A subject brought into prominence by the wet autumn of 1918 was that of arterial drainage. It was well known that much good land remained unproductive during the earlier years of the war because of the silting up of rivers, or the neglect of embankments, or because of obstructions brought about by ill-placed locks or sluices. At an early stage in the Department's existence information had been collected respecting areas which required attention, and in the summer and autumn of 1918 prisoners of war were organized in gangs to carry out remedial work. Regulation 2 M was amended so as to enable the Department to deal effectively with the subject, and in August a revised Cultivation of Lands Order was made by the Board (see Appendix II, p. 358). Much useful work of a preliminary kind in respect of the drainage of about 150,000 acres of land was undertaken under the provisions of this Order. Later, legislation was promoted, and when Parliament reassembled in the autumn the Drainage of Lands Act, 1918, was passed, conferring further powers on the Board of Agriculture and Fisheries and on Local Drainage Authorities.

Scientific and Technical Work.

Early in 1917 the scientific officers from Universities and Research Institutes who had joined the Department, with certain of the technical officers of the Board of Agriculture, were formed into a *Technical Division*, parallel with the Executive Divisions whose work was described in Chapter IX; but the Technical Division differed from the others in including a number of part-time officers whose advice was necessary, but whose other duties did not enable them to leave the institutions in which they worked. A weekly conference was held at which all members of the Division were present, and by this means contact was maintained between whole-time and part-time members of the Division.

The Division was responsible for advising other Divisions of the Department, County Executive Officers, and the agricultural public on all scientific and technical questions arising out of the Food Production Campaign.

The work necessitated not only the facilities which the offices in London could provide, but access to scientific laboratories and experimental fields. The resources of Rothamsted, the Cambridge School of Agriculture, the Oxford School of Rural Economy, the Agricultural Department of Leeds University, and other similar institutions, were placed at the Department's disposal. Thus by the time that Executive Committees were busy in every county with preparations for the harvest of 1918, scientific institutions throughout the country were studying the technical problems which the extension of cultivation under war conditions brought into prominence.

There was no lack of material for study. A continual stream of questions from the public, apart from those arising within the Department, reached the Technical Division. Most of them were dealt with by methods to be presently indicated, but there were always a number on which some discussion at the weekly conference was necessary, and of these not a few presented points on which investigations were desirable. At the conferences it was decided how and where these investigations should be carried out, and when progress, or final, reports were available, the results of the work were discussed before action was taken.

A reference to the types of work dealt with by the Technical Division will serve to illustrate the wide scope of the questions that arose in connexion with the Food Production Campaign.

In the first place there were many inquiries from the agricultural public for information on ploughing grass land, manuring crops, combating pests, feeding stock and all the other matters that occupy the farmer's daily attention. Most of these questions could be answered without delay by letter, or, when many inquiries on the same subject were received, by printed information prepared in leaflet form.

Live-stock Questions.

While the energies of the Department's other Divisions were concentrated on securing more tillage, much of the time of the Technical Division was required by live-stock questions. The ploughing of grass necessarily disturbed farmers' arrangement for keeping live stock, and suggestions for new methods of maintaining cattle and sheep were very necessary. Leaflets on the growing of catch crops, on methods of arranging tillage land so as to provide, in combination with corn-growing, the greatest possible amount of food for farm animals, and on the feeding of cows on a succession of green crops from April to November, were therefore issued. Similarly, in view of the shortage of concentrated feeding stuffs, attention was drawn by press notice or leaflet to the crops that might be grown at home as substitutes for purchased materials. Throughout the greater part of the war the economical use of the feeding stuffs available was dealt with in the *Journal* of the Board of Agriculture, by means of a monthly article provided by the Cambridge School of Agriculture; it was, therefore, unnecessary to give systematic attention to this subject at the technical conferences of the Department.[1]

The most common live-stock questions raised were those due to the supposed conflict of interest between corn-growing and stock-keeping. It was not difficult to show on paper that land under tillage could grow corn and yet supply as much food for stock as grass; but it was well known to the technical officers that to secure this result in practice was a very different matter, and the changes in the live-stock situation had therefore

[1] It will be recalled that the Ministry of Food was responsible for the supply and distribution of feeding stuffs; see p. 174.

to be closely watched. Complaints were investigated and local inquiries made, so that the true influence of the grass-ploughing campaign might be disentangled from the other factors at the time responsible for changes in the numbers of live stock. There was at no time any doubt that enough grass for the dairy herd and for working horses could be reserved ; but the future of store cattle and sheep, should the war be prolonged, raised anxious questions. The lowland grass required for corn-growing was mainly the grass on which store stock depended, and reserves of summer grazing were much wanted. In Scotland there were large reserves of summer grass in the hills, but in England and Wales the quantity was relatively small. A special inquiry into the conditions in the hill districts of both countries was made, with the double view of ascertaining the contributions being made to the food supply, and the possibilities of providing additional summer or winter provender which would relieve the strain on cultivated grass land. Some of the information collected during this inquiry has already been given in Chapter IV (see p. 78).

It was perhaps natural that stock owners themselves, unaware of the actual position, should have regarded the plough policy of the Food Production Department with disfavour. If one looked only to the difficulties of the moment there was reason for their criticism. Grass land had a specially high value in the summer of 1918 ; and undoubtedly, if one had regard merely to the Michaelmas balance sheet, grazing was a safer business than ploughing. But in the spring of 1918 when the Department decided that it was advisable to plough more grass land they were looking beyond Michaelmas, and they were then satisfied that the plough policy was as necessary for the stock owner as for the corn grower. An increase in tillage would not only increase the supply of roots and straw, but also, by saving tonnage, would enable more feeding stuffs to be imported.

When in August 1918 the importation of necessaries for the following winter was discussed between the Inter-Allied Food and Shipping Authorities, it was found to be impossible to provide all that was demanded by the Food Controllers and at the same time to provide for the transport of troops and munitions. It was therefore decided that the Allied peoples must make severe sacrifices, and that in the final allocation of shipping no space could be provided for materials required solely as feeding stuffs, except possibly some part of such tonnage as might be released because of the increased crops which were grown in 1918. The Armistice altered the whole situation, but the difficulties which stock owners experienced in the winter of 1918–19 have now shown what would have happened to the country's flocks and herds had the war continued. The inevitable reduction in the numbers of our live stock, which must have taken place, would have been brought about, not by the ploughing of part of the grazing area, but because of an insufficiency of winter fodders and feeding stuffs.

Artificial Manures.

Difficulties arising from a shortage of fertilizers have been referred to in connexion with the harvests of 1916 and 1917. The Technical Division were constantly engaged in devising measures for assisting farmers to make the best of the materials available in 1918. Leaflets were prepared and frequent press notices were issued recommending specific action. What direction this action should take was frequently debated at the weekly conferences ; for, as properly balanced manures could not be compounded, experience based on pre-war practice was at a discount. Rapid methods for testing the value of new materials that might be recommended were devised at Rothamsted, promising substances were examined there, and advice issued as to their uses on the farm if they proved to be satisfactory.

The value of waste from acetylene gas manufacture, of waste from munition factories, and of flue dust—a source of potash—were tested by experiments and, in conjunction with steelmakers, investigations to ascertain the possibility of improving the quality of the basic slag produced by the open-hearth process of steel manufacture were initiated.

Lime.

A good deal of attention was given to lime; efforts were made to increase the quantity applied to land, but labour difficulties prevented much success being achieved. The study given to the subject indicated that very large quantities must now be required by the soils of the country. Assuming the pre-war relation between the cost of liming and the value of farm produce, the immediate application of over three million tons would appear to be desirable in England and Wales, followed by the annual use of about a million tons. There seems to be little doubt that one of the factors responsible for the relatively small increase in the yield per acre of land that has taken place in our grain crops during the past century is to be found in the abandonment by most farmers of the old practice of systematic liming.

Insect and Fungus Pests.

Inquiries in connexion with insect and fungus pests were so numerous that a special sub-committee was set up to deal with this side of the technical work. The assistance of voluntary observers (mycologists and entomologists) was secured in different parts of the country. These observers reported on any crop pest likely to require special attention; thus any unusual event was quickly brought to the notice of the Department. In over two thousand cases, during the year, advice was sent to persons whose crops were being injured, and about a hundred visits were made by officers of the Division to farms where the outbreaks were of a serious or novel character. Investigations on wireworm were taken up at Rothamsted and experiments in checking the ravages of frit fly were carried out in several localities.

Seed Testing.

Just before the outbreak of war the Board of Agriculture and Fisheries decided to establish a Seed Testing Station; the project was not realized at the time, but as the difficulty of securing good seed was accentuated by war conditions it was

revived in the autumn of 1917.   One of the scientific officers
who had joined the Department in a whole-time capacity was
appointed Director, accommodation was found, and testing of
seed was begun in November ; about 7,000 samples for sowing
in 1918 were tested, and double this number of samples reached
the Seed Testing Station in the course of the first year's work.

Utilization of Straw.

While proceedings at the technical conferences related
chiefly to current questions, it was also necessary to take
account of the problems likely to arise in the course of carrying
out the Department's programme, and to arrange field experiments and laboratory investigations so that information might
be available when required.

In illustration, the case of straw may be taken.   The large
increase in the area of cereals which the Department aimed at
would provide a surplus of straw in 1918, unless the season
proved to be unusually dry.   Methods of utilizing this surplus
were therefore considered.   It was certain that the demand for
hay for the Army, and the reduction in the area of grass, would
lead to the substitution of straw for hay in feeding live stock.
Its uses were well understood by most farmers, but some
would ask for advice ; all that was necessary in this case was to
have the necessary information collated and prepared for circula-
tion.   It was also highly probable that a difficulty in securing
store cattle would result in many farmers having more straw
than they required, and at the same time less manure.   The
possibility of preparing farmyard manure by artificial methods
was therefore considered, and investigations at Rothamsted
were planned.   These investigations ultimately showed that it
was possible to make good manure from straw without the
intervention of cattle, and at no great cost.[1]

Again, shortage of concentrated feeding stuffs might have
made it necessary to prepare a digestible food from straw, by
a method then being used in Germany.   Arrangements were
therefore made for investigating the possibilities of this method.

[1] See *Journal Ministry of Agriculture and Fisheries*, vol. xxviii, p. 398.

It was shown that a suitable digestible food could be made in this country if wanted ; but, at the time, the need for this material did not justify the cost of the factories that would be required for its manufacture.

In consultation with the Paper Control Department the possibility of using surplus straw in paper-making was explored. Good paper may be made from straw pulp ; but, as compared with wood pulp and esparto, the consumption of fuel in the process of manufacture was found to be so high that, with the limited stocks of coal then available, it would have been more economical to import esparto than to use surplus straw. In the manufacture of strawboards, however, there was an opportunity for increasing the use of straw.

Reports on Farms.

The Division also prepared reports on farms in cases where Executive Committees encountered special difficulties, advised as to the methods of farming to be followed, and inspected the results of the work on farms taken in hand by the committees themselves. By the end of 1918 the committees were farming 125 holdings of more than 50 acres in area, the total area in hand being nearly 24,000 acres. Essex with 2,500, and Kent with 1,900 acres, headed the list. These farms represented the worst-managed land in the country at the time the committees took possession, and the reports on most of them in the summer and autumn of 1918 were most gratifying. Here, for example, is a note on a Kent farm from an Inspector's weekly Report, dated 27th August, in which references occur to similar farms in five counties :

'. . . Farm (230 acres), was taken over in a deplorable condition in March 1917. At that time a well-known local valuer, appointed by the Committee to make an inspection, reported that it was not worth cultivating. The arable land comprising 120 acres is now fully cropped, 100 acres are under corn and the general condition of the crops is very satisfactory.'

The writer has no information about the above case beyond what is given in the note ; he has, however, inspected a number of farms in other counties and it is not difficult to explain the wonderful success achieved on these derelict holdings in 1918. In many cases the committees wisely entrusted the management to some skilled local farmer, who took a natural pride in the task of converting a wilderness into a cornfield. To those men the season was kind—it was an ideal year for tackling neglected land; thus to many an honest farmer (who earned nothing for his work, for much of this supervision was voluntary aid) the harvest of 1918 brought the satisfaction which comes from a good crop and a good conscience.

Departmental Conferences and Committees.

The weekly Technical Conference referred to above concerned only the agriculturists and scientific staff employed in the Technical Division. The President of the Board met the Director-General and the principal officers each week at a departmental Staff Conference, at which reports presented by the head of each Division were discussed. Through these Staff Conferences all of those primarily responsible for the Food Production campaign were kept informed of the weekly changes in the situation. The topics discussed at the weekly Staff Conference referred mainly to work done, or to work projected. For dealing with the very numerous questions arising in the course of the execution of work, and for the discussion of details arising out of the development of the programme, a small Standing Committee of heads of Divisions met the Director-General each week. When special subjects required further joint discussion—as for example the orders to be placed for machinery, or the charges to be imposed for horse and tractor cultivating—the practice was to form special committees to examine and report. To facilitate an interchange of views between members of the outdoor and indoor staff, the periodical conferences with the Department's local Commissioners, referred to in Chapter IX, were continued throughout 1918 at approximately monthly intervals.

Outside the Department itself there was the Advisory Committee referred to on p. 172 which, with the President as chairman, met at frequent intervals for discussion of the general agricultural situation between January 1917 and July 1918.

All of these conferences and committees, though often dealing with the same topics, had well-defined functions, and they contributed greatly to the smooth progress of work at head-quarters and in the country.

Through the Local Organization, or one of the other Divisions of the Department, close touch was maintained with Executive Committees and their sub-committees in every county ; and these county committees, in their turn, were in equally close touch with every parish through the district sub-committees and parish correspondents.

Closing Down.

But with the Armistice the need for the special machinery at head-quarters came to an end, and shortly thereafter steps were taken to transfer a part of the war work of the Food Production Department, which it was desirable to continue on a peace footing, to the Board of Agriculture and Fisheries.

Established, like the 'cutting' of the gardener, 'on its own roots', and drawing support from that rich 'compost' the 'Vote of Credit', into which war had plunged so many of our pre-war financial devices, the Food Production Department led an independent existence for two years, connected with the Board of Agriculture only through the President. Like other War Departments it had grown rapidly, and with the Armistice came the necessity for free pruning. This work occupied the early months of 1919 ; and on 31st March, when it was possible to graft the remaining branches on to the parent stock, the Food Production Department ceased to exist.

The task set the Department, like the task which, in its turn, it had imposed upon Executive Committees, and the committees upon farmers, was no easy one ; it is doubtful if any of the bureaucrats, or at least any of those 'old contemptibles' among them who belonged to the Civil Service and were accustomed to the milder measures of the past, enjoyed the exercise of the new powers conferred on them by 'D.O.R.A.'.

In their hearts there still lurked warm affection for the green pastures of England, and they could sympathize with, if they could not listen to, the wailings of the occupiers of the scheduled fields. Nor had they much fault to find with the many criticisms of the Department and its policy and methods ; for in tillage under war conditions there had been much rough and ready work, which, naturally enough, good farmers thoroughly disliked.

These rough and ready measures were, however, a necessity in 1917 and 1918 ; and thus, although those chiefly responsible for the plough policy, and for the methods which it required farmers to adopt, were well aware that no agriculturist lamented the passing of the Department, they did not regret the action they had taken ; for the plough policy had been justified by its results.

CHAPTER XI

THE COST OF THE FOOD PRODUCTION CAMPAIGN

Accounts of the Food Production Department. Non-Trading Services. Trading Services. ' A Bad Blunder.' The Cost of Fertilizer Control. Total Cost of the Food Production Campaign in England and Wales. Value to the Taxpayer of the 1918 Harvest of England and Wales. Cost of Food Production in Scotland. Northern and Southern Expenditure. Irish Expenditure on Food Production. The Country's War Risks (Food) Insurance Policy.

The Cost of the Food Production Campaign.

In this chapter a brief reference will be made to the cost of carrying out the Food Production Campaign which was initiated at the beginning of 1917. Until the end of the preceding year the cost of the special war measures taken to increase home food production by the Agricultural Departments was small ; but the new policy called for the expenditure of considerable sums for such purposes as additional staff, the purchase of machinery, and the training of women workers.

Accounts of the Food Production Department.

The establishment of the Food Production Department, with a separate accounting staff, made it possible to effect a clear separation between the cost of war farming and of the work of the Board of Agriculture and Fisheries. After the Department ceased to exist on the 31st March 1919, a part of its Finance Branch was transferred to the Board, and the special Food Production Accounts were kept open. Expenditure in respect of the work of Agricultural Executive Committees, Women's Labour, and other similar purposes was charged to Food Production ; and receipts for tractors, horses, and other farming requisites, disposed of after the Armistice, were paid into the Food Production Account. By the 31st March 1920 nearly all the special expenditure had been dealt with, except payments in respect of compensation claims, and most of the assets had been realized ; the accounts were then closed, and certain of them were published, in 1921, with a covering Report by the Comptroller and Auditor-General (Cmd. 1368). These published Trading Accounts and Balance-sheets will be referred to presently ; meantime attention may be directed to the Food Production Department's net expenditure in 1917–18 and 1918–19, and to the subsequent expenditure, in respect of food production, by the Board of Agriculture and Fisheries in 1919–20. The accounts for the three years included (*a*) the actual cost of the work described in Chapters VIII, IX, and X, and (*b*) consequential charges arising out of that work. The latter comprised the losses incurred on stock held at the Armistice, and also the cost of carrying out certain war measures, the continuation of which was then held to be desirable. Thus while the whole expenditure set out below was caused by the war, a substantial part of it did not relate to the actual war farming described in this volume.

	1917–18 £ 000	1918–19 £ 000	1919–20 £ 000	Total £ 000
Non-Trading Services :				
Salaries, travelling, incidentals . .	175	234	182	591
Grants to Agricultural Executive Committees	294	578	510	1,382
Training of, and outfits for, women workers	229	307	69	605
Trading Services :				
Tractors, implements, and cultivation	1,836	2,561	*878*	3,519
Horses, do. do.	201	671	*487*	385
Steam tackle, do. do. . . .	—	218	*40*	178
Other Trading Services . . .	133	212	*217*	128
Total Cash Expenditure :				
Non-Trading Services . . .	698	1,119	761	2,578
Trading Services	2,170	3,662	*1,622*	4,210
All Food Production Department Services	2,868	4,781	*861*	6,788

Following the plan adopted in the Auditor-General's published accounts, the expenditure may be classed into *Trading Services,* such as the Tractor Cultivation Scheme, and *Non-Trading Services,* covering head-quarters' salaries and grants to Agricultural Executive Committees. The net payments under the main headings of expenditure, in each of the three financial years, are set out on the preceding page. In 1919–20 the receipts from the several trading schemes exceeded the payments ; the net receipts are printed in italics.[1]

Non-Trading Services.

The largest item in the payments under this heading was in connexion with the work of the Agricultural Executive Committees. During 1918–19, when expenditure was at its highest, the salaries paid to local officers, travelling expenses, and the rents and upkeep of offices accounted for £360,000 ; farming operations cost £150,000 ; and £20,000 was expended on drainage. The total payments for compensation for losses arising out of the Orders made under the Defence of the Realm Regulations, included in the sum of £1,382,000 in the above statement, was about £250,000. In the two following years claims amounting to £212,000 were paid. A certain number of claims have still to be settled, but it is unlikely that the cost will amount to more than a small fraction of the sum already paid.

The chief items in the expenditure of £605,000 on Women Workers were £280,000 for outfits, and £140,000 for training schemes ; the balance included sums paid to Women's War Agricultural Committees for administrative outlays, the salaries and travelling expenses of organizing secretaries, and grants to certain women's organizations. The greater part of the expenditure on women's work was incurred in connexion with some 17,000 land workers in the Women's Land Army, for whom outfits had to be provided, and also maintenance during training and at times when the workers were not actually employed on the land. While the aggregate is large, the cost per head for the necessary overalls, waterproofs, and boots cannot be regarded as excessive in view of the prices of clothing at the time.

[1] The writer is indebted to Sir Francis Floud, K.C.B., Permanent Secretary of the Ministry of Agriculture and Fisheries, formerly Controller of the Local Organization Division and Accounting Officer of the Food Production Department, for the detailed figures on which this abstract is based.

In the item £591,000 for salaries, travelling, and expenses incurred at head-quarters, there is included a sum of £53,000 for the salaries and expenses of about ninety officers of the Board of Agriculture and Fisheries lent to the Food Production Department in the years 1917–18 and 1918–19. It may be noted in connexion with the head-quarters' expenses that several of the principal temporary officers were unpaid.

Trading Services.

The greater part of the cash expenditure was on Trading Services, and the actual cost to the Department of these services was larger than the sum here shown, nearly half the expenditure included under salaries and travelling being incurred in respect of officers employed in connexion with the Trading Schemes. Nor do the payments made by the Food Production Department include the whole cost of these Schemes. Services were rendered by the Post Office, Stationery Office, and Office of Works, which in an ordinary business would be debited to Trading; and interest has not been charged on the capital employed. On the other hand, there was in stock on the 31st of March 1920 a considerable amount of property, the value of which is not shown in the foregoing statement.

In the Trading Accounts and Balance-sheets reported on by the Comptroller and Auditor-General (Cmd. 1368) an attempt was made to show the approximate balance of the Profit and Loss Accounts of the Trading Schemes, by debiting to each Account the services rendered by other Government Departments, apportioning Departmental Salaries, charging interest at 5 per cent. on the money provided by the Exchequer, and valuing stock unsold on the 31st March 1920. When these adjustments were made, the total of £4,210,000 in the above cash statement became £4,463,000.

The chief items in this final estimate of the total expenditure were: Tractors and tractor cultivation (£3,213,000), horses and horse cultivation (£1,021,000), steam tackle and steam cultivation (£88,000),[1] loss on binder twine held in reserve at

---

[1] This loss was incurred on sixty-six sets of steam ploughing tackle purchased and resold.

the time of the Armistice (£77,000), loss on cargoes of foreign superphosphate (£29,000), loss on purchases of American onion seed (£15,000).

There were a number of other Trading Schemes relating to the purchase of seed wheat, oats, and potatoes ; the establishment of a seed testing station ; the purchase of nitrate of soda; the distribution of superphosphate and sulphate of ammonia ; the grinding of limestones for manure ; the spraying of potatoes, and the preservation of fruit. On some of these there was a profit, but on the whole group there was a loss of £20,000.

'A Bad Blunder.'

In these war-trading transactions many mistakes were made, which to the unfortunate taxpayer, now called upon to ' foot the bill ', may well appear to have been inexcusable.

It would be a lengthy proceeding, and out of place in the present volume, to attempt to explain in detail how and why these losses were incurred ; brief explanations have been given of most of them in the Comptroller and Auditor-General's Report. On the other hand, it is very desirable that the public should realize how such losses came to be incurred. It must not be assumed offhand that they were due to lack of business knowledge, or to carelessness, or to sheer stupidity on the part of officials. One of the foregoing transactions will therefore be explained, as an illustration of the class of ' costly mistake ' that must be made by those responsible for trading on behalf of the nation under war conditions. It is selected for explanation because public attention was several times directed to the heavy loss on this transaction, the gravity of the error grew with repetition, and finally the President of the Board himself admitted in the House of Commons that a ' bad blunder ' had been made.

The Department's ' three black crows ' were three cargoes of superphosphate of lime purchased in the spring of 1917. Briefly the position was that a chance occurred of securing these cargoes, destined for another country, at a price of approximately the amount for which superphosphate was then selling in this country. There was no time to arrange the actual

freight with the Admiralty, but if ' blue-book ' rates were con-
ceded, as there was reason for expecting they would be, the
loss on the manure would have been about £12,000 ; an order
was placed, ' blue-book ' rates were refused, and the actual
cost of the 13,450 tons of superphosphate to the Exchequer
was £28,760. The two questions to which taxpayers will want
answers are : ' Why was this manure purchased ? ' ' When
purchased, why was it sold at a loss ? '

Superphosphate of lime is the most generally used of all
manures by tillage farmers ; there are many soils on which
without it the root crop would fail, involving an immediate
loss of cattle food, and a loss of corn in the following year. In
the winter of 1916–17 the outlook for supplies of superphosphate
was very disquieting. At first the difficulty was created by
the demand for sulphuric acid, used in its manufacture, by
munition factories. At the beginning of 1917 makers of superphosphate were urgently demanding acid, but the Ministry of
Munitions had informed them that for months there could be
no increase in the supply. About this time a second difficulty
arose. Fortunately there were considerable stocks of phosphatic
rock in the country when the war broke out, and though
imports fell from about 520,000 tons in each of the years 1912
and 1913 to 375,000 tons in 1915, no shortage occurred until
the end of 1916 ; then the situation underwent a rapid change.
At the beginning of 1917 great difficulty was experienced in
getting supplies of rock phosphate, and as the spring months
passed the position grew worse ; thus while in 1913 and 1914
the imports in the first four months of the year had been
189,000 and 184,000 tons respectively, in the corresponding
period of 1917 the imports were 49,000 tons. It was in these
circumstances that the chance of securing 13,500 tons of foreign
superphosphate occurred. This manure would arrive in May in
time for application to the root crop ; it would fertilize about
100,000 acres of land, on which otherwise the crops would be
poor, or might altogether fail. The view taken by the Department was that the outlook for food was then so grave, and the
consequences of shortage so dangerous, that the country could

not afford to risk the loss of crops on even 100,000 acres of land, and that it was a more prudent proceeding, from the point of view of the nation's interests, to incur the financial loss which this purchase would involve, than to lose the opportunity of making a certain addition to the home-grown food supply.

But, it may be asked, if this manure was so urgently required by farmers, if there was in May 1917 an absolute shortage, could purchasers not have been found for the cargoes at cost price?

There is little doubt that, if these cargoes had been acquired by speculators who were free to deal with them as they chose, a profit could have been made, for prices were not then actually controlled. The price of superphosphate was not controlled until the 20th August 1917. But in the circumstances of the time it would have been impossible for the Food Production Department to have sold at cost price for the following reasons. At the beginning of the year manufacturers had been informed that Government proposed to control the price of superphosphate, but no fixed prices were then introduced. Instead, there was an arrangement with makers which ensured that until the end of May, that is until the end of the sowing season, purchasers would be supplied with superphosphate by traders at rates based upon the cost of rock phosphate and acid in the second half of 1916. Although every one connected with the trade knew that the outlook in the early months of 1917 was disquieting, this fact was not allowed to affect the prices charged to farmers.

There was no binding obligation on the Department to sell the foreign superphosphate which they had purchased at the same price as the home manufactured manure, for the concessions which makers made, with respect to the prices they charged, had gained them certain advantages in the supplies of acid and the importation of rock phosphate ; but when the sale of the foreign cargoes was being negotiated arrangements for the control of manure prices were being elaborated, and apart from the undesirability of raising prices already agreed to as being reasonable prices for the home manufactured fertilizer, it would have been highly inexpedient to have disturbed the manure merchants' market at this particular time, some months before maximum prices for superphosphate were actually fixed.   In all the circumstances the officials concerned judged it to be necessary to make ' a bad blunder ', and the only real excuse which can be given to the taxpayer for this and similar transactions is that in war-trading ' bad blunders ' are sometimes inevitable.   They are part of the cost of waging war, for which all of us, however reluctantly, must subsequently pay.

The Cost of Fertilizer Control.

The responsibility for fertilizer supply was at first taken by the Ministry of Food, but was transferred to the Ministry of Munitions in March 1917 ; the purchase of superphosphate above referred to was carried through by the Food Production Department while matters were in a transition stage.   Certain other transactions in connexion with fertilizers were also carried out by the Department at a profit. Apart from the loss on foreign superphosphate, the whole cost of the provision of fertilizers after April 1917 was borne by the Ministry of Munitions, with the exception of a small loss incurred by the Board of Trade in connexion with supplies of potash.

The accounts of the Comptroller and Auditor-General (Cmd. 1368) do not disclose the actual cost of the fertilizer transactions of the Ministry of Munitions, since the published statements refer partly to materials required for munitions ;   but, so far as the costs can be accurately apportioned, the losses or profits (shown in italics), in each of the three years on the two manures which account for the whole, or almost the whole, of the outlay [1] were as follows :

	1917–18 £ 000	1918–19 £ 000	1919–20 £ 000	Total £ 000
Sulphate of ammonia . . .	—	443	402	845
Superphosphate of lime . . .	*66*	949	*46*	837
Total . . ., . .	*66*	1,392	356	1,682

[1] If the published accounts include any sums for losses on other manures, they must be very small.   They cannot be traced by the Disposals and Liquidation Commission, to whom the writer is indebted for the figures given above.

Total Cost of the Food Production Campaign in England and Wales.

If all these charges are reckoned up, and allowances are made for interest and for services rendered by other Government Departments, as has been done in the Comptroller and Auditor-General's published accounts, it will be found that the special measures taken by the Food Production Department to increase the output of food in England and Wales cost the country about £8,000,000. This was the premium we paid as an insurance against the risk of short supplies of food in the later years of war and the first year of peace.

Regarded as an agricultural enterprise the cost of the work of the Food Production Department was very high, especially the expenditure on cultivation by tractors and horses, and on training and equipping the Land Army. But the task which the Department was set was to increase home-grown food by the greatest possible amount, not to secure the largest quantity that could be grown profitably, and if this fact be realized, the expenditure can readily be justified. Now that we are able to look back on the work of 1917 and 1918 it is not difficult to point out items on which economies might have been effected. If the policy embodied in the Corn Production (Amendment) Act, 1918, had been settled nine months earlier, many cultivating implements that were ordered need not have been requisitioned; and the local organization, and consequent expenditure of Executive Committees, might have been reduced, or at least not increased, in the summer of 1918. These committees were provided with far more machinery and with many more officers in 1918–19, after their powers were curtailed, than they were in the preceding year, when they were armed with the authority that enabled them to make such large additions to the food supply. Again, if the Corn Production Acts (Repeal) Act, 1921, could have been foreseen, the expenditure on the committees' work might have been still further reduced in 1919–20. Similarly, if we take the larger items of expenditure and criticize them as if the campaign had been merely some agricultural enterprise on a vast scale, it is an easy matter to show how unprofitable they were. In proportion to the actual work done, the cost of tractor cultivation was excessive ; the loss on superphosphate incurred by the Ministry of Munitions in 1918–19 was much greater than it should have been ; the binder twine transactions involved unnecessarily high commitments ; and so we might comment on each figure. But throughout 1917, and until November 1918, we were not looking back, but looking forward ; and even as late as July 1918 there was no one—except perhaps Marshal Foch—who could have told us what we must expect in 1919.

Value to the Taxpayer of the 1918 Harvest of England and Wales.

The reasons which led to free expenditure on particular items in the Food Production programme in the period January 1917 to October 1918, indeed, call for no detailed explanation. But it may be worth while to point out that the taxpayers' losses were not nearly so much as £8,000,000 sterling, for there was a ' with profits ' clause in our insurance policy, and our ' premium ' earned a substantial bonus. It would occupy too much space to discuss the probable value of this bonus from first to last. No reference has been made in this volume to the influence of the work of Agricultural Executive Committees on the yield of the harvests of 1919 and 1920. In both years, because of adverse seasons, the crops were much less than in 1918 ; but it is undoubted that in both years the output was much greater than it would have been if farmers had not been aided by the work of Government Departments and local committees. Nor need we discuss the gains from the harvest of 1917. There was a substantial gain in this year, but its direct value to the taxpayer is not easily assessed ; in the period September 1917 to August 1918 we were so situated that if we had not grown extra food we should have had to do without, for we had not the shipping to import more than we did import.

In the year September 1918 to August 1919, however, the position was different. After the Armistice, although there would have been much suffering, we need not have starved. If the large crops of 1918 had not been grown within the country, somehow or other we would have purchased and imported most of the required supplies, and under the conditions of that year our people would have paid for the extra imports chiefly as taxpayers, not as consumers. It is possible, therefore, to make a rough estimate of the amount which the Exchequer saved because of the large harvest of 1918.

During this period the taxpayer was contributing to the Bread Subsidy—a charge which from first to last cost him about £162,000,000 [1]; he was therefore directly interested in the country's purchases of wheat. The harvest of 1918 greatly lessened our overseas purchases of wheat in the following twelve months, for England and Wales produced 871,000 tons more wheat than on the average of the years 1904–13, and grew 1,566,000 tons more potatoes. If one-seventh of this extra wheat be deducted for seed and light corn, the balance would be available for the miller, and if two-sevenths of the extra potato crop be written off for seed, pig-feeding, and waste potatoes, the balance may be regarded as having reduced our bill for overseas wheat. The home-grown wheat available for bread and the edible potatoes, if converted into the equivalent quantity of wheat, would together provide as much food as 1,000,000 tons of imported wheat, and since in 1918–19 imported wheat cost about £2 per ton more than home wheat, there was a saving to the taxpayer of at least £2,000,000. Actually the saving is likely to have been more than this figure. Consumers paid for the potatoes which they ate, but paid a part only of the cost of their bread. To the extent, therefore, to which the large supply of potatoes reduced the demand for bread, tax-payers secured an additional gain because of the saving in the bread subsidy.

There was also a saving to the taxpayer because of the extra crop of oats grown in 1918, which in England and Wales amounted to 572,000 tons. As a result of this additional supply there was a marked decrease in the imports of oats and maize in the cereal years 1918–19, and as the price of home-grown grain was £2 per ton less than that of imported oats,[2] purchasers of home-grown oats saved about £1,000,000. A part

[1] This is an approximate figure; the actual amount cannot be stated until certain adjustments, required by the pooling arrangements of the Allies, have been made.

[2] The intrinsic value of home oats is greater than that of imported oats; in the case of wheat the position is reversed. These differences in intrinsic value have been left out of account in estimating the taxpayers' savings.

of this saving would be claimed by the private horse-owner; but on account of the large demands for horse-corn by the Army, and for oats for stretching the bread supply by millers in the winter of 1918–19, it may be estimated that the 1918 oat crop saved the Exchequer not less than £750,000.

These direct savings of £2,750,000 were not the only savings effected by the taxpayer as a result of the 1918 harvest: the total value of the extra crops of wheat, oats, and potatoes grown in England and Wales in 1918 was about £30,000,000, and though this sum is but 6 per cent. of our adverse trade balance in 1919, its effect on exchange must still have been appreciable.   Again, the possession of large home crops must have helped the country's representatives in bargaining for the purchase of overseas produce.   It may be claimed, therefore, that rather more than one-third of the cost of the Food Production Campaign in England and Wales was recovered by the Exchequer on the harvest of 1918 alone.

Apart from the returns to the Exchequer, the nation benefited by the Food Production Campaign because of savings effected by individual consumers.   As above noted, horse-owners saved a substantial sum on their fodder bills in 1918–19, and consumers of potatoes saved much more on their purchases. The very large potato crop of 1918 enabled the Food Controller to fix maximum prices which must have been from 20s. to 30s. per ton less than they would have been if the yield of this crop had been no more than the average of 1904–13; thus the 1919 prices meant that a sum of about £2,000,000 was saved by purchasers of potatoes.

While, therefore, the cost of the campaign in England and Wales was admittedly high, the net cost of insuring against war risks was far short of the figure of £8,000,000, which has been arrived at by adding together the cost of the special measures adopted to encourage food production.

Cost of Food Production in Scotland.

As in the parallel case of England and Wales, a number of *Trading Services* were carried out in Scotland by the Board of Agriculture.   The net cost of these services in the three years

1917–18, 1918–19, and 1919–20 is shown in the Report of the Comptroller and Auditor-General already cited (Cmd. 1368), to have been £140,000. The only considerable deficit was that incurred on Agricultural Machinery ; the net loss in this case was £144,000. The other Trading Services, which included schemes for land cultivation, potato and manure supply, and fruit preservation, resulted in a profit of about £4,000. These results must be regarded as very satisfactory, for losses in the working of a machinery scheme were inevitable. Even more in Scotland (where tillage Orders were rarely served) than in England, it was necessary to base the rates for ploughing and other cultivation on the cost of carrying out the work by horse labour with skilled ploughmen, and not on the cost of providing imported machinery at the high rates prevailing in 1917–20, and on the wages paid to the more or less inexperienced tractor drivers then available. It would have been impracticable to have charged the full cost of cultivation to those farmers who required extra help to break up the grass land which they were willing to plough.

No separate department for supervising food production was set up in Scotland, and no separate accounts of all the expenditure on Non-Trading Services were kept by the Scotch Board of Agriculture, as they necessarily were by the Food Production Department in England and Wales ; but by the courtesy of the Scotch Board the writer is able to give the following figures, which represent the approximate cost of the special campaign in Scotland. They have been arrived at by analysing the ordinary accounts of the Board of Agriculture and apportioning, as far as possible, the expenditure of the Board between normal and special services.

Net expenditure on Food Production (Non-Trading Services) in Scotland.

	1917–18 £	1918–19 £	1919–20 £	Total £
Head-quarters' expenditure, salaries, travelling incidentals . . .	1,750	3,500	3,500	8,750
County Committees' expenditure, salaries, compensation, &c. .	10,000	15,000	13,000	38,000
Women labour outfits, training, &c. .	1,000	4,500	3,500	9,000
Total outlay on Non-Trading Services	12,750	23,000	20,000	55,750

X

From April to December 1918 the Ministry of National Service were responsible for the administration of the Woman Labour scheme, and their expenditure has not been included in the above statement; but it is clear from the figures given that the total cost of the special effort made in Scotland (excluding the cost of providing manures and certain other requisites, which were supplied by the Ministry of Munitions or the Food Production Department as agents for the Board) cannot have much exceeded, if indeed it reached, £200,000.

On the other hand, if we apply to the extra Scotch crops of 1918 the methods of valuation already adopted in the case of England and Wales, it will be found that their value to the taxpayer was about £500,000.

Much clerical work would be involved in separating out from the records of the Food Production Department the destination of the consignments of superphosphate and sulphate of ammonia sent out to farmers, and no classification of the actual quantities used in each country has been made; but the writer estimates that the cost of meeting Scotland's requirements in fertilizers was from £230,000 to £250,000, and that the total cost of the Scotch work did not exceed the sums which the taxpayers of the country saved on the 1918 harvest alone. In every sense the adoption by Scotland of a food production policy in 1917 was a profitable undertaking for the nation.

Northern and Southern Expenditure.

As one whose personal efforts were directed to increasing food supply in England and Wales, and whose material contributions to the food supply were made from Scotch land, the writer may perhaps be permitted to remark that the very low cost of the Food Production Campaign in Scotland cannot altogether be attributed to the genius of the race! Although there may be few southern administrators who would even attempt to argue that, in the matter of prudent spending, England could compete with her northern sister, it must, in the interests of clear understanding, be pointed out that England's task in the later years of war was a very different one from that which fell to Scotland. In order to justify this statement, reference must again be made to the difference in the systems of farming followed in the two countries, which was discussed in Chapter II. It may be recalled that on a thousand-acre estate typical of the cultivated land of England, 94 acres only would be found under temporary grasses and clovers, whereas on a typical Scotch estate there would be no fewer than 312 acres. England's effort to secure extra land for corn was, therefore, mainly an effort to break up permanent grass land. In Scotland, on the other hand, much temporary grass was available for growing oats and potatoes. From extensive tracts of permanent pasture in England, men, horses, implements, even necessary buildings, had disappeared. On the temporary pastures of Scotland the requisites for successful cultivation usually existed. It was a case of harder work for men and horses on most farms, and both men and horses were ready for, and were equal to, their extra task. The provision of non-local labour under war conditions was, as we have seen, a very expensive business ; it was the purchasing of tractors and horses, the training of unskilled workers, and the travelling from place to place of women workers, horse-gangs, harvesters, and threshing tackle, that brought about so great an expenditure on Cultivation Schemes in England and Wales. While in some parts of Scotland the same difficulties were met with, in general the position called for a much smaller outlay.

Whatever the relative advantages of permanent pastures as compared with temporary pastures may be from a technical point of view, there can be no question that as a safeguard against shortage of food in war time the Scotch system of farming, with its large reserves of temporary grass, has much to recommend it. Systems of husbandry which permit tillage to die out, as in many parts of the west of England, or which maintain so small an area under temporary grass that there are no reserves capable of rapid conversion to corn growing, as in the east, are not systems suited for an emergency.

The actual increase in land under crops other than grass in England and Wales between 1916 and 1918 was 1,843,000 acres : in Scotland it was 276,000 acres ; if the total cost of the special effort in each country be distributed over these areas it may be estimated that it amounted to about 87s. per acre in England and Wales, and to 36s. per acre in Scotland.

Irish Expenditure on Food Production.

In Ireland, as in Scotland, no separate department for stimulating food production was required. The measures called for by the situation which arose at the end of 1916 were taken by the Department of Agriculture and Technical Instruction, who employed the additional staff required to enforce their Compulsory Tillage regulations, and to give advice and assistance to inexperienced cultivators. Necessarily the greater part of the time of the regular staff of the Department was occupied by duties arising out of the war ; but no close estimate of the value of this time can be made. Nor, if the time could be valued, would it show the cost of the work to the Exchequer ; for, as in the other countries, war duties were added to peace duties and the extra burden fell not on the State, but on the permanent officials. The cost of the additional staff employed, and the expenditure incurred on special schemes, can, however, be ascertained. In the following statement, kindly supplied by the Department of Agriculture and Technical Instruction, this extra expenditure is shown.

In the period of three years, 1917–20, tractors, milling machinery, ploughs, sprayers, &c., were purchased for £143,018. The direct sales of these articles realized £137,167. Sprayers and milling plant transferred to the Disposal Board were sold for £3,956, leaving a loss of £1,895 as between purchases and sales in the Trading Account. Adding the cost of demonstrations and instruction in the use of tractors, freight, storage, insurance, and charges for administrative expenses and interest on advances at 5 per cent., the net total expenditure in connexion with the provision of machinery and implements was £10,876.

The cost of technical and other expert staff engaged in connexion with the campaign of increased food production, including the operations of County Committees of Agriculture and the enforcement of the compulsory tillage regulations, amounted to approximately £336,000.

An advance of £122,000 was made for loans to farmers, of which £102,000 has already been repaid to the Treasury in the period ended 31st March 1922.

In addition to the sums referred to above there was Ireland's share of the cost of providing fertilizers; this may be estimated at £275,000, making the total cost of Ireland's Food Production Campaign in the three years 1917–20 about £625,000 (excluding outstanding loans), a very small figure as compared with the cost in England and Wales; and, relatively to the extra area tilled, much less even than in Scotland.

On the other hand, if the extra crops of the 1918 harvest can be valued by the methods applied to British crops (it is questionable if they should be, because of differences in Food Control), the total saving to taxpayers because of the Irish harvest of 1918 would amount to about £1,200,000. The increase in Irish production in 1917 was about equal to that in 1918, and the value to the Exchequer of the extra crops grown from 1917 to 1920 must have largely exceeded the expenditure incurred by the Department of Agriculture.

As was the case in Scotland, Irish farmers had at their disposal a large quantity of temporary grass land suitable for ploughing; and, in contrast to the position in Scotland, there was in Ireland a good supply of local labour in 1917 and 1918. These conditions made a Compulsory Tillage Scheme possible; and from a financial point of view this scheme gave highly satisfactory results.

The Country's War Risks (Food) Insurance Policy.

Summarizing the figures given in this chapter, it may be stated that while the special measures taken to increase the home food supply after January 1917 cost the taxpayer rather more than £9,000,000,[1] there were direct savings to the Exchequer

---

[1] This figure does not include outlays by the Ministry of Food on schemes which directly or indirectly stimulated food production. The Ministry's outlay in respect of the 1917 and 1918 potato crops was about £1,290,000, while schemes for supplying or preserving fruit and vegetables cost about £1,265,000. But it may be claimed that the cost in these cases did not fall on the taxpayer. The policy of the Ministry aimed at the carrying out of all its work without imposing a charge on public funds. In this policy it was successful. At March 31st 1921 the net result of all transactions was a profit of £6,390,000. Against this sum there were some outstanding claims; but when these have been adjusted the remaining profit should still be a substantial one.

on the harvest of 1918 alone of about £4,500,000. If we were to reckon up the value of the savings effected in 1917, and in the two years following the Armistice, it would be found that the cost of the Food Production Campaign was reduced to an amount small in comparison with even one day's war spending. But we need not now attempt such estimates ; it is sufficient for our purpose to note that the premium paid by the country for this war risks (food) insurance policy was a negligible one, if judged by the criteria which the ordinary man applies to any insurance premium that he may find it necessary or prudent to pay.

Nor is it only as a small and altogether justifiable insurance premium against the risks of a temporary blockade, or the failure of those overseas harvests on which we depended, that we must regard our expenditure on food production in the war years. The additional supplies which the increased cultivation of the land of the country placed at the disposal of the public between August 1917 and August 1919 meant more to the comfort and well-being of our forty-seven million people than 99 per cent. of them will ever realize. Without these millions of tons of extra home-grown food there would undoubtedly have been hunger for many of us, and want for not a few, in spite of all the resources and the efforts of the Ministries of Shipping and of Food. Even the final victory of the Allied Armies in the autumn of 1918 would not have averted many hungry weeks after the Armistice, if we had failed in our campaign on the land.

CHAPTER XII

FROM FOOD PRODUCTION BACK TO FARMING

Summary of the War Changes. Changes in Area. Average Crops of War Period. Total Produce of Principal Crops. Live stock Changes. The Effect of the War on the Home-grown Food Supply. Could the United Kingdom produce its own Food ? Problems of Peace Farming. The Consumer's Interests. The Farmer's Point of View. Increasing Production. Prospects for Extension of Tillage. Grass *v.* Tillage a National Question. The Farmer's Difficulty. Influence of Education and Research. Relief for Tillage in Taxation and Rating. Land used for Sport. Country Industries. Unity necessary for increasing the Production of the Land.

In concluding this survey of Food Production in the United Kingdom during the war some of the main features of the changes that took place may briefly be alluded to. The *Efforts* made by agriculturists, the *Conditions* under which they worked, and the final *Results* are respectively reflected in, and summarized by, the figures in Tables XX to XXIII.

Changes in Area.

Table **XX** gives the area under the principal crops in 1904–13, and in each of the years 1914 to 1918. The changes in area show the directions which farmers' activities took. The normal management of the land is indicated by the figures for the average of the ten-year period 1904–13.

Referring first to the whole cultivated area, it will be seen that, except for a slight increase in 1916, there was a continuous shrinkage from 1914 to 1918. At the outbreak of war the total area was some 250,000 acres less than in the average year of the preceding decennium, and it had fallen by a further 500,000 acres in 1918 ; a small part of this loss was due to the occupation of land for war purposes, but most of it would appear to have been due to incomplete returns, and it may be doubted whether the total area at the farmer's disposal was substantially less in 1918 than it was in 1914.

TABLE XX

AREA UNDER PERMANENT GRASS AND TILLAGE CROPS IN THE UNITED KINGDOM
ON THE AVERAGE OF THE TEN YEARS 1904–13, IN EACH OF THE YEARS 1914
TO 1918, AND ON THE AVERAGE OF THE FIVE YEARS 1914–18.

Figures, Millions of Acres

Crop	Av. 1904–13	1914	1915	1916	1917	1918	Av. 1914–18
Total cultivated area .	47·08	46·76	46·67	46·69	46·34	46·27	46·55
Permanent grass . .	27·63	27·35	27·33	27·19	26·59	25·05	26·70
Total arable land . .	19·45	19·41	19·35	19·50	19·75	21·22	19·85
Arable land under clover and grass .	6·32	6·61	6·46	6·76	6·04	5·52	6·28
Arable land not in grass .	13·13	12·80	12·89	12·74	13·71	15·70	13·57
Wheat	1·78	1·91	2·33	2·05	2·11	2·80	2·24
Barley	1·87	1·87	1·52	1·65	1·80	1·91	1·74
Oats	4·11	3·90	4·18	4·17	4·79	5·71	4·55
Potatoes . . .	1·17	1·21	1·21	1·12	1·38	1·51	1·28
Turnips, swedes, and mangolds . . .	2·34	2·28	2·13	2·08	2·17	2·11	2·15
Minor crops and fallow .	1·86	1·63	1·52	1·67	1·46	1·66	1·61

The area under arable land was largely increased in 1918
and the area under permanent grass was decreased to a somewhat greater extent. There was further a substantial decrease
in the area under rotation grasses and clovers, and there was
a notable increase in the cultivated area not occupied by grass;
the change began in 1917, and in 1918 the increase over the
1914 area was nearly 23 per cent. The result of this change
was that, on the average of the years 1914–18, 440,000 more
acres were available for growing grain and other tillage crops
than in the years 1904–13.

There was a large increase in the areas under oats, wheat,
and potatoes, and a decrease in barley, roots, and minor crops.
The immediate changes produced by the war are shown by the
1915 figures; wheat and oats were increased at the expense
of barley, roots, and minor crops. Barley more than recovered
its pre-war area in 1918. Not until 1917 was there any increase

in the land planted with potatoes. Minor crops and fallow reached the 1914 level in 1916 and 1918. Throughout the war the area under roots was abnormally small.

Average Crops of War Period.

The general conditions under which the farmer worked during the war are indicated by the figures in Table XXI, which compare the average crops secured in each of the five harvests 1914 to 1918 with the average yield of the years 1904–13. The yield depended chiefly on the weather, but the manure and the labour supply were also responsible for the results. Labour shortage told heavily against most crops in 1916, and especially against spring-sown cereals, swedes, turnips, and potatoes in England, and against potatoes in Scotland. In all the war years swedes and turnips suffered from insufficient hoeing. In 1916, and to some extent in 1917, most crops were adversely affected by advances in manure prices and the scarcity of both phosphates and potash ; on the other hand, the cereal crops of 1918 benefited by increased applications of sulphate of ammonia; and it is likely that the yields of both potatoes and mangolds were also improved by the free use of this nitrogenous manure.

TABLE XXI

Yield Per Acre of the Principal Crops of the United Kingdom on the Average of the Ten Years 1904–13, and in each of the Five Years 1914–18.

Crop	1904–13	1914	1915	1916	1917	1918
	bus.	bus.	bus.	bus.	bus.	bus.
Wheat	31·88	32·77	31·68	29·13	30·58	33·3
Barley	34·03	34·48	30·80	32·02	32·00	33·8
Oats	41·94	42·63	42·91	41·16	43·70	44·5
	tons	tons	tons	tons	tons	tons
Potatoes	5·63	6·25	6·27	4·78	6·30	6·1
Turnips and swedes . .	14·66	13·83	15·13	14·49	14·81	14·3
Mangolds . . .	19·42	18·50	19·48	19·60	21·47	20·6
	cwt.	cwt.	cwt.	cwt.	cwt.	cwt.
Hay, clover and rye-grass	32·49	29·01	31·91	35·95	30·58	31·3
,, permanent grass .	28·85	25·25	24·78	29·78	25·96	26·7

The weather of the years 1914 to 1918 exercised a greater influence on the farmer's crops than it would have done if peace had been maintained. Rain, temperature, and sunshine were not directly influenced by war ; theories to the contrary notwithstanding, the gun-fire in France did not modify the rainfall of the south-eastern counties. On the other hand, the effects of the weather on crops were accentuated by war conditions. Stripped as the country was of labour, timely frosts in winter had an unusual value in ameliorating the state of the land, and untimely rains in spring or autumn were unusually hurtful in curtailing the farmer's opportunities of sowing, or harvesting, his crops. It was the mellowing action of the winter's frosts that lightened the task of the allotment holder in 1917, and it was the deplorable harvesting weather experienced by farmers' depleted staffs that completed the ruin of the potato crop of 1916, and reduced to rotting straw so much of the splendid oat crop grown on newly ploughed grass land in Wales and the north of England in 1918.

In two of the five years in which war harvests were gathered in, the yield per acre of the wheat crop exceeded the decennial average. Barley reached the average yield per acre only in the harvest of 1914. Were it not that it had been frequently sown, as a last resort, on land on which wheat or oats failed, it might have been an average crop in 1918. Oats and potatoes, on the other hand, fell below the average in one only of the five years. The potato crops of 1914, 1915, and 1917 were very satisfactory. The 1916 crop was worse than any since 1907. The turnip crop, though under average in three of the five years, did not differ much from average in any year except 1914, while the yield of mangolds was over average in four years, and was very good in 1917. The only war year in which hay was an over average crop was 1916. In other years hay, whether grown on arable land or on permanent meadows, was indifferent or poor, and, as the demand for hay for the Army was large, many difficulties were created for the farmer and the forage officer in their mutual dealings.

Total Produce of Principal Crops.

Table **XXII** shows the total crops secured as the combined results of the farmer's efforts and of the weather conditions. The total produce of the three important cereal crops is stated in millions of quarters (not tons as in Chapters **VI** to **IX**); the quantities of the other crops are in millions of tons. The first column of figures shows the average yield of the period 1904–13, and the last, the average of the harvests 1914–18. With the exception of the clover and rye-grass hay, and part of the meadow hay of 1914, all these crops were harvested during the war.

TABLE XXII

TOTAL PRODUCE OF THE PRINCIPAL CROPS OF THE UNITED KINGDOM ON THE AVERAGE OF THE TEN YEARS 1904–13 ; IN EACH OF THE YEARS 1914 TO 1918 ; AND ON THE AVERAGE OF THE FIVE YEARS 1914–18.

Figures, Millions of Quarters or Tons

Crop.	Av. 1904–13	1914	1915	1916	1917	1918	Av. 1914–18
	qrs.	qrs.	qrs.	qrs.	qrs.	qrs.	qrs.
Wheat	7·09	7·80	9·24	7·47	8·04	11·64	8·84
Barley	7·96	8·07	5·86	6·61	7·18	8·07	7·16
Oats	21·56	20·66	22·31	21·33	26·02	31·51	24·37
	tons	tons	tons	tons	tons	tons	tons
Potatoes . . .	6·59	7·48	7·54	5·47	8·60	9·22	7·66
Turnips, swedes, mangolds	36·83	33·72	34·13	32·33	35·21	33·16	33·80
Hay, clover and rye-grass	4·82	4·21	4·53	5·49	4·77	4·39	4·68
,, permanent grass .	9·33	8·19	7·92	9·71	8·43	7·94	8·44

In each of the war years, even in 1916, the total wheat crop of the country exceeded the pre-war average—the mean increase in the five years was nearly 25 per cent. ; the increase in 1918 was no less than 64 per cent. The total barley crop in 1915, 1916, and 1917 was less than the pre-war average, but in 1918 slightly more ; over the five years the average decrease was 10 per cent. The oat crops of 1914 and 1916 were below, but in 1917 and 1918 much above, the pre-war totals. The average for the five years exceeded the 1904–13 average by 13 per cent., while the 1918 crop was 46 per cent. in excess of the pre-war crop. In each year except 1916 the potato crops of the war period exceeded the pre-war yield. The average yield was 16 per cent. more than in 1904–13, and in 1918 a potato crop 40 per cent. in excess of the average pre-war crop was secured. In no war year did the total yield of turnips, swedes, and mangolds reach the pre-war level; the poorest crop was in 1916 and the best in 1917; the deficiency in the average crop amounted to 8 per cent. The total quantity of hay grown on arable land was over-average in 1916, but somewhat less than average in all of the other war years; the average crop of the five years was 3 per cent. less than in 1904–13. The hay crop produced by permanent grass also exceeded the average in 1916, but in the other years was relatively rather worse than the produce of temporary grass; on the average, it was 10 per cent. less than in 1904–13. A poor hay crop in both 1917 and 1918, the demands for forage for army and town horses, and the lack of concentrated feeding stuffs made hay very scarce in the winter of 1918–19; it was at this period that the stock owner's greatest difficulties occurred. Although farmers had frequently had cause for anxiety, they themselves little knew how precarious was the position of their live stock in the autumn of 1918, and not until months after the Armistice was signed did they realize how very fortunate they had been in bringing their herds and flocks through the war without serious losses.

Live Stock Changes.

The losses in number were, indeed, remarkably small, and until towards the end of 1917, except in the case of pigs, the effects produced by war had been slight. The position from year to year between 1914 and 1919 is shown by the figures in Table XXIII. In each case the figures are those which were collected by the Agricultural Departments at the June census.

The dairy herd fell off slightly in 1915, but recovered, and in 1919 was within a few thousands of the 1914 size. The total number of cattle from 1916 onwards was somewhat greater than at the outbreak of war. In 1918 there was a decrease of about

50,000 in cattle over two years old, as compared with the previous year, and of about 40,000 as compared with 1914, chiefly because of the heavy slaughter which took place after prices were controlled in the autumn of 1917. There was, however, a noteworthy increase in the cattle of this age in 1919.

TABLE XXIII

NUMBERS OF CATTLE, SHEEP, AND PIGS IN THE UNITED KINGDOM IN EACH OF THE YEARS 1914 TO 1919.

Figures, Millions

Description of stock	1914	1915	1916	1917	1918	1919
Cows and heifers in milk or calf .	4·59	4·49	4·50	4·51	4·60	4·59
Other cattle, under one year .	2·66	2·79	2·81	2·77	2·67	2·68
,, ,, one to two years .	2·60	2·67	2·80	2·76	2·75	2·77
,, ,, over two years .	2·33	2·22	2·34	2·34	2·29	2·46
Total cattle . . .	12·18	12·17	12·45	12·38	12·31	12·49
Ewes for breeding . . .	11·26	11·34	11·60	11·44	10·98	10·03
Other sheep under one year .	11·67	11·54	11·67	10·89	11·17	9·79
,, ,, over one year .	5·04	5·40	5·58	5·53	4·91	5·30
Total sheep . . .	27·96	28·28	28·85	27·87	27·07	25·12
Sows for breeding . . .	0·49	0·44	0·43	0·37	0·41	0·36
Other pigs	3·46	3·36	3·18	2·63	2·40	2·56
Total pigs	3·95	3·80	3·62	3·01	2·81	2·92

The position in the case of sheep was less satisfactory. The numbers were well maintained until 1917, but thereafter there was a large decrease. To some extent the decline was due to natural causes. The winter of 1916–17 was a hard one for hill flocks, and the crop of lambs in 1917 was poor. But over the south of England, where sheep are extensively kept on roots and other products of tillage land, further causes were at work. The cost of growing roots and of ' folding ' sheep had increased, and there was much difficulty in securing capable shepherds in 1915 and 1916; later, feeding stuffs became scarce and expensive, and the prices fixed for lamb and the best mutton were unsatisfactory. It was not possible after prices were controlled to discriminate sufficiently in price between mutton of different qualities, hence in some districts it was profitable to sell ewes, but not profitable to rear lambs. The combined influence of these various factors in the situation resulted in a 10 per cent. decrease in the sheep flocks of 1919 as compared with those of 1914.

The ox and the sheep are seldom competitors with man for their food supply. In normal times they consume a certain quantity of milling offals and oats, which in time of scarcity may be required by man ; but broadly it may be said that their requirements in this respect do not give rise to serious difficulties, for there are many foods which may be substituted. In the case of pigs it is different ; if the milling offals, barley meal, and maize meal, on which they are largely fed, are required by man, the pig keeper is likely to be faced with great difficulties. The changes in policy which were necessary, as the food situation fluctuated at different periods of the war, caused much dissatisfaction, and no doubt involved many stock owners in losses. But the fact is that a settled pig-policy in war-time, when the conditions are dictated by the enemy, is impracticable. Pigs are not only most valuable meat-making animals, but breed very quickly, and when opportunities present themselves of securing suitable foods everything possible must be done to encourage pig-keeping; but directly pigs come into direct competition with man, and the food situation is difficult, they must be sacrificed, for it is better to keep five men alive on barley meal than one comfortably nourished on pork. In this country the alternative did not arise, but it was this consideration that finally settled the hotly debated pig-policy of Germany. Although a sharp fall in the number of our pigs had taken place by June 1917, we had, in 1919, 74 per cent. of the number of pigs which we had in 1914; a final result which, all things considered, must be admitted to be satisfactory.

In examining the numbers of live stock maintained during the war it must be remembered that, as has already been stated, man was not their only new competitor for provender. The demands of the War Office were large ; the industrial horse-owner, too, deprived of the usual overseas supplies, made greater calls on home produce than in peace time. The approved arrangement was that the forage officer was to take

only what the farmer could spare after providing enough for
the essential needs of his live stock. The practical difficulty,
caused by the short hay crops of 1917 and 1918 and the scarcity
and high price of feeding stuffs, was the interpretation to be
placed on ' enough '.

The War's Effect on the Supply of Home-Grown Food.

In the foregoing pages we have summarized the combined
effects produced by the farmer's efforts and by war conditions on the crops and live stock of the United Kingdom.
We must now look at the war changes from the consumer's
point of view. What was the final result? Was the home food
supply reduced or increased because of war?

The years 1914–17 call for little comment. In the first, it was
the harvesting of the crops only that was influenced by war;
and a glance at the figures in Table **XXII** will suffice to show
that in 1916 production was below the average, but that in
1915 and 1917 there must have been some increase in the food
supply. The year 1918, however, deserves more attention.
It was in this year that, for the first time, the Food Production
policy adopted at the end of 1916 became effective, and a comparison of the quantity of food provided in 1918 with the
pre-war supplies is of special interest.

In Tables **XXI** and **XXII** a comparison of the war crops
with those of 1904–13 has been made; but as the food supply
estimates made by the Food (War) Committee were for 1909–13,
this period will be selected for comparison with the results
secured in 1918.

At the time of the Armistice all questions relating to food
supply and consumption were so modified by war conditions
that a comparison of the food value of the 1918 and of the
pre-war farm produce cannot readily be made, and our present
purpose will best be served by answering the question: What
contribution would the output of 1918 have made to the
nation's food supply, if the produce had been available under
the normal conditions of 1909–13?

First with respect to the gains. We had at the time of the
Armistice 4,188,000 qrs. more wheat, 229,000 qrs. more barley,

10,317,000 qrs. more oats, and 2,608,000 tons more potatoes available than we had on the average of the period 1909–13. It will at least be agreed that we could have made the extra wheat into bread, and the barley into beer ; but the destination of the oats and potatoes is less certain. With so large a supply of oats, porridge might have been more popular, and potatoes, too, might easily have been consumed in excess of the 1909–13 quantities.

If in 1909–13 the nation had been as poor as it now is, and if our use of food were dictated by considerations of thrift, the whole of the extra oatmeal and extra potatoes would have been gratefully accepted and eaten by the people themselves ; but in the prosperity of 1909–13 and with our acquired habits (of which we cannot even now rid ourselves) these extra supplies would largely, in the case of oats, and to some extent in the case of potatoes, have been fed to live stock. The result would have been that about one-third of the available energy in the former case, and three-fourths in the latter, would have been available for man. In this case 4,780,000 million Calories [1] would have been added to the home output of 1909–13.

With respect to the minor crops, there was no doubt some decrease in the production of certain field-grown vegetables of small food value, partly because of labour difficulties and partly because their growth was discouraged by the Food Production Department; but the increase of the produce of allotments was so considerable, and the total food value of these minor crops is so small in comparison with the main products, that no account need be taken of them in our estimate.

On the other side of the account there were in 1918 certain losses in meat and milk production. The extent of the losses which may have been due to the ploughing of grass land has been discussed in Chapter IX ; but these are not the only losses with which we are now concerned.

[1] It will be recalled that one million Calories approximately equals a year's supply of energy for one person ; the numerals may therefore be read as persons provided with food.

There were changes in the supplies of the fodder crops grown on arable land. Straw was more abundant than before the war, and so were home-produced milling offals, light grain, and waste potatoes ; roots, on the other hand, were less plentiful.

Again, the output of 1918 was affected by abnormal conditions, other than the actual supply of food for live stock. We have seen that the milk yield was reduced by the substitution of inefficient milkers for the skilled men who had joined the Army ; and meat production was reduced by the irregular supplies of feeding stuffs, as well as by the limited quantities. It is thus not possible to answer off-hand the question, ' What would the production of meat and milk in the United Kingdom have been if the crops of 1918 had been available under normal conditions ? ' The writer's opinion is that if there were any reduction it would have been very small. There would at least be no difficulty in showing (on paper) how, given the produce actually available in 1918, the 1909–13 output of meat and milk could have been produced. But for the present purpose it will be assumed that a substantial part of the losses which actually took place were caused by a deficiency of home produce.

The total loss in milk production in 1918, as we have seen in Chapter IX, was estimated by Lord Astor's Committee at 390,000,000 gallons, and it was ascribed largely to the scarcity of feeding stuffs. We have already estimated that, at the most, 80,000,000 gallons may have been lost by the ploughing of cow pastures, and we may now put the total loss, because of a reduction in home-grown crops, at 100,000,000 gallons.

We have estimated, in Chapter IX, that the reduction in beef and mutton because of the ploughing of pastures amounted to 60,000 tons. The small quantities of home grain available in 1918–19 were mostly fed to cows. Other cattle and sheep were deprived of their usual rations. We may, therefore, estimate the total reduction in the beef and mutton output, because of the shortage of home fodders and feeding stuffs, at 100,000 tons, thus leaving 71,000 tons only to be accounted for by the reduction in imported feeding stuffs and by all other war consequences.

The statistics collected by the Ministry of Food pointed to

a decrease of 209,000 tons of pig meat in 1918–19 as compared with the five pre-war years. This large decrease was due chiefly to the lack of milling offals, maize, and feeding barley, that is chiefly to imported materials. The whole quantity of home-grown grain used in pig-feeding before the war may be estimated to have produced about 45,000 tons of pork. Sound grain for pig-feeding was available in very limited quantities in 1918–19; on the other hand, there was much damaged grain. Further, the potato crop—and therefore suitable material for pig-feeding—was largely in excess of the pre-war crop. From these considerations it would appear to be safe to conclude that the absence of sufficient supplies of home-grown pig foods in 1918 cannot have reduced the production of pig meat by more than 25,000 tons.[1]

The losses which have been assumed in meat and milk if converted into terms of energy would be equivalent to 730,000 million Calories; thus it may be concluded that the net gain which the country secured from the produce of the 1918 harvest was not less than 4,050,000 million Calories.

We have seen, in Chapter V, that in 1909–13 the average food supply of the United Kingdom provided 49,430,000 million Calories, and that the total product of the home soil was 16,872,000 million Calories; the gain in the output of home-grown food in 1918 was therefore about 24 per cent.

In other words, whereas the country began the war with supplies provided by its own soil which would have sufficed for 125 days out of the 365, in the year in which the Armistice was signed it had secured a harvest that would have sufficed for 155 days out of the 365. The crops were grown and the live stock were fed under conditions that were altogether abnormal; but the land's extra produce was equivalent to the supply of 30 days' food for the nation living its normal life.

For many months after the Armistice the ordinary conditions of peace did not return; statistics indicate, however, that the total consumption of food per head of the population, when measured in terms of energy, did not differ markedly

---

[1] It should be noted that this figure represents loss due to a *deficiency* of home produce; further loss would occur because the *efficiency* of much home produce would be lessened owing to the absence of imported feeding stuffs.

from the pre-war rate. But if the dietary of our people was not markedly deficient, our live stock were abnormally hungry, and it may be surmised that, in spite of the vigilance of the Food Controller, the compassion of their owners and the wretched harvest weather enabled them to consume a larger proportion of the produce of the harvest of 1918 than they did in the period 1909–13.

It should be noted that the extra month's supply, which the 1918 harvest represented, falls far short of the total quantity of human food that the 1918 harvest could have furnished, if the prolongation of the war had compelled us to stretch our resources to the uttermost. As was stated at the time, if we had reserved for live stock the pre-war oat crop, but closely milled all other grain and used it for bread, and if we had made the full use of potatoes that a hungry nation might make, we could, from our cereals and potatoes, have provided a quantity of food equivalent to forty weeks' consumption of bread stuffs ; and by slaughtering our live stock the additional foods required by the population in this period would have been procurable. But fortunately for us no such drastic methods were necessary.

Could the United Kingdom produce its own Food ?

In connexion with the large increase in food supply that resulted in 1918 from the Food Production Campaign, reference may be made to a subject often raised in the war years. It is sometimes assumed that it is merely the want of enterprise of our farmers, or the lack of application of scientific principles, or the unwise policy of our statesmen that prevents the country from producing nearly all the food it needs ; and it has been seriously asked, ' Is it not possible for the United Kingdom to feed its entire population, or at least to supply all necessary foods, except the small percentage that could only be grown in tropical or semi-tropical climates ? ' From the purely agricultural point of view it may be answered that there would be no special difficulty, if the people of this country were content to place themselves under the direction of some all-powerful Food Controller, who would feed them with what was necessary, as a farmer feeds his cattle. If they would be satisfied with the rations of protein, fat, and carbohydrate which their bodies must have, and if they would be prepared to pay for their food on a calorie basis the farmer could no doubt supply the necessary protein and energy.   But the public would not be content with rations of protein, fat, and carbohydrate, and would not pay on a calorie basis.   They must have bread and meat and many other things in certain customary quantities ; and thus under present circumstances, or under any circumstances that can be foreseen, there is no possibility of providing the foods they demand, from the soils of the United Kingdom.   It would require more than twenty million acres of land to supply the grain alone that is consumed in the country, and to secure this quantity of grain it would be necessary to plough every acre of cultivated land not subject to flooding and not too far above sea-level to prevent corn from ripening.   The cost would be prohibitive, and the suggestion that we might furnish our people with their normal food supply may be dismissed as absurd.

But between the 34 per cent. of our food requirements supplied by our land in 1909–13 and 100 per cent. there is a wide margin; and if the vanished hand of the Food Controller could be restored, and he compelled us to satisfy from 40 to 50 per cent. of our total needs from our own land, it might be no bad thing. There is great scope for economy in the selection and use of foodstuffs, and a Food Controller who could compel us to purchase and use food wisely would quickly solve most of our pressing economic difficulties.

Problems of Peace Farming.

As the people of this country are chiefly fed upon imported food, and are interested in the quality and price of their foodstuffs rather than in its origin, the ordinary consumer takes little interest in the well-being of agriculture.   The farmer, on the other hand, finds almost the whole of his market in this country, and is very directly interested in the prosperity of other industries.   For him bad trade creates a most perplexing situation, for although he knows what his customers would like to buy, he does not know what they will be able to buy.   This one-sided interest makes the position of the food producer in peace-time quite as difficult as it was in war-time ; indeed, in a sense more difficult. In war-time the farmer knows that all he can grow is required, and should the price be controlled in the interests of consumers, he is satisfied (although he may not admit it) that in fixing prices due regard is paid to fair dealing. In peace-time he realizes that his prices are controlled by his competitors in other lands, and that the cost of production to him is not considered by his customers. The solution of these difficulties appears to the farmer to present an almost impossible problem, but he is satisfied that if the cost of production in other industries could be reduced and his customers were prosperous his own anxieties would be lessened.

Other classes too, all indeed who are dependent on our great industries, are as directly interested as the farmer in this question of lessening the cost of production and improving trade.

The essential interests of producers and of the great majority of consumers are therefore not divergent, and, when we examine this peace difficulty carefully, we find that in one respect it closely resembles our war-time food problem. Then the need was for foods supplying energy in abundance, now the need is that the sources of energy sought after by consumers should be abundant and cheap. We have heard much since the Armistice of the harmful effect on industry of dear calories in coal ; but food, too, is a fuel, and high-priced calories in our foodstuffs, even more than in coal, have increased the cost of output and depressed trade.

The Consumer's Interests.

Let us then, and first from the point of view of the general public, ask what direction the farming of our land should take in order to increase the output and to lessen the cost of the energy supplied to us in food. The subject has been discussed in Chapters III and IV, and it has there been shown that the chief factors in determining the cost of energy in food are, the quantity of land used in its production, and—if converted into animal produce—the kind of animal used for the purpose. From the agricultural point of view the green-leaved plant is essentially an organism for securing new energy for use on, or sale from, the farm, the animal an organism for manufacturing the energy already existing on the farm into a new product. The plant adds to, the animal dissipates, the stocks of energy with which the farmer works.

The cultivator himself, no doubt, considers that any particular crop, such as wheat, is the result of his own efforts. He has grown it on land for which he has paid rent, by labour which he has hired, from seed which he has supplied, and with manures which he has purchased. Moreover, he tells himself, it is his own skill that has produced a satisfactory yield. All this is true ; but if we' were to analyse his crop, and seek the source of the materials, and of the stored-up energy, we should find that some 5 per cent. only of the materials have come from soil and manure, and that but a trivial quantity of the energy has come from the seed. The farmer has prepared the land and sown the seed and tended the crop ; but almost the whole substance of the crop has come from the air, and the large store of energy, which in the wheat grown on a single acre may amount to two or three million Calories, has come from sunlight. Nature has worked with man, and, as Adam Smith says, 'at no expense' has made this great contribution to wealth ; and thus the resulting energy is cheap.

In the case of the pasture the farmer gives little assistance to Nature ; he may perhaps apply some manure, cut and clear drains, and harrow and roll the surface, otherwise he does nothing; hence, to the agriculturist grass-growing is inexpensive. The benefit of this cheapness cannot, however, be passed on to the human consumer ; to him the energy stored up in grass is worthless until converted into meat or milk, and in the process of conversion most of the energy collected by the plant is dissipated; so that ultimately not more than one-fifth, or more often not more than one-tenth or one-twentieth, is available for man.

The business of the farmer, it will be seen, is thus partly concerned with the production of raw material, and partly with the manufacture of raw material. In a sense it is a matter of indifference to him on which side of his business he concen-

trates chief attention. But conditions might easily arise—
if they do not already exist—which might force this country
to exploit its soils for the production of more raw material.

Although the farmer may devote his entire energies to
live stock, as in the case of the grazier, or concentrate wholly
on crop-growing, as in the case of the market gardener, it must
not be supposed that under British conditions the production
of raw material by crops, and the manufacture of meat and
milk, could be carried on extensively as independent industries.
It is indeed possible, though not probable, that the farmer
might almost wholly abandon tillage in favour of grazing;
but it is not possible that he could extend tillage and neglect
live stock. To the farmer of the United Kingdom his live stock
must always be the principal source of income.

Moreover, quite apart from their own need for meat and
milk, the general public have good reasons for desiring a prosperous live stock industry and the maintenance of a large head
of live stock in this and the other countries from which they
draw supplies. Live stock not only cheapen the cost of production of grain and other vegetable foods, but they stabilize
supplies, and thus prevent violent fluctuations in the cost of
living. They constitute our real reserves and protect us from
famine in adverse seasons; for it is in the bodies of live stock
and not in granaries that we can economically store our surplus
grain. Whereas nations who depend almost entirely on vegetable foods increase in numbers close to the limits set by the
average harvest, and suffer severely in bad years, nations
depending largely on live stock are scarcely affected, since the
grain consumed by stock in average seasons may be diverted
to man's use when the need arises.

This stabilizing of the supplies, indeed, constitutes a principal part of the farmer's business. When corn prices fall
because of over-abundant supplies, the farmer relieves the
market by feeding more grain to his cattle, sheep, and pigs;
in so doing he dissipates 80 to 90 per cent. of the original
energy value of the grain, but he converts it into meat and milk,
which pay him better. A rise in corn prices follows, he reverses

his procedure, and automatically a larger supply of energy, in cheap vegetable foods, goes to market.

Looking at the subject broadly, therefore, and from the consumer's point of view, it may be stated that what the public require is an abundant supply of energy-producing materials at steady prices, and further that abundance and uniform prices require both an extension of tillage farming and the maintenance of a large head of live stock. From the purely technical point of view these two requirements are not incompatible, and it is to the furtherance of this policy that the efforts of those who study the consumer's needs should be directed.

The Farmer's Point of View.

In war we were forced to consider the needs of the consumer, and as we had not too closely to consider his tastes we were able to concentrate our efforts on increasing the soil's output of energy in a form available to man. We reckoned up Calories as we counted rifles or shells ; every million represented the food required by one of our people, every billion reduced by some 500,000 tons the demands made on our shipping, and this again, in 1918, meant 100,000 additional American troops on the Western Front. Thus we insisted on the vital importance of tillage, ignored peace-time rules of husbandry, abandoned ordinary considerations of profit and loss, purchased tractors as we purchased guns, and secured manures, binder twine, and other farming requisites as we secured munitions.

But with the coming of peace the conditions that dictated our war policy disappeared. The Food Production Department and the Food Ministry went, control of all kinds was abolished, and the general public were quickly left to look after their own energy requirements. The consumer still requires his 3,000 Calories per day, but he asks for bread and meat and milk. Calories no more satisfy his tastes than the price he offers for them fills the farmer's purse. Food Production has become *farming*, and farming must pay its way.

Farmers and their men have now to live by their labour.

Pre-war experience proved that this was then no easy task, and post-war experience has already made it plain that there must be no decrease in the skill of the master, and no relaxation in the industry of the labourer, if they are now to earn a livelihood on the land.

It needs no argument to prove that the problem of increasing production, and at the same time maintaining a solvent agricultural industry, is a most difficult one. The struggle in the generation before the war was hard. None of the three partners in the industry had grown fat on the land. The owner, unless he had other resources, with difficulty maintained the condition of his estate; the tenant seldom, himself, acquired the full capital needed for successful farming, and the task of keeping what money he had was often too much for him; the labourer's remuneration was notoriously low.

It was not to be expected, and it is not claimed, that all our pre-war owners were model landlords, that all our farmers were enterprising cultivators and skilled managers of live stock, or that all our ploughmen, shepherds, and other farm workers were reliable and industrious men; but taking the industry as a whole, it is claimed that it was well served by those engaged in it; as well as were any of our other industries. Far from being unskilled, War Tribunals revealed the farm labourer as a man possessed of knowledge and qualities which many a town artisan might envy; and although the townsman may at times be disposed to regard the farmer as a slow-witted person, who fails to make money because he neglects cost-accounting, our Controllers discovered, in their dealings with him, that his grasp of questions affecting his own business was thorough, and that in bargaining he had few equals.

Now that war has ceased and we are striving after real peace it would be well if town consumers—who so frequently express dissatisfaction with the farming of our land, and assume that all would be well if the farmers, in leading-strings, could be told what to do by some central authority—would set themselves the task of tackling some of the real difficulties of food production in this country, such for example as marketing costs. We in the towns point out to the farmer that he has the finest market in the world at his doors, and that we are paying high prices for all that he sends us. But we do not take sufficient account of his side of the transaction. He receives, perhaps, half of what we pay for meat and one-third of what we pay for milk ; while for the potatoes, other vegetables, and fruit which he grows on his tillage land he often gets not even one-fourth of what we are required to pay.

This is not proof of his lack of skill in transporting and marketing commodities, any more than it is proof of our lack of skill in securing our supplies. It is indeed our business rather than his to see that transport and marketing charges are reduced ; for it matters more to the nation than to the farmer that his land should be tilled. Moreover, his voting strength is small ; it is the townsman who can control the nation's business.

One point clearly brought out by war experience must be emphasized, and it is that only by enlisting the voluntary co-operation of the farmer can the nation secure any large increase in the home production of food. The Food Production Department succeeded when, and only when, it had the whole agricultural population co-operating in its effort to increase production. And this war lesson is equally true in time of peace.

Increasing Production.

Apart from considerations of profit, it may be stated that there would be no technical difficulty in largely increasing the output of food from the soils of the United Kingdom. Much of the grass land of the country is of poor quality ; given reasonably good management, it should be well within the capacity of graziers to raise the annual production of meat by pastures from about 65 lb. to 100 lb. per acre and even to double the present output. But the large demands which extensive improvements would create for manures would raise their prices, already high ; the future value of meat is quite uncertain, and any prospect of doubling the yield of pastures is at present remote. The most that could reasonably be looked for would be an increase in yield of from 25 to 30 per cent., and if we achieve this within the next generation we shall have made remarkable progress as compared with earlier periods.

Improvement of pastures might result in a similar increase in the milk supply ; and, by selection of cows, a further addition to the yield might be made, so that an increase of 50 per cent. in our dairy produce might be possible in the same period. If these two great improvements could be made, we should, by the year 1950, have added the maintenance of 2,365,000 persons (i. e. million Calories) to our home food supplies, a net increase over the 1909–13 production of 14 per cent.

Improvements in our tillage crops may also be expected ; but here the scope is less than in the case of our pastures, for the existing management is better, and it would be more difficult to add 15 per cent. to the yield of tillage crops than to add 30 per cent. to the yield of pastures ; the advances to be expected depend chiefly on the work of the plant-breeder.

Taking a sanguine view of the improvements that might be made in our pastures and tillage crops, it may be stated that, if the country adheres to the proportions of grass and tillage cultivated at the outbreak of war, the most that could be expected would be that the United Kingdom should provide food for nineteen million persons by the middle of the present century. And this figure depends upon a rate of progress in our agricultural output for which our experience, since the middle of the nineteenth century, gives no warrant.

As has been stated in previous chapters, the only certain way to secure a substantial increase in the country's home-grown food is to increase the area under tillage.

Every one who has studied the history of agriculture in the nineteenth century must know that when home-grown food was essential the United Kingdom was farmed so as to support a larger population than at present. Those ignorant of our history were shown in 1918 that, under the extreme difficulties of war, and denied all the requisites that facilitate cultivation, the farmers of the country added 40 per cent.[1] to the pre-war

[1] See diagram, p. 258.

crops of grain and potatoes, and some 24 per cent. to the total output of food. The war effort resulted in the production of a much greater quantity of food than there is any prospect of growing in the next generation, if we return to our pre-war tillage area.

The difficulties in securing an increase in tillage farming are not of a technical kind ; there is much land in the United Kingdom, well suited for tillage, which now grows grass. The climate is not unsuitable for tillage ; taken as a whole it is a fine climate for tillage farming, one of the best in the world, as is proved by the yield of our crops ; but it is still better suited for grass-growing. Thus the farmer has a choice of the methods of management which he may adopt, and is not, as in dry hot climates, compelled either to till or to abandon agriculture. British tillage farming has declined in comparison with the tillage of other lands for reasons not altogether inherent in the soil, or in the industry itself. Land went down to grass in the end of the nineteenth century because, although good, it was not good enough. As the industrial and commercial prosperity of the country increased, its land became of less value to those engaged in tilling it, for other industries offered more remunerative employment. It was not only bad seasons and cheap transport that led to the substitution of grass for arable land ; it was not merely a case of the misfortune of the farmer, but of the good fortune of his fellows. If there had been no bad seasons land would have gone down to grass; and, unless we were to assume that the industrial prosperity of the country was entirely dependent on cheap breadstuffs—which it manifestly was not—it may further be stated that, in the conditions existing before the war, there would have been a marked decline in tillage farming, even if wheat had maintained the prices of the early 'seventies.

Prospects for an Extension of Tillage Farming.

Assuming the country's pre-war policy to be continued, there would seem to be no immediate prospect of an increase in the area under the plough. Even with the confidence which it was expected that guaranteed prices would give to the corn-grower, the area under grass increased rapidly after the Armistice.

The diagram on p. 334, which indicates the area under crops other than grass in 1874, and for each year in the period 1914–21, shows clearly enough what are the views of farmers on the prospects of tillage farming. In every part of the United Kingdom the rapid increase in land under the plough, which took place between 1916 and 1918, has been followed by an equally rapid fall. There can be no doubt that the Agricultural Returns of the next year or two will show a further decline, and there is no likelihood that when the 1914 level has been reached the down-to-grass movement will be stayed.

It is of some interest to compare the nation's post-war purchases of wheat and meat from overseas with the farmer's management of his land. The imports of wheat and meat in the two years following the Armistice, with the similar imports of the years 1912 and 1913, are therefore given in Table XXIV.

TABLE XXIV

MEAT AND WHEAT IMPORTS, BEFORE AND AFTER WAR.

Weight, Total Value in Sterling, Calorie Value, Calorie Value per head of population. Calories purchased per £1, and Calories purchasable in Wheat for one Calorie purchased in Meat.

	Averages	
	1912, 1913	*1919, 1920*
Meat of all kinds, tons	1,092,000	1,233,000
Wheat and wheat flour, tons .	6,158,000	5,552,000
Value of meat in pounds sterling . . .	50,524,000	156,063,000
„ wheat „ „ . .	51,080,000	131,121,000
Calories in meat, millions	3,249,000	3,773,000
„ wheat „	16,018,000	14,438,000
Calories per head of population in meat . .	70,940	79,430
„ „ „ „ „ wheat . .	349,710	303,960
Calories purchased for £1 in meat . . .	64,300	24,200
„ „ „ „ wheat . . .	313,600	110,100
Calories purchasable in wheat for one in meat .	4·88	4·55

It will be seen from these figures that in spite of our huge war debt, of our greatly diminished exports, and of the sale

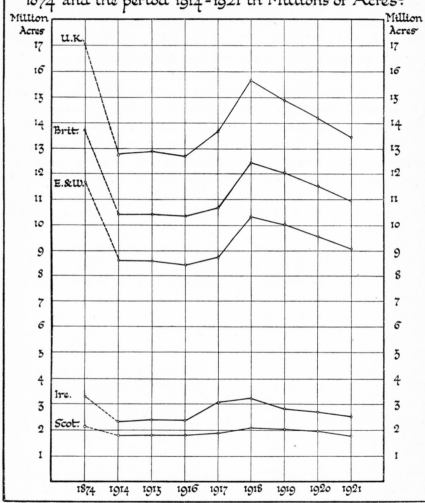

Area of CULTIVATED LAND (excluding Permanent and Temporary Grass) in the United Kingdom, Great Britain, England & Wales, Ireland, and Scotland in 1874 and the period 1914-1921 in Millions of Acres.

of our foreign securities—which before the war paid for many millions worth of our imported foodstuffs—the quantities of meat and wheat imported differed but little after the Armistice from the quantities imported before the war. We imported less wheat because we grew much more at home, and more meat as we produced less. The actual consumption per head changed very slightly. The price we paid for these staple foods rose from £101,604,000 to £287,184,000. Further, although a much poorer nation than before, and although energy in wheat could be purchased at one-fourth of the cost of energy in meat, we were not persuaded into increasing the use of the cheaper foodstuff. We incurred outlays on expensive food which contributed to the rise in the cost of production, by which we lost trade. The burden of our extravagance, although felt by nearly every one, fell chiefly on those unfortunate workers to whom lost trade meant lost employment.

The figures in Table XXIV, and the course of prices after the Armistice, which show that the war brought about no marked alteration in the demand for, or in the relative prices of, wheat and meat, appear to justify the farmer's anxiety to get back to the 1914 tillage area. Moreover, the increase in the cost of labour, which affects arable land to a much greater degree than grass land, points to the conclusion that, if in future the pre-war relative values of wheat and meat are not altered, the area under the plough must be still further reduced before stability is reached. But it is much too soon to draw any conclusions from post-Armistice imports; the years 1919–20 were of a very exceptional character, and there are reasons for thinking that, as a result of the war, we may find in the no distant future substantial changes taking place in the relative values of imported wheat and British meat.

The stock-feeder who reflects on his experience during periods of industrial depression during the thirty years before the war may well view with uneasiness his future prospects, in spite of the prices current since the Armistice. Between 1890 and 1910 wheat was subject to fierce competition, but British meat was largely protected by natural causes, and in

years of good trade there was a ready demand for it. The war
has brought about great changes in the meat trade. The first
effect of war, owing to the requirements of the Armies, and the
increased wages of civilian workers, was to stimulate the
demand for meat ; and naturally all civilians who could afford
it, and who could get it, purchased native fresh meat. But in
the course of the war chilled and frozen meat became much
more popular, and millions of consumers in western Europe
who had never eaten imported beef and mutton before 1914
have learned to use it. This development of the frozen meat
trade may affect the British farmer's management directly and
indirectly. Directly, it will bring keener competition into the
home meat markets, and it will accentuate the effects of
industrial depression on the British stock-feeder's business.
Foreign competition, which before the war was seriously felt
only by meat of third quality, will now affect second quality
meat as well, and it may even sharply restrict the market for
first quality beef and mutton. Indirectly the development of
the refrigerated meat trade will affect our farming methods
by its influence on grain prices. If farmers in new countries
can develop their markets for meat, they will secure an advantage which hitherto they have been without—the opportunity
of converting grain into meat when grain prices are low.

There were evidences before the war that wheat prices had
reached their lowest level at the end of last century, and that
the combination of causes which brought about the very low
prices of the 'nineties were not likely to recur. While the war,
by increasing poverty, has profoundly influenced the demand
for cereals, and so far has lowered the relative value of wheat
to meat, its ultimate effects are more likely to increase than to
lower the relative price of wheat to other necessary foods.
The poverty of central and eastern Europe has greatly affected
food prices since the Armistice ; but in speculating on the
future course of wheat and meat prices, it should be noted that,
as regards the former, there has been a large decrease in the
production of certain important wheat-growing countries as
well as a reduction in purchasing power, and as regards
the latter, that the German, Austrian, and Russian peoples

were not consumers of refrigerated beef and mutton, so that the poverty of these nations has not directly affected this trade.

To what then do these recent changes in farming and probable changes in the markets point ? Land is going back to grass, the dairy farmer has already experienced the effects of trade depression and high marketing costs on his industry, and the prospects of the meat producer are not more hopeful. While it is unlikely that the nation, unless reduced to dire straits, will reduce its total consumption of meat, it is only too probable that consumers will refuse to purchase British meat at the relative prices, and in the relative quantities, current before 1914. Economy must be effected and the consumer will prefer to spend the sum which he can afford for the purchase of meat on the cheaper foreign product. Thus it is likely that the home farmer must be content with a lower (relative) level of prices than he has hitherto secured ; or he must curtail his supplies so that they do not exceed the demands of those consumers who are prepared to pay much higher prices for home than for foreign meat. In practice reduction in quantity, and in many cases also reduction in the cost of production, would be secured by curtailing the use of purchased feeding stuffs.

This then is the probable result on British farming of a reversion to this country's pre-war agricultural policy :— a rapid extension of grazing in the immediate future, a reduction in the 1909–13 output of meat, and possibly of milk, and then a slow increase of tillage because of changes in the relative values of cereals and meat.

But the subject is one on which it is impossible to dogmatize. The position now is such that a series of poor harvests across the Atlantic would force up grain prices to a figure to which our corn areas would quickly respond ; on the other hand, a succession of crops such as, with the exception of that of 1916, America has produced since 1915, would, in conjunction with high labour costs, bring about a great increase in the area under grass. Bad seasons on this side of the Atlantic, by depleting the farmer's capital, would similarly extend the grass area.

If changes are forced upon us by the last of these causes farmers themselves would suffer severely. Otherwise it would make relatively little difference to agriculturists whether the country's tillage area expands or contracts. Provided the changes are not caused by emergencies which leave them no time for adjustment, farmers would respond automatically, and without serious inconvenience, to economic influences.

Grass v. *Tillage a National Question.*

Although, for the present, the heavily taxed public have had enough of Corn Production legislation, and are for the most part anxious to leave the farmer out of their political questions, and the farmer is equally anxious to be left alone, it is unlikely that this subject of the relative merits of grass and tillage farming will long remain dormant. In the years preceding the war, as we have seen, it mattered little to the British consumer whether our land was tilled or not. Food in abundance reached the country from overseas ; our exports enabled us to pay without difficulty for what we required ; and industry provided our workers with better wages than they could earn on the land. But war has radically altered our circumstances. Temporarily at least the sources of our food have been restricted ; we can no longer pay without difficulty for what we import. Our credit is good, it is true, but however good our credit may be, we must ultimately pay for our food by our work ; and the longer we try to postpone payment the greater are the difficulties that will be created for those among us who, in an economic sense, are the weakest.

A comparison of the trend of production as disclosed in the diagram on p. 334 with the post-war purchases of wheat and meat shown in Table XXIV points to what is, perhaps, the greatest of all our national difficulties. Almost all of us were willing to pay for war ; few among us are willing to pay for victory. Although there may not be many of those, who have thought about the subject at all, who can suppose that after a world war there could be spoils for the victors, man's primitive instincts, which throughout centuries asserted themselves, and

in many cases successfully asserted themselves after wars, have
been given rein since the Armistice. The war has been won ; it is
impossible, we argue, that we should be worse off than we were
before these years of conflict and sacrifice, of heroism on the
battlefields, and of toil in munition factories and on the land.
Thus even now, after three years' experience of the results of
our efforts to provide homes and employment for heroes in our
cities, or homesteads and small holdings for ex-service men at
reasonable rents in the country, after three years too of efforts
to coax corn from the land by legislation and to relieve unemployment by reclaiming wastes, we cannot bring ourselves
to admit that there are no spoils for the conquering nations,
and that projects which would have been carried through
easily enough before 1914 have now become impossible because
all of us are determined to secure some share in the ' fruits of
victory '—fruits which, in fact, have no existence.

But although this is our attitude in public affairs, and
although conditions worse than in 1914 will not be accepted
readily by masses of our people, we must all of us admit that
somehow or other our imported food has got to be paid for.
If our industries recover so that our exports not only pay our
war debts to creditor nations, but pay for the foods we import,
and if we can find plentiful supplies abroad, as we did before
the war, all will be well. It would clearly be economically
unwise and socially undesirable to expend on our land labour
which can be used more profitably in other industries. But if
our industries cannot pay—what then ? Are we to continue
reiterating the opinion that a return to less favourable circumstances than we enjoyed in the pre-war period is unthinkable ?
Should we not rather admit that victory, under the conditions
of modern warfare, has been only less ruinous than defeat,
and that the first step towards recovery must be a step backwards, not forwards—backwards to the simpler fare and harder
work of an earlier period.

And if we are compelled to pay this price for victory there
is at least the consolation that our own natural resources could
be more fully used than they now are. There is within the

country much land which—though not fertile enough to keep the ploughman at work in the opening years of this century—was tilled industriously by our forefathers ; land from which we might secure useful employment and more food, as they did.

Whatever the future may have in store for our industries it is, at least, obvious that we cannot long afford to maintain both idle men and idle acres.

This book will have failed in its purpose if it has not shown that within the United Kingdom there are several million acres of land which, although not idle from the farmer's point of view —for they are paying rent and providing some profit—are idle from the national standpoint, inasmuch as they employ very little labour and produce far less essential food than they did in former years. The effect of the tillage of these acres on our national welfare is under-rated by those who count only the additional labourers they could employ ; for the gross value of the produce of this land would be available for distribution among our own people if they were unable to find more remunerative work on commodities for export. Not agricultural labourers alone would be provided with employment, but the other workers who supply them with necessaries ; moreover, although the farmer and landowner might not themselves benefit from the increased output, the extra produce of tillage land would give further employment to the transport worker, business to the agricultural merchant, and work to village tradesmen.

Although in 1914 it no doubt paid the country to export the products of industry and to import food, the difficulties created by the war would almost certainly be lessened if, cultivating the land as we did fifty years ago, our soils now provided one-half instead of one-third of our people with the food which they require.

From the national point of view, too, the problem, although difficult, is not so formidable as it would at first sight appear to be. There is a very large area in the United Kingdom which under any probable combination of circumstances would be used for grass, and a second, but much smaller, area which would in any case grow other crops. At the present time the first of these areas may be put at 28,000,000 and the second at 12,000,000 acres ; the balance of about 6,000,000 acres consists of land on the ' margin ' of tillage. Under the conditions assumed above, it is anticipated that with a *laissez-faire* policy nearly all of this third area would remain in grass ; but the balance against tillage is not very heavily weighted, and a counterpoise should not be impossible.

The ' counterpoise ' of the guaranteed price has been tried, and for the time being, at least, has been abandoned ; it need not be discussed further. The reasons for the failure of the Act of 1920 are sufficiently obvious. But the difficulty, which this Act attempted to meet, remains. Farmers who contemplated cultivating these 6,000,000 marginal acres would be debarred from doing so by a sense of insecurity. And in respect of a percentage of the 6,000,000, varying with prices and costs, farmers are justified. At the time of writing[1] this percentage is undoubtedly very high.

The Farmer's Difficulty.

The position of the tillage farmer is this. He requires for the successful cultivation of his land a much larger capital than is involved by most kinds of grass farming. His wages bill must be met punctually, and seed and manures are necessary many months before his crop is ready for market. But, as compared with the variations in the gross annual value of the crops he grows, his capital is small ; thus a single very bad year may embarrass him, and two or three bad seasons in succession might leave him without any working capital. Under these circumstances, although he might contrive to carry on, his farming would suffer, and even when good seasons returned he would recover his position slowly. To compensate for these risks and anxieties tillage farming must show substantially greater prospects of profit than grass farming. But this is not all. In the case of a great part of the 6,000,000 acres in question it might, even now, be argued confidently that over a long period of years the profits from tillage were certain to exceed the profits

[1] Autumn of 1921.

from grass, and that national and individual interests would
be equally served by tillage ; and the farmer would agree.
But even those occupiers of marginal land who were convinced
that in the long run tillage would yield the greater returns
would be found unwilling to abandon grass ; for, assuming the
period for which it might safely be estimated that the profits
of tillage would exceed the profits on grass to be thirty years
(because within this period an average season, and yield of a
certain given amount, might be expected), the occupier would
have no guarantee that the seasons which were worse than
average would not occur within the first fifteen years, and if
they did and his capital were reduced he could not then recover
his position in the period of good years which followed. It is
for the reasons above indicated that education in itself cannot
much affect the tillage of marginal land. A good education
is no substitute for an insurance policy ; nor can it command
credit facilities in ' bad times ', when credit is urgently required.

Influences of Education and Research.

Agricultural education and research are undoubtedly of
great value to the country ; by benefiting the tillage of the
12,000,000 acres which we have here assumed to be ploughed
annually, and improving the management of the 28,000,000
acres which we assume will remain under grass, educational
efforts might add many millions to the annual value of the
output of our land ; but as already stated, unless the marginal
land is tilled, it is scarcely possible that, as the result of these
improvements, our soils could be made to feed nineteen million
people a generation hence. From a technical point of view, too,
it must be recognized that the difficulty of increasing the output
of food by improving cultivation is very considerable ; most of
the existing arable land is relatively well cultivated, and the
crops have reached a point at which the law of diminishing
returns operates against large additions to the yield. On the
other hand, the conversion of marginal land from grass to
tillage would at once add largely to the food supply, as the
country's experience in peace and in war has abundantly
proved. In one sense, too, it may be stated that the technical

difficulty in effecting a change would be slight. We know how to break up grass land and how to crop it—it can quickly be converted into useful tillage. The real difficulties are economic : the provision of landlord's capital for buildings, drainage, &c., and of tenant's capital for stock, implements, and wages. And, above all, there is the uncertainty of the answer to the question put by the individual cultivator, ' Will it pay *me* to till ? '

Thus while progress will be made as the result of the work of teacher and investigator, the respective areas in grass and tillage may undergo little alteration because of improved education. The instructor can help the tillage farmer, but meantime he can do even more to help the grass farmer. The work of the investigator may, perhaps, be expected to favour growers of tillage crops, since their problems receive most attention ; but pasture plants and pastures, too, are being closely studied, and the scope for improvement and for an increase in productiveness in them is great.

In connexion with education and the possibility of changes in methods which may favour tillage, there is one point arising out of war experience that may again be referred to—this is the influence of mechanical cultivation. At a high cost, because of conditions forced upon us by war, the tractor everywhere became a valued aid to the tillage farmer in 1918. Efforts are now being concentrated on improvements and on the designing of implements suited for use with the tractor ; it may therefore be hoped that, as a result, the cost of cultivation will be reduced and a corresponding impetus given to tillage farming. Meantime, however, it is not possible to forecast the influence of the tractor, for though the war taught us the uses of mechanical cultivation, it has also so greatly increased the cost of machinery and implements as to tell against, rather than in favour of, these aids to tillage farming in the immediate future.

Relief for Tillage Land in Taxation and Rating.

We have defined ' marginal land ' as land in which the advantages of grass and tillage are equipoised. Under present conditions, over nearly all of these (assumed) 6,000,000 acres, lack of capital and uncertainty for the future weight the balance in favour of grass. Can anything be done to tilt it in the other direction ?

Guarantees have been abandoned. Education does not provide the appropriate remedy. Even if ignorance were the main factor in the position, which it is not, ignorance in this particular case would be very unresponsive to all kinds of educational influences. There remains a method of altering the economic balance which deserves consideration and has not yet been attempted, viz. the adjustment of the burdens on land. These burdens are very heavy, and if, by applying principles familiar in connexion with the income tax, relief could be given to land under the plough, the balance might be tilted in favour of tillage. Appropriate measures resulting in discrimination in rating and taxation might, indeed, so alter the economic position as to bring much ' marginal ' land under the plough.

It would seem to be equitable that land which is being put to full use in the production of food, which is employing labour, which requires much capital for its equipment, and which involves greater weather risks, should be required to contribute less to public burdens than land giving little employment and producing little food. There would, no doubt, be many practical difficulties to overcome (chief among them the provision of the credit necessary to tide tillage farmers over ' bad times ') ; but if the nation needs to trade with the ' talent ' now buried beneath its greensward these difficulties must be faced.

One point only requires mention here. We have written of the 6,000,000 marginal acres as if they formed a well-defined area within the United Kingdom ; but this is not so. These acres are everywhere intermingled with other types of land. A field on one farm, several fields on another ; ten fields in one parish, fifty in the next, and so on. It is true that in certain districts fields suitable for conversion into tillage would be much more numerous than in others ; but they could not, in practice, be separated readily from other grass or tillage land. Any relief given to tillage land should therefore apply to all tillage, whether marginal land or not. Any other method of treatment would be both ineffective and unworkable.

Land used for Sport.

During the war, measures were taken to reduce game, and, in the interests of food production, parks, golf links, and many a suburban lawn and playground were broken up. These measures were justified in an emergency, when land was being used wherever labour could be found, and when no source of food required for man or domestic animals could be neglected ; but in the interests of food production there are some who would justify a similar policy in time of peace. The fate of the suburban lawn we may leave to its owner ; but it may be stated that the destruction of the amenities of the country would be a most undesirable policy to adopt in the interests of food production. Any contribution to the food supply which would result from the continuance of these war measures would be trivial in comparison with the loss which would follow their adoption. The amenities of land have, in the past, been largely responsible for providing the first essential for successful tillage farming—cheap capital. Had it not been that landowners were willing to provide land, buildings, fencing, and drainage at very low rates of interest, the home-grown food supply of the United Kingdom would have been much less than was actually the case in 1909–13. The chief danger which now threatens the well-being of tillage farming is that, as a result of the war, cheap capital may no longer be available, and the consumer who feels aggrieved by the game laws, as they now operate, and by the other amenities of the land that lead rich men to seek a country life, literally quarrels with his bread and butter. The rabbit takes a serious toll from our fields, but he has few protectors ; and the food destroyed by the animals preserved for sport is negligible in comparison with the losses caused by the existence of our untilled soils. If the reformer who thinks that our food supply suffers loss because of the sporting value of land would concentrate his energies on securing the use of landlord's capital in the extension of tillage, rather than on measures which would prevent that capital reaching the land of the country in future, as it has done freely in the past, he would be doing useful work for food production.

Country Industries.

But it is not the rich only that we must attract to the land. In far greater numbers we want those who have only labour to give. It is scarcely necessary to mention the desirability of providing more allotments. The allotment movement made great strides during the war, and still further progress should be expected in peace. Many individuals among all groups of workers are skilled gardeners, and in some industrial groups the proportion of successful allotment cultivators is high.

The value of the allotment, not only in producing food but in providing healthy relaxation for workers, is curtailed in this country by the great extent to which our industries have congregated in towns ; and we have not yet succeeded in establishing the cheap means of transport which enable so many Belgian workers to live in the country and travel miles to the factories and shops in which they are employed. Extensions in this direction may be hoped for ; but, if the industrial population of Britain is to go on increasing, a great effort should be made to imitate the policy of our late enemies and to establish industries in the country. The experience of Germany has shown that it is possible to do this in the case of a number of industries, with satisfactory results to employers, and with great benefit to employees.

The development of road transport and the possibility of transmitting electric power by cable for long distances have removed the original chief hindrances to the growth of industries in the country, and the benefits which would follow the vitalizing of our villages by new industries are obvious. Workers themselves would get access to cheap land, and, with the opportunity, many would till larger allotments than those very small plots usually cultivated near towns, and could thus combine pig, poultry, and bee-keeping with gardening.

To food production on a large scale the spreading of our industrial population over the country would be equally advantageous ; a market would be created for meat, dairy and other products in the locality ; transport and handling costs would be reduced, and there would be a corresponding increase in the demand. The consumption of many things is now severely curtailed by the distributing charges.

But the advantages would not be confined to the local market; for, as in Germany, the existence of a large industrial population in rural areas would provide the occasional labour at busy seasons which is so necessary for the successful farming of tillage land, hence direct aid would be given to the development of tillage farming.

Unity necessary for Increased Production.

While there may be a number of palliatives for the condition into which our agriculture has fallen in the past fifty years, there can be no single remedy. Further, the remedies which are possible are not remedies which agriculturists by themselves could adopt. There must be unity of policy, or at least substantial agreement, before any great increase in food production can be achieved. If we could secure unity of policy, there would be no difficulty in adding largely to the output of the soil. War brought us many new proofs of the power of unity. Unity of purpose gave us the Kitchener Armies, unity of action created munitions, unity of endeavour produced the harvest of 1918, and unity in command brought us victory. Now that peace has returned let us give this same unity of national effort to the problems presented by our idle acres.

There is no real reason to quarrel about them. Those whose interests lie in food production need not fear the encroachment of their neighbours from the towns, whether rich or poor. If, in place of herding together in cities as we did in the nineteenth century, we learn by the experience of others and spread ourselves over the land there will be room for all. Our seventy-six million acres provide space enough for the industrialist and the sportsman, as well as for the farmer and the allotment holder.

It is not within our heaths and moorlands that ' The sustenance of Nature hidden lies '; they could add but little to our food supply. A large increase could only come from the tillage of our grass land, and we have seen that any great extension of tillage is, for economic reasons, impossible at present. While in war Hesiod's vision of land's latent riches may well inspire our action, in peace we must not imagine that all the 'food concealed' in our soils could be profitably recovered, or dream that any land policy, however sagacious, would enable us to 'lay the rudder by'.

Thus such changes in our pastures and our plough lands as we may effect need give no cause for continuing the ancient feud between the tiller of the soil and the owner of flocks and herds. Their divergent interests may have been acute enough in the world's early history to have suggested an appropriate setting for the first recorded tragedy. But we have learnt much about stock and tillage since Cain slew his brother Abel. The experience of British farmers themselves has, indeed, proved that stock and tillage may wax and wane together. Our forty-seven million acres of cultivated land can spare many acres for the plough without defrauding our live stock of their necessary pastures. Although in the war years echoes of the old conflict were revived by the ploughing Orders of the Food Production Department, now that peace has returned agriculturists may quickly agree as between the interests of live stock and tillage.

There is one further cause of dispute which should be settled. The ancient feud between the tiller of the soil and his brother has its modern counterpart in the feud between consumers and producers, which again war has brought into prominence. High food prices have led town consumers to think and say hard things about farmers; and the very difficult conditions under which farmers worked during the war have led them, in turn, to resent the words of the spokesmen of the towns. Buyer and seller must haggle over prices in the market; but the producer's real interests are bound up with those of the consumer. There must be certainty of supply and abundance for the consumer, and in providing that supply and securing that abundance the producer earns his livelihood. Any successful attempt to develop the resources of the country must rest on a basis of goodwill. In order that prosperity and plenty may return, and the ravages of war be repaired, we must endeavour to rid ourselves of distrust, of selfishness, and of envying and grieving at the good of our neighbours. For these causes of unrest there is no room on the land; they create no useful energy; they promote neither Food Production nor Peace.

APPENDIX

I

REGULATIONS RELATING TO FOOD PRODUCTION MADE BY ORDER IN COUNCIL UNDER THE PROVISIONS OF THE DEFENCE OF THE REALM CONSOLIDATION ACT, 1914.

(In Great Britain Regulation 2 L was made use of chiefly in connexion with allotments. Regulation 2 M gave authority for the issue of Orders relating to ordinary agricultural land. In Ireland Regulation 2 L was used in connexion with both agricultural land and allotments ; and the application of Regulation 2 M was limited to certain sections (see p. 355). Regulation 2 P applied only to Ireland.)

REGULATION 2 L.

(1) Where the Board of Agriculture and Fisheries are of opinion that, with a view to maintaining the food supply of the country, it is expedient that they should exercise the powers given to them under this regulation as respects any land, the Board may enter on the land and cultivate the land or use the land (including any buildings or erections thereon) for the keeping or breeding of live stock, poultry, or bees, or arrange for its cultivation or use as aforesaid by any person either under a contract of tenancy or otherwise.

(2) The Board may after entry on any land do or authorize to be done all things which they consider necessary or desirable for the purpose of the cultivation of the land or its use as aforesaid or for adapting the land to cultivation or to such use as aforesaid including the erection of fences or buildings, and may also during their occupation of the land or on the termination thereof remove any fence, building, or other work erected or constructed under this provision.

(3) Any person who cultivates or uses land under any such arrangement shall, on the determination, by or on behalf of the Board, of the arrangement, if the determination takes effect before the first day of January nineteen hundred and twenty, receive from the Board such compensation as may have been agreed under the terms of the arrangement, or, in default of any such agreement, as the Board may consider just and reasonable, and shall not be entitled to any other compensation.

(4) On the determination of the occupation of any land by the Board under this regulation, compensation shall be paid by the Board to any person injuriously affected by the exercise of the powers under this regulation, the amount of that compensation to be determined, in default of

agreement, by a single arbitrator under and in accordance with the provisions of the Second Schedule to the Agricultural Holdings Act, 1908.

(5) The Board may with respect to any land authorize any local authority to exercise on behalf of the Board any of the powers of the Board under this regulation.

(6) A local authority authorized to exercise on behalf of the Board any of the powers of the Board under this regulation may exercise such powers in respect of land of which the local authority is owner or occupier and may retain the rents and profits arising from such exercise of these powers, but shall not be entitled to receive from the Board any rent or compensation for the use thereof or for the exercise by the local authority of any powers under this regulation in respect of that land.

(7) This regulation shall apply to Scotland with the substitution of the Board of Agriculture for Scotland for the Board of Agriculture and Fisheries, of arbiter for arbitrator, and of the Agricultural Holdings (Scotland) Act, 1908, for the Agricultural Holdings Act, 1908.

(8) This regulation shall apply to Ireland subject to the following modifications :

  (i) The Department of Agriculture and Technical Instruction for Ireland shall be substituted for the Board of Agriculture and Fisheries :

  (ii) The following sub-section shall be substituted for sub-section (1) :
      Where the Department of Agriculture and Technical Instruction for Ireland are of opinion that, with a view to increasing the production of food in the country, it is expedient that they should exercise the powers given to them under this regulation as respects any land the Department may enter on and take possession of the land,

      (a) without any consent, if the land is for the time being unoccupied, or if the Department are of opinion that it is not being cultivated according to the rules of good husbandry ;

      (b) without any consent, if, at any time after the first day of February in any year, it appears to the Department that the occupier of the land has not taken the necessary steps to cultivate the minimum tillage portion of his holding in accordance with the requirements of any Order made by the Department under the Third Schedule of the Corn Production Act, 1917, and applying to the holding ;

      (c) without any consent, if the land is situated in or near a town to which the Towns Improvement (Ireland) Act, 1854, or any part thereof applies or an urban district, and the Department are of opinion that in order to provide necessary food for residents in the locality land in or near that town or district is immediately required for the purpose of being cultivated in allotments, and that the use of the land for that purpose is unreasonably withheld ; and

(d) in any other case, with the consent of the occupier and the person in receipt of the rent of the land,

and cultivate the land or any part thereof or use the land (including any buildings or erection thereon) or any part thereof for the keeping or breeding of live stock, poultry or bees, or arrange for its cultivation or use as aforesaid, by any person in such manner and upon such terms and conditions as the Department may direct.

(iii) For the purposes of this regulation the Department may :

(a) on entering on any land enter on and take possession of any buildings thereon ; and

(b) provide accommodation for persons, machinery, implements of husbandry or plant, farm produce, stock or animals, employed or used by the Department, or by any person authorized by the Department, for the cultivation of land or the increase of the food supply of the country, and for that purpose take or retain possession of any land or buildings.

(iv) Any person authorized by the Department in that behalf may, for the purposes of this regulation and upon the production, if so required, of his authority, enter on and inspect any land or building and inspect any machinery, implements of husbandry, farm stock or produce thereon.

(v) For the purposes of this sub-section the expressions 'cultivation' and 'cultivate' shall have the same respective meanings as in the Third Schedule to the Corn Production Act, 1917, and the expressions 'occupier' and 'unoccupied' refer to such occupation as involves liability to payment of poor rates :

Provided that where the poor rate is made in respect of a half rent under section sixty-three of the Poor Relief (Ireland) Act, 1838, instead of upon the occupier of the land, the land shall not on that account be deemed to be unoccupied.

(vi) Sub-sections (4) and (6) shall not apply.

(vii) The powers conferred by this regulation on the Department shall be in addition to and not in derogation of any other powers of the Department, and all such powers may be exercised concurrently in respect of any land.

REGULATION 2 M.

(1) Where the Board of Agriculture and Fisheries, after such consultation with the Food Controller as may be arranged, are of opinion that, with a view to maintaining the food supply of the country, it is expedient that they should exercise the powers given to them under this regulation, the Board may

(*a*) enter on and take possession of any land which in their opinion is not being so cultivated as to increase, as far as practicable, the food supply of the country, and, after entry thereon, do all things necessary or desirable for the cultivation of the land or for adapting it for cultivation ; and for such purposes enter on and take possession of any buildings on the land or convenient for such purposes ; and

(*b*) take possession of any machinery, implements of husbandry or plant (other than machinery, implements, or plant in the possession or under the control of a dealer or manufacturer), or any farm produce, stock or animals, which, in the opinion of the Board, are required for the cultivation of land or the increase of the food supply of the country ; and

(*c*) provide accommodation for persons, machinery, implements of husbandry or plant, farm produce, stock or animals, employed or used by the Board for the cultivation of land or the increase of the food supply of the country, by taking or retaining possession of any land or buildings ; and

(*d*) utilize any water supply or motive power for any such purposes ; and

(*e*) by notice served on the occupier of any land require him to cultivate the land in accordance with such requirements as the Board may think necessary or desirable for maintaining the food supply of the country and may prescribe in the notice ; and

(*ee*) by notice served on the occupier of any land require him in accordance with the terms of the notice to adapt the land for cultivation by repairing or removing any hedge or fence on the land, or by clearing or repairing any ditch or drain, whether natural or artificial, by which the land is capable of being drained ; and

(*eee*) by order, applicable generally or to any specified area, and published in such manner as the Board may consider to be best adapted for informing persons thereby affected, prohibit or regulate the use of land for the cultivation of any crop specified in the order and by any such order require the ploughing up within such time as may be specified in the order of any land in use at the date thereof for the cultivation of any such crop ; and

(*f*) by notice served on the tenant of any land which or part of which, in the opinion of the Board, is not being so cultivated as to increase as far as practicable the food supply of the country, determine his tenancy of the land on such date as may be specified in the notice, or on the application of the landlord by order authorize him in any such case to determine the tenancy in accordance with the terms of the order ; and

(*g*) after entry on any land arrange for its cultivation by any other person whether by contract of tenancy or otherwise ; and

(*h*) where, in the opinion of the Board, any land is injured or is likely to be injured by any such neglect on the part of the proprietor or occupier of any other land in relation to the maintenance of banks or the cleansing of channels as is mentioned in section fourteen of the Land Drainage Act, 1847, and subject to, and after the expiration of seven days from, the service of such notice as is required by that section, exercise such powers of executing all necessary works and recovering the expenses thereof as are by that section conferred on the proprietor or occupier of any land which is injured by any such neglect, and for any such purpose enter on any land without any warrant or authority ; and

(*i*) by notice served on the occupier or person in control of any dam, mill, lock, sluice, weir, or other structure affecting the flow of water in any river or stream, require such occupier or person to keep open or closed any mechanical appliance by which the inflow or outflow of water is capable of being regulated during such times and in such manner as the Board, having regard to the use by such occupier or person of the structure and of the water thereby impounded, consider to be necessary or desirable for the prevention of floods or for the draining of land adjoining or near the river or stream ; and

(*j*) where, in the opinion of the Board, any land is injured or likely to be injured by flooding or inadequate drainage which might be remedied wholly or partially by the exercise of powers which are conferred by any general or local Act, or by any award made under any Act, or by any Commission of Sewers, and which are not being exercised or in the opinion of the Board are being insufficiently exercised, exercise any such power and also any power conferred by any such Act or award or commission for defraying the expenses so incurred or for any purpose incidental to the exercise of any such power ; and

(k) enter on or take possession of any dam, mill, lock, sluice, weir, or other structure affecting the flow of water in any river or stream and remove or repair or alter or maintain and use the same where such action is in the opinion of the Board necessary or ‚desirable for the prevention of floods or for the drainage of agricultural land ; and

(l) for the purpose of removing any obstruction to or otherwise improving the flow of water in any river or stream, or maintaining or improving the banks of any river or stream or any sea defence or drainage outfall, enter on the river or stream or any land adjoining or near the river, stream, defence, or outfall ; and

(m) where any expenses are incurred by the Board in the exercise of any of their powers under paragraphs (k) or (l) of this regulation, recover those expenses, so far as they are directly attributable to the default of any person in carrying out his obligations under statute or otherwise, from that person ; and

(n) on the application of any drainage authority empowered by a local Act to levy rates to a limited amount, by order increase the amount that may be so levied ; and

(o) by notice served on the occupier of any agricultural land or the person having the management of any such land require him to make within such time and in such form and to such person as the notice may prescribe a return in writing with respect to the cultivation of the land or the crops or live stock thereon or any other matter as to which the Board may desire information for the purpose of the proper exercise of their powers under this regulation, but so that no such return or any part thereof shall be published or disclosed except for the purposes of a prosecution under this regulation.

(2) An occupier of land may, with a view to maintaining the food supply of the country, submit to the Board a scheme for the cultivation of the land in a manner not consistent with the contract of tenancy of the land, and the Board, if satisfied that the adoption of the scheme is necessary or desirable for the maintenance of the food supply, may direct that the land shall be cultivated in accordance with the scheme, subject to any modification which the Board may think fit to make therein.

(3) If any person obstructs or otherwise interferes with or impedes any officer in the execution of his powers under this regulation, or discloses or publishes any return or part thereof in contravention of this regulation or negligently or wilfully fails to comply with the requirements of any order made under this regulation, or with any condition subject to which a licence under any such order has been granted, or,

being an occupier of any land or building of which the Board require possession, or of which the tenancy of the occupier has been determined by notice served under this regulation, without lawful excuse, refuses to give possession thereof to the Board or to quit such land or building or, having been served with a notice under this regulation requiring him to do any act, negligently or wilfully fails to comply with the requirements of the notice, or, where the notice requires him to make a return, makes a false return, he shall be guilty of a summary offence against these regulations.

(4) If the Board at any time withdraw from possession of any land of which possession has been taken under this regulation, they may recover from any person then interested in the land as owner or tenant or otherwise such amount as represents the value to him of all acts of cultivation or adaptation for cultivation executed by the Board ; such amount to be determined, in default of agreement, by a single arbitrator under and in accordance with the provisions of the Second Schedule to the Agricultural Holdings Act, 1908.

(5) Any person authorized by the Board in that behalf may, for the purposes of this regulation and upon production if so required of his authority, enter on and inspect any land or building and inspect any machinery, implements of husbandry, farm stock or produce thereon.

(6) The Board may with respect to any land or land in any district authorize any person or any body constituted by the Board for the purpose to exercise on behalf of the Board any of the powers of the Board under this regulation and prescribe the procedure of any such body, and the authentication of any notice or other instrument issued by any body or person so authorized.

(7) The powers conferred on the Board by this regulation shall be in addition to and not in derogation of any other powers of the Board.

(8) In this regulation the expression ' cultivation ' includes use for grazing and the expression ' cultivate ' has a corresponding meaning.

(9) This regulation except paragraph (ee) and paragraphs (h) to (n) (both inclusive) of sub-section (1) shall apply to Scotland, with the substitution of the Board of Agriculture for Scotland for the Board of Agriculture and Fisheries, of arbiter for arbitrator, and of the Agricultural Holdings (Scotland) Act, 1908, for the Agricultural Holdings Act, 1908 ; and sub-section (1) of this regulation so far as the powers conferred by paragraphs (h) to (n) (both inclusive) thereof are concerned, and sub-sections (3), (5), (6) and (11) of this regulation shall apply to Ireland, with the substitution of the Department of Agriculture and Technical Instruction for Ireland for the Board of Agriculture and Fisheries, and of section fifty-eight of the Drainage (Ireland) Act, 1842, for section fourteen of the Land Drainage Act, 1847, and with the omission of the references to the Food Controller and to Commissioners

of Sewers, but save as aforesaid this regulation shall not extend to Ireland.

(10) With a view to increasing food production by the conservation or improvement of grazing land, the occupier of any land in Scotland shall be entitled, after due notice in writing to the owner of such land and to the owner of any woodlands adjoining such land, or to their respective agents or factors, and with due care to prevent damage to any woodlands on or adjoining such land, to ' make muirburn ' or set fire to any heath or muir within the boundaries of such land, at any time or times between 1st October and 30th April when the same would otherwise be unlawful or be in contravention of the lease or other contract affecting the land : Provided that nothing herein contained shall affect any duty to comply with any regulation, order, or instruction in regard to the use, display or ignition of lights or fires, in force for the time being.

(11) Any notice under this regulation may be served on the person to whom it is to be given, either personally or by leaving it for him at his last known place of abode, or by sending it through the post in a registered letter addressed to him there.

REGULATION 2 P.

(1) Subject to the provisions of this regulation, it shall be the duty of every occupier of arable land in Ireland to cultivate in the year nineteen hundred and seventeen, so much of the arable land held by him, and hereinafter called the ' holding ', as is specified in that behalf in this regulation and if he fails or neglects to do so, he shall be guilty of a summary offence against these regulations.

(2) The portion of the holding to be cultivated pursuant to this regulation shall be as follows :

(a) If no part of the holding was cultivated in the year nineteen hundred and sixteen, a portion equivalent in extent to one-tenth of the area of the holding ;

(b) If any part of the holding was cultivated in the year nineteen hundred and sixteen, a portion equivalent in extent to the part so cultivated and to one-tenth of the area of the holding in addition : provided that the occupier shall not be required by virtue of this provision to cultivate more than one-half of the area of the holding.

(3) This regulation shall not apply to :

(a) any holding of less than ten acres in extent ; or

(b) any holding or class of holdings as to which not later than the twenty-fifth day of March nineteen hundred and seventeen it shall be declared in writing by the Department of Agriculture and Technical Instruction for Ireland that the cultivation of the holding or class of holdings would be of less service for the production of food than the use of the holding or class of holdings in some other manner in which the same is being used or proposed to be used.

(4) Land under a first or second year's crop of rye-grass shall be deemed to be cultivated, and cultivation by any person under a conacre letting made by the occupier shall be deemed to be cultivation by the occupier.

(5) This regulation shall have effect notwithstanding any covenant, agreement, condition, or provision as to the user of a holding whether contained in any lease or other instrument affecting the holding or in any verbal contract of tenancy or implied by law, and no such covenant, agreement, condition, or provision shall operate so as to penalize, impede, or interfere with such cultivation as is required by this regulation.

(6) Any person duly authorized by the Department of Agriculture and Technical Instruction for Ireland in that behalf shall have power to enter on and inspect any land for the purpose of ascertaining whether the requirements of this regulation are being or have been complied with.

(7) Any application to the Department of Agriculture and Technical Instruction for Ireland for a declaration as to a holding under sub-section (3) of this regulation shall be made in writing on or before the twenty-eighth day of February nineteen hundred and seventeen, and shall set out the particulars of the holding, the manner in which it is used or proposed to be used, and the grounds of the application.

(8) If at any time after the twenty-eighth day of February nineteen hundred and seventeen it appears to the Department of Agriculture and Technical Instruction for Ireland that the occupier of a holding does not intend to fulfil the requirements of this regulation the Department may enter on the holding and may cultivate the same or any part thereof, or arrange for its cultivation by any person in such manner and upon such terms and conditions as the Department may direct, and may exercise as respects the holding all or any of the powers given to the Department by Regulation 2 L.

(9) It shall be the duty of an occupier of a holding to furnish to the Department of Agriculture and Technical Instruction for Ireland, if and when required by them, such particulars with respect to the holding and user thereof, as may be required by the Department for the purposes of this regulation, and any occupier who fails or neglects to comply with such requirement shall be guilty of a summary offence against these regulations.

(10) For the purpose of this regulation ' arable ' means cultivated or capable of being cultivated ; and ' occupier ' means the person rated or liable to be rated to the poor rate, and in the case of a holding of which the half rent is rated means the actual occupier although not liable to be rated.

II

STATUTORY RULES AND ORDERS RELATING TO FOOD PRODUCTION

THE CULTIVATION OF LANDS ORDER, 1918 (NO. 2), DATED AUGUST 19, 1918, MADE BY THE BOARD OF AGRICULTURE AND FISHERIES UNDER REGULATION 2 M OF THE DEFENCE OF THE REALM REGULATIONS.[1]

Whereas under Regulation 2 M of the Defence of the Realm Regulations (which so far as the same is applicable to England and Wales, is set out at the foot of this Order), the Board of Agriculture and Fisheries (hereinafter referred to as ' the Board ') are empowered, after such consultation with the Food Controller as may be arranged, to exercise certain powers with a view to maintaining the food supply of the country, and to authorize any person, or any body constituted by the Board for the purpose, to exercise on behalf of the Board the powers conferred on the Board by Regulation 2 M, and to prescribe the procedure of any such body and the authentication of any notice or other instrument issued by any body or person so authorized.

And whereas the Board, after consultation with the Food Controller, are of opinion that for the purpose aforesaid such Order as is herein contained should be made.

Now the Board of Agriculture and Fisheries do hereby order as follows:

1. The persons who are for the time being appointed by a county council of an administrative county to act as members of the War Agricultural Committee for the county are hereby reconstituted as the body to exercise in manner herein provided such of the powers conferred on the Board by Regulation 2 M as are hereby authorized to be so exercised.

2. The body hereby reconstituted shall maintain an executive committee consisting (1) of members appointed by the said body, not less than four nor more than seven in number, unless the Board otherwise direct, and (2) of additional members appointed by the Board. In the case of a county in Wales (including Monmouthshire), two of the members so appointed by the body hereby reconstituted shall be the members representing the council of the county on the Welsh Agricultural Council. If any vacancy occurs among those members of an executive committee who are appointed by the body hereby reconstituted, the executive committee may appoint any person to fill the vacancy so arising.

3. (1) The body hereby reconstituted for a county, acting through the executive committee, may on behalf and at the expense of the

[1] This Order was first made on 12th January 1917. The revised form printed above was in force at the time of the Armistice.

Board, but subject to such directions as to approval of expenditure or otherwise as may from time to time be given by the Board, and subject also to the restrictions imposed by this section, exercise within the county any of the powers of the Board under Regulation 2 M (except the powers conferred by paragraphs (*eee*), (*f*), (*k*), (*l*), (*m*), (*n*), and (*o*) of Section (1) of that Regulation) and appoint such officers and incur such expenses as the committee may consider necessary or expedient for such purposes ; provided always that

(*a*) the committee shall not enter on or take possession of any common land as defined by this Order, or take possession of any inhabited dwelling-house, without a further consent given by the Board ; and

(*b*) where any notice is served under the powers contained in paragraph (*i*) of section (1) of the Regulation such notice shall contain a provision to the following effect :

This notice shall take effect at the expiration of seven days from the date of service hereof, unless before such expiration notice of appeal to the Board of Agriculture and Fisheries is given in writing to the Secretary to the War Agricultural Executive Committee, and in the event of any such appeal this notice shall take effect on such date (if any) as the Board shall determine after considering the appeal.

(2) The rights of any person dealing with the committee shall not be affected by any question as to compliance by the committee with any directions so given by the Board to the committee, or the requirement of consent in the case of common land or an inhabited dwelling-house.

4. (1) The Corn Production (Amendment) Act, 1918, provides that any person who on or after the 21st August, 1918, is, under the powers of the Defence of the Realm Regulations exercisable by the Board with a view to maintaining the food supply of the country with respect to matters dealt with in Part IV of the Corn Production Act, 1917, served with a notice which requires any change in the mode of cultivating or in the use of land in his occupation and is not solely for the purpose of securing that the land shall be cultivated according to the rules of good husbandry may within the time prescribed by the Board require a reference to arbitration of the question whether it is undesirable in the interest of food production that the change should apply to any portion of the land included in the notice. A copy of any such notice served on a tenant is at the same time to be served on the landlord.

Every such notice shall contain the notification of a right to appeal referred to in paragraph (4) of this section.

(2) The Act of 1918 also provides that before possession is taken

under the said powers on or after the 21st August, 1918, for the purpose of securing any change in the mode of cultivating or in the use of land other than the conversion of the land into gardens or allotments, notice of intention to take such possession shall be served on the owner and occupier of the land if they can reasonably be ascertained, unless the notice is served solely for the purpose of securing that the land shall be cultivated according to the rules of good husbandry, and that an owner or occupier so served shall have the same right of reference to arbitration as is set out in the preceding paragraph of this section.

Except where possession is taken for the purpose of converting the land into gardens or allotments or solely for the purpose of securing that the land shall be cultivated according to the rules of good husbandry, a notice is required to be thus served, and every such notice shall contain the notification of a right to appeal referred to in paragraph (4) of this section.

(3) Where possession is taken by the Committee of any land for conversion into gardens or allotments or solely for the purpose of securing that the land shall be cultivated according to the rules of good husbandry, the Committee shall on or before the taking of possession give notice in writing to the owner and the occupier of the land if they can reasonably be ascertained, of the purpose for which possession has been or is to be taken.

(4) Except in the case of a notice to which the last preceding paragraph of this section relates, any notice to which this section relates which is served under this Order on or after the 21st August, 1918, shall contain a provision to the following effect :

> The occupier or owner of the land to which this notice relates is entitled by notice given to the Secretary of the War Agricultural Executive Committee within fourteen days from the date of the service of this notice on him to require the reference to arbitration of the question whether it is undesirable in the interest of food production that the change in the mode of cultivating or in the use of the land required by this notice should apply to any portion of the land.

5. An executive committee shall from time to time report their proceedings to the body reconstituted by this Order for the county, but the acts of the committee shall not be subject to confirmation by that body.

6. A member of an executive committee shall not take part in any decision of the committee which relates to land of which he is the owner or occupier, or the agent of the owner or occupier, or enter into any contract with the committee, unless such contract has been approved by the Board.

7. Accounts shall be kept by an executive committee of their

receipts and expenditure and be open to inspection by any officer of the Board and those accounts shall be made up and audited in such manner as the Board shall direct.

8. An executive committee shall appoint a chairman of the committee. At any meeting at which the chairman is not present a person appointed by the meeting shall be entitled to act as chairman of the committee. At any meeting of an executive committee the chairman shall, in case of an equal division of votes, have a second or casting vote.

9. The quorum proceedings and place of meeting of an executive committee shall be such as the committee determine.

10. The proceedings of an executive committee shall not be invalidated by any vacancy among its members, or by any defect in the appointment or qualification of any of its members.

11. Minutes of the proceedings of an executive committee shall be kept in a book provided for that purpose and a minute of those proceedings signed at the same or the next ensuing meeting by a person describing himself as, or appearing to be, chairman of the meeting at which the minute is signed shall be received in evidence without further proof.

12. Any notice, direction or other instrument signed by a person describing himself as, or appearing to be, chairman of an executive committee shall be received in evidence without further proof as a notice, direction or instrument issued by the executive committee.

13. Until the contrary is proved an executive committee shall be deemed to have been duly constituted.

14. An executive committee may, subject to any directions given by the Board, appoint such sub-committees as the committee thinks fit. A sub-committee may consist either wholly or partly of persons not being members of the executive committee.

15. An executive committee may act on behalf of the Board in any arbitration under the Corn Production (Amendment) Act, 1918, whether relating to compensation or any other matter.

16. In this Order, the expression ' common land ' includes any land subject to be enclosed under the Inclosure Acts, 1845 to 1882, and any town or village green and any other land subject to any right of common.

17. The Cultivation of Lands Order, 1918, is hereby revoked, but so that such revocation shall not affect the previous operation of such Order or anything done under it, or affect any right or liability acquired or incurred under such Order and any reference in any document to the Order hereby revoked or to any body constituted by any such Order shall be considered as a reference to this Order or to the body reconstituted by this Order.

18. This Order applies only to administrative counties in England and Wales.

19. This Order may be cited as the Cultivation of Lands Order, 1918 (No. 2).

In witness whereof the Board have hereunto set their Official Seal this nineteenth day of August, nineteen hundred and eighteen.

(L.S.)

T. H. Middleton,
Assistant Secretary.

THE CULTIVATION OF LANDS (ALLOTMENTS) ORDER, 1918, DATED AUGUST 21, 1918, MADE BY THE BOARD OF AGRICULTURE AND FISHERIES UNDER REGULATION 2 L OF THE DEFENCE OF THE REALM REGULATIONS.[1]

Whereas under Regulation 2 L of the Defence of the Realm Regulations, which, as subsequently amended, is set out at the foot of this Order, the Board of Agriculture and Fisheries (hereinafter referred to as ' the Board ') are empowered to exercise certain powers with a view to maintain the food supply of the country and to authorize any Local Authority to exercise those powers on behalf of the Board.

And whereas the Board are of opinion that for the purpose aforesaid such Order should be made as is herein contained.

Now the Board of Agriculture and Fisheries do hereby authorize the council of the administrative county of London and the council of each municipal borough and urban district to exercise on behalf of the Board the powers conferred by Regulation 2 L as amended as respects any land within the county of London or the borough or district, or which in the opinion of the council can conveniently be cultivated or used for the purposes of the Regulation by persons residing in the county of London or the borough or district, subject nevertheless to the provisions of this Order :

1. A council shall not enter on any garden or pleasure ground occupied or usually occupied together with a dwelling-house or on any common land, as defined in this Order, without a further consent given by the Board, or on any occupied land, which is not within the county of London or in a county borough, except with the written consent of the occupier of the land or with the sanction of the War Agricultural Executive Committee of the county.

2. A council shall not enter on any land for the purpose of using it for the keeping or breeding of live stock, or use for such purpose any land on which the council have entered under Regulation 2 L, without the sanction of the Board.

3. A council shall as soon as possible after entry on any land give

[1] This Order was first made on 8th December 1916. The revised form printed above was in force at the time of the Armistice.

notice of the entry to the occupier (if any) of the land, and also to the owner thereof.

4. A council may in the case of occupied land agree to make a periodical payment as compensation for the use thereof but not in excess of the rent payable by the occupier for the land, or if held with other land, in excess of a fair proportion of the total rent so payable, or where the land is occupied by the owner, in excess of the annual value for the purposes of income tax together with the tithe rentcharge (if any).

5. A council may arrange with any society having for its object the cultivation of vacant land for the cultivation or use of any land on which the council has entered, and may delegate to such society such of the powers of the council under this Order as may be necessary for the purposes of the arrangement.

6. A council may purchase any seed manures or implements required for the cultivation of the land and sell any article so purchased to the cultivators, or allow their use of the implements at a price or charge sufficient to cover the cost of purchase. A council may also, but only with the express sanction of the Board, adapt any land (including any buildings or erections thereon) for use for the keeping or breeding of live stock, poultry or bees.

7. A council shall as far as practicable arrange that the payments made by the occupiers for the use of the land shall cover the cost incurred by the council in providing the land or adapting it for cultivation or use, and shall not incur any expenses in the exercise of the powers hereby conferred (except in respect of compensation payable under subsection (3) of Regulation 2 L or payable under subsection (4) of that Regulation in respect of any deterioration of the land) which will involve the Board in a liability to repay the council a total amount exceeding two pounds for each acre provided by the council.

8. An arrangement with a person or society for the cultivation or use of the land shall be subject to determination by the council or the Board at any time by notice to that person or society, and shall not provide for payment of compensation to that person or society in excess of the value at the time of quitting of the crops growing on the land and the labour expended upon and manure applied to the land since the taking of the last crop in anticipation of a future crop or provide for the payment of any compensation if the determination takes effect on or after the 1st January, 1920.

9. The land shall not be used for the production of vegetable crops which continue productive for more than one year.

10. A separate account shall be kept by a council of all its receipts and expenditure under this Order or the Order hereby revoked, which shall at any time be open to inspection by an officer of the Board.

11. In this Order the expression ' common land ' includes any land

subject to be enclosed under the Inclosure Acts, 1845 to 1882, and any town or village green and any other land subject to any right of common.

12. The Cultivation of Lands Order, 1917 (No. 2), is hereby revoked, but so that such revocation shall not affect the previous operation of such Order or anything done under it, or affect any right or liability acquired or incurred under such Order, and any reference in any document to the Order hereby revoked shall be construed as a reference to this Order.

13. This Order applies only to England and Wales.

14. This Order may be cited as the Cultivation of Lands (Allotments) Order, 1918.

In witness whereof the Board have hereunto set their Official Seal this twenty-first day of August, nineteen hundred and eighteen.

(L. S.)   *T. H. Middleton,*
                                               Assistant Secretary.

III

STAFF OF FOOD PRODUCTION DEPARTMENT

The total number of persons employed in the work of the Department was about one thousand. The following were those chiefly responsible for the direction of the work of preparation for the 1918 harvest :

President : The Rt. Hon. Rowland E. Prothero, M.P., M.V.O. (now Lord Ernle), President of the Board of Agriculture and Fisheries.

Director General : The Rt. Hon. Lord Lee of Fareham, G.B.E., K.C.B.

Deputy Director General : Sir Thomas H. Middleton, K.B.E., C.B.

Principal Agricultural Adviser : The Hon. E. G. Strutt, C.H.

Controllers :

  Local Organization : F. C. L. Floud, C.B.

  Labour : The Rt. Hon. Viscount Goschen, C.B.E.

    Women's Branch : Miss M. L. Talbot, C.B.E. (Director).

  Cultivation : Sir Sothern Holland, Bart.

    Lt.-Col. H. M. Stobart, D.S.O. (Deputy Controller).

  Supplies : Laurence Weaver, C.B.E.

  Horticulture : F. Keeble, C.B.E., F.R.S., D.Sc.

Chief Commissioners :

  England. Sydney Mager, C.B.E.

  Wales. C. Bryner Jones, M.Sc.

General Secretary : H. L. French, O.B.E.

Sir Charles Fielding, K.B.E., succeeded Lord Lee as Director General in July 1918. Several other voluntary workers, notably Lord Ailwyn, the Rt. Hon. F. D. Acland, M.P., and Sir Percival Perry, K.B.E., gave the Department valuable assistance in the early months while a regular staff was being assembled.

INDEX

OUTLINE OF PLAN

FOR THE

ECONOMIC AND SOCIAL HISTORY OF THE WORLD WAR

I

EDITORS AND EDITORIAL BOARDS
(Further arrangements to be announced later.)

GREAT BRITAIN
Sir William Beveridge, K.C.B., *Chairman*.
Mr. H. W. C. Davis, C.B.E.
Mr. Thomas Jones, LL.D.
Mr. J. M. Keynes, C.B.
Mr. F. W. Hirst.
Professor W. R. Scott, D.Phil.
Professor James T. Shotwell, *ex officio*.

AUSTRIA-HUNGARY
Joint Editorial Board.
    Professor J. T. Shotwell, *Chairman*.

    Editors, Austrian Series.
    Professor Dr. Friedrich von Wieser (*Chairman*).
    Dr. Richard Riedl.
    Dr. Richard Schüller.

    Editor, Hungarian Series.
    Dr. Gustav Gratz.

    Editor, Public Health Series.
Professor Dr. Clemens von Pirquet.

THE BALTIC COUNTRIES
Professor Harald Westergaard (Denmark), *Chairman*.
Professor Eli Heckscher (Sweden).
Mr. N. Rygg (Norway).
Professor James T. Shotwell, *ex officio*.

BELGIUM
Professor H. Pirenne, Editor.

FRANCE
Professor Charles Gide, *Chairman*.
M. Arthur Fontaine.
Professor Henri Hauser.
Professor Charles Rist.
Professor James T. Shotwell, *ex officio*.

GERMANY
Dr. Carl Melchior, *Chairman*.
Professor Dr. Albrecht Mendelssohn Bartholdy.
                    (Executive Secretary).
Vice-Chancellor Gustav Bauer.
Dr. Hermann Bücher.
Dr. Carl Duisberg.
Professor Dr. Max Sering.
Professor James T. Shotwell, *ex officio*.

ITALY
Professor Luigi Einaudi, *Chairman*.
Professor Pasquale Jannaccone.
Professor Umberto Ricci.
Professor James T. Shotwell, *ex officio*.

THE NETHERLANDS
Professor H. B. Greven, Editor.

RUMANIA
Mr. David Mitrany, Editor.

RUSSIA
Editor, First Series.
Sir Paul Vinogradoff, F.B.A.

YUGO SLAVIA
Professor Velimar Bajkitch, Editor.

MONOGRAPHS

(This list includes only those published and in course of preparation, and may be added to or changed from time to time. The monographs fall into two main classes, those which may be said to constitute full numbers in the series, volumes of about from 300 to 400 pages; and partial numbers or special studies of approximately 100 pages or less, which may ultimately be incorporated in a full volume along with others dealing with cognate subjects. Monographs already published are indicated by an asterisk, partial numbers by a double asterisk.)

BRITISH SERIES

British Archives in Peace and War, by Dr. Hubert Hall.

*Manual of Archive Administration, by Captain Hilary Jenkinson.

*Bibliographical Survey, by Miss M. E. Bulkley.

The War Government of Great Britain and Ireland with special reference to its economic aspects, by Professor W. G. S. Adams, C.B.

*War Government in the Dominions, by Professor A. B. Keith, D.C.L.

The Mechanism of Certain State Controls, by Mr. E. M. H. Lloyd.

Rationing and Food Control, by Sir William Beveridge, K.C.B., and Sir Edward C. K. Gonner, K.B.E.

*Prices and Wages in the United Kingdom 1914–1920, by Professor A. L. Bowley.

Food Statistics of the War Period, by Sir Edward C. K. Gonner, K.B.E.

Taxation during the War, by Sir J. C. Stamp, K.B.E.

The General History of British Shipping during the War, by Mr. E. Ernest Fayle.

*Allied Shipping Control; an Experiment in International Administration, by Sir Arthur Salter, K.C.B.

The British Coal Industry and the War, by Sir Richard Redmayne, K.C.B.

The British Iron and Steel Industries during the War, by Mr. W. T. Layton, C.H., C.B.E.

The Wool Trade during the War, by Mr. E. F. Hitchcock.

**The Cotton Control Board, by Mr. H. D. Henderson.

Food Production in War, by Sir Thomas Middleton, K.B.E.

English Fisheries during the War, by Sir W. A. Herdman, K.B.E.

The Labour Unions; Transport and Railway Trade Unions; Workshop Organization; Trade Unionism and Munitions; Labour in the British Coal Mining Industry, by Mr. G. D. H. Cole.

Labour Supply and Regulation, by Mr. Humbert Wolfe, C.B.E.

The Agricultural Labourer during the War, by Mr. Arthur Ashby.

The Health of the Civilian Population during the War, by Dr. A. W. J. Macfadden, C.B.

The Clyde Valley during the War, by Professor W. R. Scott and Mr. J. Cunnison.

Scottish Agriculture and Fisheries (with a supplementary chapter on the Jute Industry). A Series of War-time Economics, by Mr. H. M. Conacher, Mr. Joseph Duncan, Mr. D. T. Jones, and Dr. J. P. Day ; with Introduction by Professor W. R. Scott.

The Effects of the War on the Economic and Industrial Development of Ireland, by Professor Charles H. Oldham.

War-time Profits and their Distribution, by Sir Josiah C. Stamp.

Liquor Control in War-time, by Dr. Arthur Shadwell.

The National Savings Movement, by Sir William Schooling.

The Effect of the War upon Women and Women's Work, edited by Mrs. M. A. Hamilton.

British War Budgets and Financial Policy, by Mr. F. W. Hirst.

Wales in the World War, by Dr. T. Jones.

Dictionary of Official War-time Organizations, by Dr. N. B. Dearle.

An Economic Chronicle of the War, by Dr. N. B. Dearle.

Manchester and the War ; a Survey of Local History, by Professor H. W. C. Davies.

A Guide to Local War Records, by Miss Wretts Smith.

The War and Insurance ; a Series of Studies dealing with Life Insurance, by Mr. S. G. Warner ; Fire Insurance, by Mr. E. A. Sich and Mr. S. Preston ; Shipping Insurance, by Sir Norman Hill ; Friendly Societies and Health Insurance, by Sir Alfred Watson ; Unemployment Insurance, by Sir William Beveridge.

AUSTRO-HUNGARIAN SERIES

Austria-Hungary :

Bibliography of Printed Materials, by Dr. Othmar Spann.

War Government in Austria-Hungary, by Professor Dr. Joseph Redlich.

Austro-Hungarian Banking and Financial History, by Dr. Alexander Popovics.

Military Economic History, a series of studies directed by Professor Wieser, Generals Krauss and Hoën.

The Economic Use of Occupied Territories : Serbia, Montenegro, Albania, by General Kerchnawe.

Military Economic Administration, by Director Fritz Hornik.

The Peace Negotiations of Brest Litovsk and Bucharest, by Dr. Gustav Gratz and Dr. Richard Schüller.

'Mittel-Europa': the Preparation of a new Joint Economy, by Dr. Gratz and Dr. Schüller.

The Exhaustion and Disorganization of the Hapsburg Monarchy, by Professor Dr. Friedrich von Wieser.

Conditions in Austria immediately following the Break-up of the Monarchy, by Dr. Richard Schüller.

Empire of Austria :

Regulation of Industry in Austria during the War, by Dr. Richard Riedl.

Documents and Statistics relating to the War-time Administration of Industry in Austria, by Dr. Richard Riedl.

Food Control and Agriculture in Austria during the War, by Dr. H. Löwenfeld-Russ.

Labour in Austria during the War, a series of studies directed by President Ferdinand Hanusch.

Austrian Railways in the War (Civil Control), by Ing. Bruno Ritter von Enderes.

Coal Supply in Austria during the War, by Ing. Emil Freiherr von Homan.

Public Health and the War in Austria-Hungary :

General Survey of Public Health in Austria-Hungary, by Professor Dr. Clemens von Pirquet.

Studies in Public Health and the War in Austria, by Drs. Helly, Kirchenberger, Steiner, Raschofsky, Kassowitz, Breitner, Bokay, Schacherl, Hockauf, Finger, Kyrle, Elias, Economo, Müller-Deham, Nobel, Wagner, Edelmann, and Mayerhofer, edited with Introduction by Professor Clemens von Pirquet.

Kingdom of Hungary :

General History of the War Economics of Hungary, by Dr. Gustav Gratz.

Description of the Economic Conditions of Hungary at the Outbreak of the War, by Dr. Alexander Matlckovits.

The Effects of the War upon Government Administration and Public Spirit in Hungary, by Count Albert Apponyi.

Hungarian Industrial History during the War, by Baron Joseph Szterenyi.

The History of Commerce during the War, by Dr. Alexander Matlckovits.

The History of Hungarian Finance during the War, by Dr. John Teleszky.

Agricultural Production and the History of the Agricultural Classes, by Dr. Emile Mutchenbacher.

Social Conditions during the War, by Dr. Desider Pap.

Hungarian Food Policy during the War, by Professor John Bud.

Belgian Series

Belgium and the World War, by Professor H. Pirenne.

The Deportation of Belgian Workmen and the Forced Labour of the Civilian Population during the German Occupation of Belgium, by M. Fernand Passelecq.

The Food Supply of Belgium during the German Occupation, by M. Albert Henri.

German Legislation with Reference to the Occupation of Belgium, by Drs. M. Vauthier and J. Pirenne.

Unemployment in Belgium during the German Occupation, by Professor Ernest Mahaim.

Destruction of Belgian Industry by the Germans, by Count Kerchove.

Economic Policies of the Belgian Government during the War, by M. F. J. Van Langenhove.

CZECHO-SLOVAKIA

Financial Problems and Policy of Czecho-Slovakia during the first year after the War, by Dr. A. Rasin.

FRENCH SERIES

Bibliographical Guide to the Literature concerning France for the Economic History of the War, by Dr. Camille Bloch.

Administrative and Constitutional Changes caused by the Economics of the War in France, by M. Henri Chardon.

French War-Time Administration, by M. A. Boutillier du Retail.

French Industry during the War, by M. Arthur Fontaine.

French Textile Industry during the War, by Albert Aftalion.

The Organization of War Industries, by M. Albert Thomas.

Rationing and Food Control, by MM. Adolphe Pichon and P. Pinot.

Statistical Study of Prices and Wages during the War, by M. Lucien March.

French Commercial Policy during the War, by MM. Etienne Clémentel and Daniel Serruys.

The Blockade, by M. Denys-Cochin and M. Jean Goût.

Changes in French Commerce during the War, by Professor Charles Rist.

French Merchant Shipping during the War, by M. Paul Grunebaum-Ballin.

Internal Waterways, Freight Traffic, by M. Georges Pocard de Kerviler.

French Ports during the War, by M. Georges Hersent.

French Railroads during the War, by M. Marcel Peschaud.

Supply of Coal and Petroleum, by M. Henri de Peyerimhoff.

Metallurgy and Engineering, by M. Robert Pinot.

The Chemical Industries, by M. Eugene Mauclère.

Aeronautic Industries, by Colonel Paul Dhé.

The Development of Hydraulic Power, by Professor Raoul Blanchard.

Forestry and the Timber Industry during the War, by General Georges Chevalier.

French Agriculture during the War, by M. Michel Augé-Laribé.

Labour during the War, by MM. William Oualid and M. Picquenard.

Unemployment during the War, by M. A. Crehange.

Women in Industry under War Conditions, by M. Marcel Frois.

Co-operative Societies, &c., and the War, by Professor Charles Gide and M. Daudé-Bancel.

Syndicalism, by M. Roger Picard.

Foreign and Colonial Labourers in France, by M. B. Nogaro and Lieutenant-Colonel Weil.

Prisoners of War in France, by M. Georges Cahen-Salvador.

The Damage inflicted by the War, by M. Edmond Michel.

Problem of Housing during the War, by M. Henri Sellier.

Statistics of Population, by M. Michel Huber.

The Cost of the War to France, by Professor Charles Gide.

War Costs : Direct Expenses, by Professor Gaston Jeze.

War Finances, by M. Henri Truchy.

The Money Market and French Banks, by M. Albert Aupetit.

Public Health and Hygiene, by Docteur Leon Bernard.

Regionalism ; French Local Government and Economic Problems, by Professor Henri Hauser.

The Refugees, by M. Pierre Caron.

The Organization of Labour in the Invaded Territories, by M. Pierre Boulin.

Food Supply in the Invaded Territory, by MM. Paul Collinet and Paul Stahl.

The Economic History of French Cities during the War, by MM. Henri Sellier (Paris), Edouard Herriot (Lyon), Henri Brenier (Marseille), J. Levainville (Rouen), Paul Courteault (Bordeaux), Claude Joseph Gignoux (Bourges), etc.

The Colonies, by M. Arthur Girault.

Northern Africa, by M. Augustin Bernard.

Alsace-Lorraine, by M. Georges Delahache.

GERMAN SERIES

A Bibliography of German War Literature, by Professor A. Mendelssohn Bartholdy and Dr. E. Rosenbaum.

German War Government and the Effect of the War upon the German Constitution, by Professor A. Mendelssohn Bartholdy.

(Others to follow.)

ITALIAN SERIES

The Economic Legislation of the War, by Professor Alberto De' Stefani.

Agricultural Production in Italy 1914–19, by Professor Umberto Ricci.

The Agricultural Classes in Italy during the War, by Professor Arrigo Serpieri.

Food Supply and Rationing, by Professor Riccardo Bachi.

Italian War Expenses and War Taxation, by Professor Luigi Einaudi.

Currency Inflation in Italy and its effects on prices, incomes and foreign exchanges, by Professor Pasquale Jannaccone.

Vital Statistics and Public Health in Italy during and after the War, by Professor Giorgio Mortara.

The Italian People during and after the War : A Social Survey, by Professor Gioacchino Volpe.

Social and Economic Life in Piedmont as affected by the War, by Professor Giuseppe Prato.

The Food Supply of the Italian Army during the War, by Professor Gaetano Zingali.

Bibliography of Italian War Literature, by Professor Vicengo Porri.

THE NETHERLANDS

The Financial Effects of the War upon the Netherlands, by M. J. Van der Flier.

(Others to follow)

PORTUGAL

The Economic and Social History of Portugal as affected by the War, by Professor George Young.

RUMANIAN SERIES

The Rural Revolution in Rumania and South-Eastern Europe, by Mr. D. Mitrany.

(Others to follow)

FIRST RUSSIAN SERIES
(To the Bolshevist Revolution)

The Effects of the War upon the Central Government in Russia, by Professor Paul P. Gronsky.

State Finances in Russia during the War, by Mr. Alexander M. Michelson.

Currency in Russia during the War, by Professor Michael B. Bernazky.

Russian State Credit during the War, by Mr. Paul N. Apostol.

Private Banks in Russia during the War, by Mr. E. M. Epstein.

Life of Russian Municipalities during the War and the All-Russian Union of Towns, by Mr. N. J. Astroff.

The Zemstvos and the War, by Mr. T. J. Polner.

The All-Russian Union of Zemstvos and the ' Zemgor ' (The Union of Zemstvos' and Towns' Unions), by Mr. Sergius P. Turin.

The Russian Army in the World War ; a study in social history, by Lieutenant-General Nicholas N. Golovine.

Rural Economy in Russia and the War by Professor Dr. Alexis N. Anziferoff, Professor Dr. Alexander Bilimovitch, and Mr. G. A. Pavlovsky.

Agrarian Conditions and Problems in Russia during the War, by Professor Dr. V. A. Kossinsky.

The Land Settlement in Russia and the War, by Professor Dr. Alexander D. Bilimovitch.

The Problem of Food Supply in Russia during the War, by Professor Dr. Peter B. Struve, Fellow of the Russian Academy of Sciences.

Co-operative Credit and Agricultural Co-operation in Russia and the War, by Professor Dr. Alexis N. Anziferoff.

Co-operatives and Consumers in Russia during the War, by Professor Dr. V. T. Totomianz.

State Control of Industry in Russia during the War, by Mr. Simon O. Zagorsky.

The Effects of the War upon Separate Branches of Industry :
    (a) Coal mining, by Mr. Boris N. Sokoloff.
    (b) Petroleum, by Mr. Alexander M. Michelson.
    (c) Mining and Metallurgy, by Mr. Alexander V. Rutchenko.
    (d) Manufacturing of metal goods (to be arranged).
    (e) Chemical Industry, by Mr. Mark A. Landau.
    (f) Flax and Wool Industry, by Mr. Sergius N. Tretiakoff.
    (g) Textile (Cotton) Industry, by Mr. Theodor G. Karpoff.

The Effects of the War upon the Problems of Labour :
    (a) Wages, by Miss Anna G. Eisenstadt.
    (b) Workmen's Budgets (to be arranged).
    (c) Changes in the Composition of the Working Classes, by Mr. Vladimir T. Braitwaite.

Internal Russian Trade during the War, by Mr. Paul A. Bouryshkine.

Russia in the Economic War, by Professor Baron Boris E. Nolde.

Russian Transport during the War, by Mr. Michael B. Braikevitch.

German Capital in Russia and the War, by Mr. Basil B. Eliashevitch.

Russian Universities and other Academic Institutions during the War, by Professor Paul J. Novgorodzeff.

Russian Elementary and Secondary Schools during the War, by Mr. Dimitry M. Odinez.

Medicine and Sanitary Organizations in Russia during the War, by Professor Dr. V. A. Jurevitch.

The Psychology of the Zemstvos Workers and the War, by Mr. Isaac V. Shklovsky.

Social Conditions and Movements in the Ukraïna during the War, by Mr. Nicholas M. Mogilansky.

Vital Statistics of Russia during the War, by Professor Dr. A. A. Tschuproff.

Distribution of National Income, by Professor Dr. Peter B. Struve.

The Standard of Living (to be arranged).

Russia and the World War ; a historical synthesis, by Sir Paul Vinogradoff.

Scandinavian Series

The Economic Effects of the War upon Sweden, by Professor Eli Heckscher.
The Economic Effects of the War upon Norway, by Professor W. Keilhau.
The Economic Effects of the War upon Denmark, by Dr. Einar Cohn.
The Economic Effects of the War upon Iceland, by Mr. Thorstein Thorsteinsson.
Inter-Scandinavian War Studies, edited by Professor Harald Westergaard.

Yugo-Slavia Series

The Economic Situation of Serbia prior to the War, by Professor Velimir Bajkitch.
Serbia during the First Year of the War, by Professor Velimir Bajkitch.

The United States

Guide to American Sources for the Economic History of the War, by Mr. Waldo G. Leland and Dr. N. D. Mereness.
(Others to follow.)